Recent Approaches to Participatory Forest Resource Assessment

Jane Carter

Recent Approaches to Participatory Forest Resource Assessment

Jane Carter

with:

Bianca Ambrose, Peter Branney, Om Prakash Dev,
Robert Dunn, Mario Godoy, Jane Gronow,
Andrew Ingles, Bill Jackson, Anna Lawrence,
Jackson Mutebi, Daniel Otu, Felipe Sánchez Román,
Eric Safo, Penelope Scott, Hukum Bahadur Singh,
Mary Stockdale and Joe Watts

Rural Development Forestry
Study Guide 2
Rural Development Forestry Network
Overseas Development Institute
London
1996

© Overseas Development Institute 1996

First published 1996

Published by the Overseas Development Institute,
Regent's College, Inner Circle, Regent's Park,
London NW1 4NS

ISBN 0 85003 232 6

Typeset by ODI, London.
Printed by Russell Press Ltd, Nottingham.

Cataloguing in Publication Data for this book is available from
the British Library.

The production of this book was financed by the
Forestry Research Programme
University of Oxford,
Halifax House, 6 South Parks Road,
Oxford OX1 3UB

Contents

List of Figures

List of Boxes

List of Photographs and Illustrations

Acronyms

The following acronyms and abbreviations have been used throughout the text. Those specific to particular case studies are listed at the end of the relevant chapters.

BA	Basal Area
dbh	Diameter at Breast Height
FAO	Food and Agriculture Organisation (of the United Nations)
FSC	Forest Stewardship Council
GIS	Geographical Information System
GPS	Global Positioning System
IIED	International Institute for Environment and Development
ITTO	International Timber Trade Organisation
NGO	Non-Governmental Organisation
NTFP	Non-Timber Forest Product
ODA	Overseas Development Administration (of the British Government)
PSP	Permanent Sample Plot
PRA	Participatory Rural Appraisal
RRA	Rapid Rural Appraisal
TSP	Temporary Sample Plot
UNESCO	United Nations Education, Science and Cultural Organisation
WWF	World Wide Fund for Nature

Foreword

In many societies, the responsibility for forest management is changing. Traditionally forests were either privately owned, communally owned or state owned; in a very few cases they were owned by corporations or public companies. Because the beneficiaries of the forest products and services often live outside its boundaries, forest management has tended to be centralised in, or controlled by, state forest services. Now the increase in rural populations has resulted in a rise in the demand for forest products locally, the fragmentation of forest areas, and a need to ensure that the remainder is managed effectively to provide the basic needs of those dependent on the forest. More and more, local communities, who are dependent on the forest, are being empowered to manage it.

The Overseas Development Institute, through its Rural Development Forestry Network, has begun the publication of a series of study guides to assist communities embarking upon participatory forms of forest planning and management. The purpose of the guides is to communicate pertinent field experience to policy-makers, mid-level professionals and programme co-ordinators. This, the second of the series, is a guide to participatory methods for assessing a community's forest resources. The guides use a method of analysis and style suited to their employment in a variety of training contexts ranging from post-graduate courses to short workshops.

The techniques of forest resource assessment used in the past were developed for the needs of national planners, and of managers of extensive forests mainly concerned with the production of timber or the raw materials of wood-using industries. These, mainly sophisticated, techniques included remote sensing imagery, mapping, electronic data handling and advanced statistical analyses, and are largely inappropriate to serve the needs of communities unused to the problems of management, hampered by limited human and financial resources, and concerned with a much wider range of forest products. The community's management situation is very different from that of a forest department served by professional foresters.

This guide takes the form of seven case studies which examine the local situation and describe the steps taken in the development of appropriate resource assessment techniques. In all but one of the studies, the process is a very recent development and the stories are far from complete. Nevertheless they are informative, intriguing and thought-provoking. The guide is mainly concerned with resource assessment techniques, but the studies inevitably draw attention to wider facets of participatory forest management. I was particularly interested in three questions:

- How can the sustained production of the goods and services of the forest be guaranteed?

- How can the local, national and international objectives of management be balanced in a situation of local management?

- What is the appropriate level of technology for participatory forest management?

The Classical approach to the first question has been to set aside forest in what has been termed a 'permanent forest estate' and, through central legislation, seek to ensure the integrity of its boundaries and production of the goods and services of the forest on a sustained basis. In some countries this has been successful, but in others less so. The seven case studies could not throw much light on the dynamics of policy within the community, so that there are few clues about how security of forest tenure will be developed. Nevertheless there are signs of hope in that some of the communities have clearly announced an intention to sustain the forest for future generations. As management develops, I hope that this question will receive attention.

Economists would, I believe, tackle the second question by means of some pricing mechanism. If a nation or the wider international community values some product from the forest more than do the local people, then those outside should pay at least the difference in value to the local community in order to compensate them for their more direct benefits foregone. This is relatively easy if the choice is between a luxury timber for export and, say, a tree whose fruits are consumed locally. The difficulty arises as the benefits become less and less marketable or an intangible. There must be a role for national planning, and there must be local input into national plans if they are to be relevant and acceptable. Somehow a mechanism has to be found that allows both synthesis from local needs to national plans and the analysis of national needs incorporated into local management. Is there a potential role for existing marketing or other forms of rural cooperatives in forest management?

The final question of the definition of appropriate technology is clearly signalled in the case studies. In fact it is part of the wider question of sustainability – not of harvests but of community effort – which is, without doubt, the most important facet of community involvement in forest management. Facilitation of participatory management has an important catalytic role but, in my opinion, facilitators may be unwise to remove any of the management process, including the summary and analysis of data, outside the community before the community itself is in a position to design, employ and control the service it needs. Undoubtedly such a strategy will slow progress and raise enormous difficulties in tropical forest management, not least in measuring growth, mortality and recruitment and in monitoring biological diversity – all of which are likely to involve the management of permanent sampling units and the handling of voluminous data over long periods of time. The alternative of hiring appropriate expertise whilst skills are acquired locally may be feasible – as is suggested by the experience in Quintana Roo. Ideally this is the area for cooperation between the national forest service and the community, and could lead to mutual respect and benefit. Undoubtedly generalisations are inappropriate and the definition of appropriate technology must be chosen locally.

The form and style of the guide draws attention to the many important questions and dilemmas facing both communities and co-ordinators attempting to introduce participatory forest resource assessment. The variety among the cases militates against general deductions but stimulates discussion; hence this guide can make no recommendations for approved practices but will certainly assist practitioners to reach their own conclusions. I congratulate both the authors and contributors on the production of such a penetrating analysis of such apposite experiences.

Michael S. Philip
Reader (Hon) in Forestry, University of Aberdeen

Acknowledgements

This book was made possible through a generous grant from the Forestry Research Programme component of the British Overseas Development Administration's Renewable Natural Resources Strategy. The grant covered fieldwork in all but one of the countries from which the case studies are drawn, as well as background research, writing, compilation and publication costs. I am most grateful for this financial support, and would particularly like to express my thanks to **Howard Wright**, **Anne Bradley** and **Tony Greaves** of the Forestry Research Programme for their advice and assistance.

The case studies are based on field reports written by an ODI Research Associate or myself, in close collaboration with field staff. Each report was then subject to heavy editing before reaching its present form as a chapter. My warm thanks to all the authors and contributors for their time and insights, and in particular for the patience of many of them in responding to queries during the editing process. I trust that they feel the final result was worth the effort involved. Since a large number of people assisted the case study authors and contributors in their work, they are acknowledged separately, by chapter.

Chapter 2
I am grateful to the ODA for separately funding Robert Dunn to write the report that led to this chapter, and to **John Hudson**, Senior Forestry Adviser, for instigating this. However, it should be noted that ODA does not necessarily share the views expressed. Helpful comments on an early draft of the chapter were provided by **John Hudson** and **Graham Chaplin** of the ODA and **Kirsti Thornber**, the VSO Forester currently working with the Ekuri villagers.

Chapter 3
The assistance of **Jacques de Cuypère**, Project Leader, Awá Sustainable Forest Management Project, is gratefully acknowledged, both in organising Anna Lawrence's field visit, and in his helpful comments on the draft. Discussions were held during fieldwork with **Daniel Rubio** of UTEPA, and **Martha Mondragón** and **Douglas Ferguson** of CIBT, and with many members of the El Pan and Arenales communities who made an invaluable contribution. Useful comments on an early draft of the chapter were provided by **Jorge Recharté** of the Facultad Latinoamerica de Ciencias Sociales (FLASCO), Ecuador. I would also like to thank **Desmond Chaffey**, ODA Forestry Adviser, **Chris Cox**, former director of ETC, and **Lucinda Leach**, cabinet maker, for advice and comments provided at various times during the chapter's evolution. Special thanks are due to **Jim Bampton**, for making his valuable contributions from his hospital bed.

Chapter 4
Hugo Galletti, **Salvador Gutiérrez**, **Eduardo Ramírez**, **Luis Poot**, **Henning Flachsenberg**, **René Forster**, **Helmut Janka** and **Alfonso Arguelles** of the PPF are all thanked for giving willingly of their time to discuss their work. The assistance provided by **ejidatarios Fausto Aké**, **Benito Martínez**, and **Juvencio Taveo** is also gratefully acknowledged. In addition, Anna Lawrence would particularly like to thank **Tim Synnott** of the Forest Stewardship Council for his insights; **Juán Peón** of PIQRO; and **Christopher Briggs** and **Henrique Fernández** of the British Council.

Chapter 5
Jane Gronow and Eric Safo would like to thank the members of the Ghana Forestry Department who have supported them in their work, and all the people of Assin Akropong, Wurakese and Akinkausu who participated in the activities described. In addition, I would like to express my appreciation for the support provided by **John Francois**, Chief Conservator of Forests, and **Kofi Smith** of the Ministry of Lands and Forests during my visit to Ghana. **Jane Gronow** deserves many thanks for all her assistance and stimulating companionship, both regarding the Ghana case study and in the wider context of this book's preparation.

Chapter 6
I would like to thank all those at the NACFP and the NUKCFP who made me welcome during my visit to Nepal. Of those who did not contribute directly to the writing of the chapter, **Nick Roche**, NUKCFP Project Co-ordinator and **Hugh Gibbon**, Area Leader, NUKCFP Koshi Hills Project Office, are particularly thanked for their assistance. **Janet Seeley**'s warm support and always pertinent advice is also gratefully acknowledged.

Chapter 7
Although they cannot be named individually, the major contribution to this chapter made by all the participating villagers is gratefully acknowledged. In addition, **Tim Jessup**, the Kayan Mentarang Project Leader, supported the writing of the report on which the chapter is based, as well as the initiatives described within it. Two non-governmental organisations, Plasma and Puti Jaji, assisted greatly in organising and running the participatory inventory workshop. Mary Stockdale especially wishes to thank **Panthom**, **Nuripto** and **Sarah Cooke**, as well as **Tanja Tabel** for her companionship and assistance in the field, and **Peter Kanowski** for his valuable comments on the draft field report.

Chapter 8
In conducting fieldwork for this chapter, Joe Watts held discussions with many people. He is particularly grateful to **Barnard Akunda**, Warden (acting in Charge) for Law Enforcement and Multiple Use, BINP; **Philip Franks**, Project Manager, DTC; **Erin Gubelman**, Peace Corps Volunteer, ITFC; **Henk Hoefsloot**, Chief Technical Adviser, MECDP; **Frederick Kigenyi**, Assistant Commissioner, Forestry Department, Kampala; **Masereka Augustine**, Warden (Community Extension Education), Rwenzori Mountains National Park; **Dan McCall**, Project Leader, Rwenzori Mountains Conservation and Development Project; **Alex Muhweezi**, Head of Office, IUCN Uganda Country Office; **Gershom Onyango**, Project Manager, MECDP; **John Otekat**, Deputy Director, Uganda National Parks; and **Jaap Schoorl**, Park Management Adviser, DTC. I would also like to thank **Robert Wild**, formerly Project Manager, DTC, and **Henk Hoefsloot** for their valuable comments and suggestions on an early draft.

A number of other people assisted in the compilation of this book either through commenting on various chapters or in providing useful additional information. Amongst them, I would particularly like to thank **Stephen Adlard**, former ODA Associate Professional Officer, CIAT, Bolivia; **Julia Falconer**, ODA Technical Co-operation Officer, Forest Inventory and Management Project, Ghana; **Irene Guijt**, Research Officer, IIED, UK; **Drake Hocking**, Steep Associates Ltd; **Stewart Maginnis**, ODA Technical Co-operation Officer, **Proyecto de Manejo Integrado del Bosque Natural**, Costa Rica; **Clive McKay**, Avian Ecologist sponsored for his work in Cameroon by the Royal Society for the Protection of Birds; **Daniel Nepstad**, Woods Hole Research Center, USA; **John Nittler**, Team Leader, BOLFOR, Santa Cruz, Bolivia; **Forova Oakiva**, PNG Forest Research Institute, Lae, Papua New Guinea; **John Palmer**, Tropical Forestry Services Ltd; **Darrell Posey**, Linacre College, University of Oxford; and **Janette Young**, formerly based in Cameroon with BirdLife International. In addition, I am grateful to **Kathrin Schreckenberg**, ODI Rural Development Forestry Network for checking on the botanical names and authorities of the plant species mentioned in the text, and **Rosemary Wise** and **Richard Wise** for preparing some of the figures.

Two external reviewers, **Michael Philip** (Honorary Reader in Forestry, University of Aberdeen) and **Jenny Wong** (ODA Technical Co-operation Officer, Forest Inventory and Management Project, Ghana) had the time-consuming task of reading and commenting on all the chapters. Their pertinent advice, stemming from their depth of understanding of forest resource assessment, was invaluable. Although it was not possible to follow all their suggestions exactly, their comments vastly improved the original text. Michael Philip is further thanked for kindly writing the Foreword.

At the ODI I am grateful for the assistance provided by both past and present staff of the Rural Development Forestry Network, in particular **Ingrid Norton** for all her support, **Edwin Shanks** for providing the catalyst for this book, and **Mary Hobley** for shared thoughts. I also thank **Peter Gee** and **Pippa Leask** for undertaking the publishing; **Margaret Cornell** for the copy-editing and the general indexing; and the library staff **Graham Hurford**, **Mark Perkins** and **Christopher Pescud** for their assistance in obtaining sometimes obscure references.

Finally, my special thanks to **Christian Lengeler** for his constant support and understanding, **Elsa Lengeler** for ensuring that I kept the Study Guide in perspective, and **Noelie Lengeler** for waiting until I had finished writing.

Authors and Contributors

Jane Carter has a first-class degree in Agricultural and Forest Sciences from the University of Oxford, where she also read her doctorate. The latter investigated on-farm tree cultivation in the middle hills of Nepal, focusing on local knowledge and practice. It entailed 16 months of fieldwork in a remote Nepali village. The study was set in the context of community forestry developments in Nepal, and suggested a number of possible strategies regarding private tree cultivation and management in Nepal's middle hills.

Jane Carter worked in forestry overseas for a number of years between graduating and beginning her doctoral studies. She was employed by the National Academy of Sciences based in Nairobi, Kenya on a programme investigating the potential of indigenous nitrogen-fixing tree species, and then spent two years in Sri Lanka as a VSO Forest Officer, working for the Sri Lankan Forest Department on a number of reforestation and community-oriented tree planting programmes. This was followed by a period in Australia where she collected seed, and wrote a manual on the propagation of Australian tree species used in developing countries.

On completion of her doctorate, Jane Carter joined the ODI in early 1992. She assisted in running the Rural Development Forestry Network, and in this capacity taught rural development forestry on a variety of workshops, short courses and Masters degree courses. She has conducted research on a number of topics including the organisation of small-scale tree nurseries (published as the first in this series of Study Guides), participatory forest management in India and Cameroon, the potential of urban forestry to meet the needs of the urban poor, and alley farming. Her latest research on participatory forest resource assessment methods spanned a period of eighteen months, and was carried out in addition to other networking duties. Entailing the organisation and co-ordination of fieldwork in six different countries (two of which, Ghana and Nepal, she visited herself) as well as the collation of information from a variety of secondary sources, it was a collaborative piece of work with many people and institutions.

Chapter 2

Robert Dunn is a forester who worked as an ODA Technical Co-operation Officer (TCO) on the Cross River State Forestry Project between March 1991 and November 1994. His previous work experience was two years with the ODA-assisted Forest Resources Management Project in Ghana. He and his wife, Justine, are currently managing a 7,000 ha natural pine estate in Belize.

Daniel Otu is a senior member of the Cross River State Forest Department, for which he has worked since 1972. With Robert Dunn, he ran the Inventory and Management Section of the Cross River State Forestry Project from 1991 to 1994. His current position is Inventory Officer, Forestry Development Department.

Chapter 3

Anna Lawrence is a forester who has worked in Latin America for a number of years. As an ODI Research Associate, she visited the Awá Sustainable Forest Management Project in July 1994 in order to conduct fieldwork for this chapter. She is currently employed on a two-year research programme at the Agricultural Extension and Rural Development Department, University of Reading, UK.

Mario Godoy is a forest engineer who worked in 1990/91 on the preparation of what became the Awá Sustainable Forest Management Project together with CIBT in El Pan. During the time taken for project approval to be reached (1991–4), he worked for UTEPA. Since January 1994, he has been the Field Manager of the Awá Sustainable Forest Management Project, based in San Lorenzo.

Jim Bampton is a forester employed as an ODA Associate Professional Officer on the Awá Sustainable Forest Management Project. He joined the project in January 1995, and has particular responsibility for inventory. He is based in San Lorenzo.

Leonel Quiñónez is employed as a part-time social communicator for the Awá Sustainable Forest Management Project. He is also the Regional Co-ordinator for UTEPA, based in San Lorenzo. In his former capacity, he has particular responsibility for the preparatory phase of project activities in each community, overseeing issues such as the granting of **comunas** status to communities, land titles, and general matters of social organisation.

Chapter 4

Anna Lawrence visited the Quintana Roo Forestry Project in May–June 1994 as an ODI Research Associate, to conduct fieldwork for this chapter. Further details about her are given above.

Felipe Sánchez Román is a forest statistician working on the Quintana Roo Forestry Project for the AMA (**Acuerdo México Alemania**). He is based in Cancún.

Chapter 5

Jane Gronow is a forester who worked in community forestry in Nepal for eight years. She began work for the Collaborative Forest Management Unit (CFMU) in Ghana in 1993, and is employed there by the ODA as a technical co-operation Officer. She has been particularly involved in the development of the collaborative forest resource assessment surveys described in the chapter.

Eric Safo is a Technical Officer assigned to the Collaborative Forest Management Unit (CFMU). He has considerable experience working with the national inventory teams and recently moved to work at the Adwenaase pilot site, where he was involved in the early development of collaborative forest resource assessment surveys.

Patrick Owusu Asante, **Orteng Darko** and **Daniel Assan** are all members of the Assin Akropong community, and dedicated forest volunteers. Daniel Assan previously worked as an agricultural extension officer and has taken particular responsibility for mapping Adwenaase forest. Patrick Asante has played a lead role in survey and compass work, and Orteng Darko has focused on the NTFP surveys.

Chapter 6

Peter Branney is a consultant with LTS International Ltd based in Edinburgh, UK, specialising in rural development forestry. He has worked in community forestry in Nepal for over three years in total since 1983. He initially worked as a VSO (Voluntary Services Overseas) forester in a remote part of the Mid-Western Region, and more recently as Forest Management Adviser to the Koshi Hills Community Forestry Project based in Dhankuta. Since 1993 he has conducted periodic consultancies on community forest management for the Nepal-UK Community Forest Project.

Om Prakash Dev is a forester who has worked in community forestry in Nepal for over 12 years. Seven of these have been spent in the Koshi Hills. In 1990 he was seconded from the Department of Forests to work on the ODA-assisted Koshi Hills Community Forestry Project, now part of the Nepal-UK Community Forestry Project. His current position on the project is that of Forest User Group Support Officer.

Andrew Ingles was Forestry Adviser and Deputy Team Leader of Nepal-Australia Community Forest Project for two years (early 1993 – early 1995). He is a forester with five years experience in community forestry in Nepal. He is a co-author of the NACFP community forestry training manual and author of a number of publications on community forestry, religious forests and biodiversity conservation. He has also undertaken consultancy work related to PRA in Africa.

Bill Jackson is the Team Leader of NACFP, a position he has occupied since mid-1992. A forester with over five years experience of community forestry in Nepal, he previously held the position of Forestry Adviser with NACFP. He is co-author of the NACFP community forestry training manual and author of a number of publications on community forestry.

Hukum Bahadur Singh is Training Co-ordinator for NACFP, a post he has occupied for four years. He has a background in education and has spent over eight years with NACFP in various positions including Senior Extension Officer. He is co-author of the NACFP community forestry training manual and author of a number of publications on training in community forestry.

Chapter 7

Mary Stockdale recently completed her doctorate on rattan inventory and management at the Oxford Forestry Institute, University of Oxford. Fieldwork for this entailed five months living in a community-managed forest in the Kayan Mentarang Nature Reserve. She revisited East Kalimantan in November–December 1994 as an ODI Research Associate to conduct fieldwork for this chapter.

Bianca Ambrose is a forester who recently completed an MSc in Forestry and Land Use at the Oxford Forestry Institute, University of Oxford.

Godwin Limberg, Frank Momberg, Samuel ST. Padan, Dolvina Damus, Martua T. Sirait, Ketut Deddy and Mathilde Snel are all either past or present staff of WWF-Indonesia based in Samarinda or Jakarta.

Chapter 8

Joe Watts is a forester with over four years experience of conservation and development issues in West Africa, where he worked as the ODA Technical Co-operation Officer for Forest Conservation on Mount Cameroon. He conducted the fieldwork for this chapter as an ODI Research Associate in October–November 1994, and has been working since then in British forestry.

Penelope Scott is currently working as a consultant, advising on community-based natural resource management for the Rwenzori Mountains Conservation and Development Project. She has worked in Uganda for nearly four years, conducting fieldwork for her Masters degree in Bwindi Impenetrable National Park, after which she spent two years working with the Mount Elgon Conservation and Development Project.

Jackson Mutebi has worked in and around the Bwindi Impenetrable National Park for the last four years as an extension/community officer under CARE-International's Development through Conservation Project. His current position on the project is Community Conservation Officer.

1   Introduction: Defining the Issues

Recent Approaches to Participatory Forest Resource Assessment may seem a broad title, but so also is the subject material of this book. It grew from a recognised need to document and learn from the growing body of recent field experience involving local people in forest resource assessment. This was made possible through specifically commissioned field studies and the gathering of secondary information by extensive correspondence with field workers in different parts of the world. The result focuses on case studies from seven countries, in which the involvement of local people in quantifying forest resources for various purposes is described in detail. Collectively, they provide examples of a diverse range of assessment methods, from mapping to quite complex inventories of many species. In the concluding chapters, the lessons to be drawn from them are supplemented by experience from a wider range of countries and contexts.

In this introductory chapter, the need for participatory forest resource assessment is set in the context of general developments in forestry. A number of key aspects are then discussed – including the definition of key terms, local people's reasons for participating (or hesitating to participate) in forest resource assessment, and the different techniques that may be used in forest assessment by or with local people.

1.1   Forest Resource Assessment in the Context of Participatory Forestry

Participatory forestry is increasingly seen as both a desirable and a feasible option in many parts of the world, but particularly in the tropics. As used here, the term implies a two-way exchange of experience and knowledge, in a partnership between local people and forestry or related professionals. Such participation may range from the recognition and strengthening of forestry activities already

1

being implemented by local people, to new initiatives requiring considerable outside technical as well as institutional support. There are many reasons for supporting forestry activities by local people, as has been discussed by numerous authors (for example, Westoby, 1987; Gilmour and Fisher, 1991). One argument is the sheer impracticality of ignoring or giving inadequate attention to local people's forest interests. This may be seen wherever forests are part of local people's livelihoods, but particularly in areas of high population density and/or in remote areas poorly supplied by government services. Another argument rests on the moral justification of involving people in the control and management of their traditional lands. In addition, many national governments are increasingly interested in decentralisation and reducing management costs borne by the state. Greater local responsibility for natural resources can appear attractive from this point of view, although in practice any potential cost-effectiveness of participatory management is unlikely to be seen in the immediate term. However, the most cogent argument of all for greater local participation in forestry activities is when this is demanded by local people themselves. The instances of this occurring without any external stimulus tend to be associated with threats to forest land that local people have viewed traditionally as theirs. As the world's tropical forest area shrinks and is placed under increasing pressure from agriculture, logging and other 'development' activities, more indigenous groups and organisations are campaigning for rights to control and manage forest land.

Participatory forestry necessitates considerable emphasis on social aspects, which in early work may take precedence over technical forestry issues. Important social aspects include:

- Establishing rapport and lines of communication between local people and forestry/development professionals.

- Investigating existing indigenous knowledge, covering aspects such as the value and uses attributed to forests and forest plants, knowledge of forest management practices, and any current or former indigenous forest management systems.

- Identifying or facilitating the formation of appropriate local organisations through which activities can be channelled.

- Investigating power structures within the community, with a view to conducting activities (particularly the distribution of costs and benefits) in an equitable manner.

A number of the case studies in this book clearly indicate the importance of such work. It is, or should be, the foundation on which subsequent activities are built.

Although indigenous knowledge alone may be sufficient for local people to control and manage forests where there is very low pressure on resources, this circumstance is increasingly rare. In establishing formal rights to control and manage forests, the need arises for systematic, quantified information – whether to campaign for tenure rights, for compensation, or to manage the forest resource in a rigorous manner according to agreed objectives. Resource assessment is an essential tool in management, forming the basis on which decisions are made and their consequences later evaluated. A comment by one of the case study authors serves to illustrate this latter point:

> The ecology, botany and uses of trees are often well known to local people, but to manage a forest as a whole they need systematic information on how many trees there are, and where they are. Once they have the two sets of data, they move from being people with knowledge to people who are in a position to manage. (Jane Gronow, 1995, pers. comm.)

Thus a need has arisen for assessment methods in which local people can participate to gather systematic, quantified information about the forest resource. In some circumstances this has been addressed by modifying existing survey or inventory techniques, and training local people in their use. This may be particularly appropriate where the main focus of assessment is timber production – an aspect of forest management in which professional foresters are highly experienced. Modified survey and inventory techniques may also be suitable for the participatory assessment of forests for a wider range of products. Local people often value many non-timber forest products (NTFPs) such as game (bush meat), bamboos, canes, fruits, fodder for livestock, medicines and spices. They may wish to include all these in forest resource assessment, although clearly it presents a complicated task.

In other situations, the relatively recent and local availability of sophisticated tools such as remote sensing, global positioning systems (GPS) and computerised data management systems has led to new opportunities for local people to participate in forest mapping and assessment. Such approaches may be particularly relevant for local people campaigning for control over forest resources, since they provide a means of producing highly accurate territorial and resource maps.

1.2 Definitions

A Participatory Approach

The term *participation* is so widely used in development literature, and so variously interpreted, that brief comment on its use in this book is necessary. What is meant by participation can range from almost complete outside control, with the token involvement of local people, to a form of collective action in which local people set and implement their own agenda in the absence of outside initiators and facilitators (see, for example, Biggs, 1989; Pretty,

---

Indigenous knowledge can often provide much information on resource *quality* (as locally perceived) and *general distribution*. Forest resource assessment may be used to build on this, providing details on *quantity* and *location* on which to base systematic forest management.

1995). Between these two extremes are various intermediate forms of participation, on a sliding scale of outsider involvement. Cornwall (1995) identifies six modes of local people's participation, as outlined in Box 1.1.

Box 1.1 Participatory Research and Action: A Continuum of Approaches

Mode of local people's participation	Type of participation	Outsider control	Potential for sustaining local action and ownership	Role of local people in research and action
Co-option	Tokenism – representatives are chosen but have no real input or power	***********		Subjects
Co-operation	Tasks are assigned, with incentives; outsiders decide agenda and direct the process	********		Employees/ subordinates
Consultation	Opinions asked; outsiders analyse information and decide on a course of action	******		Clients
Collaboration	Local people work together with outsiders to determine priorities; outsiders have responsibility for directing the process	*****	***	Collaborators
Co-learning	Local people and outsiders share their knowledge to create new understanding and work together to form action plans; outsiders facilitate.	***	******	Partners
Collective action	Local people set and implement their own agenda; outsiders absent		***********	Directors

Cornwall (1995) (with minor modifications)

Using such definitions, most of the participatory approaches to forest resource assessment described in this book fall into the categories of consultation or collaboration. However, some of the activities described are closer to co-operation, whilst others may be considered to entail co-learning. Some of the case study initiatives are aiming for eventual collective action; others are not. Certainly all currently involve outside input, as is to be expected when new methods are being developed.

Participatory Rural Appraisal

In a number of the case studies described, Rapid Rural Appraisal (RRA) or Participatory Rural Appraisal (PRA) methods are used. The basic principles of these two approaches are summarised in Box 1.2. PRA is often viewed as the successor to RRA, the latter thus being considered out-dated. However, many practitioners, including those who were involved in the early stages of the development of both approaches, argue that they are equally valid and that the essential difference lies in how the information collected is used, and by whom (Chambers, 1994a and b; Chambers and Guijt, 1995). RRA implies consultation with local people, whilst PRA (if conducted effectively) should be closer to co-learning and in some cases, collective action. PRA is described as

> ....a growing family of approaches and methods to enable local people to share, enhance and analyse their knowledge of life and conditions, to plan and to act. In most cases, the use of PRA is initiated by outside development workers. But when used well, PRA can enable local people (rural or urban), to undertake their own appraisal, analysis, action, monitoring and evaluation. (Chambers and Guijt, 1995: 5)

Box 1.2 Basic Principles of RRA and PRA

These may be summarised as follows:

- Offsetting biases – of a spatial, project, person (gender, elite), seasonal, or professional nature.

- Courtesy – demonstrating respect for local people.

- Rapid progressive learning – flexible, exploratory, interactive, inventive.

- Reversal of roles – learning from, with and by local people; eliciting and using their criteria and categories; and finding, understanding and appreciating local people's knowledge.

- Optimal ignorance and appropriate imprecision – not finding out more than is needed and not measuring when comparing is enough. We are trained to make absolute measurements but often trends, scores or ranking are all that are required.

- Triangulation – using different methods, sources and disciplines, and a range of informants in a range of places. Cross-checking to get closer to the truth through successive approximations.

- Principal investigators learn directly from and with local people.

- Seeking diversity and differences.

Source: Chambers and Guijt (1995)

It is important that those using RRA/PRA methods to collect information are aware of the true nature of local people's participation in the process, and treat the results accordingly. Expectations are raised and misunderstanding arises when claims are made to more local control over analysis and planning than actually occurs. Further information on RRA and PRA may be found in the series of RRA Notes produced by IIED, and texts such as Davis-Case (1990), Molnar (1990), Freudenberger (1994) and Messerschmidt (1995).

Sustainable Forest Management

The term *sustainable* forest management is often used throughout this book, although it has been included with some hesitation. Like participation, sustainable is a word which is currently popular in development literature, but which is often used without adequate definition. One succinct definition, provided by the World Commission on Environment and Development, is as follows:

> Sustainable development is development that meets the needs of the present without compromising the ability of future generations to meet their own needs. (WCED, 1987: 43)

Sustainable forest management may be described as the management of an area of forest to ensure no significant change in its composition over a substantial period of time. However, this is too simplistic. The term can have quite different meaning for different people. For example, local people may express the concept in the quite vague terms of the forest continuing to exist and supply their needs for future generations – similar, in fact, to the WCED definition. Traditional foresters have tended to view sustainable forest management in terms of non-diminished timber supplies over a series of rotational felling cycles, whilst conservationists are concerned that there should be no loss whatsoever in habitat richness and species diversity. Economists usually evaluate sustainability more in terms of overall management costs set against production profits over a substantial time period. For rural development workers, an important additional aspect to consider is social and institutional sustainability. In other words, how feasible will it be in the long-term for local people to continue the given initiative, once external assistance is no longer available? Factors to be considered here may include the robustness of organisations established by local people to oversee and determine activities, local political support, and appropriate national legislation, as well as training in necessary skills.

All these interpretations of sustainable forest management may not be mutually exclusive, but they are certainly not the same. Furthermore, sustainability is something that is very difficult to prove without the benefit of hindsight – as well as foresight. At the

As defined by the FSC (1994),

Environmentally appropriate forest management ensures that the harvest of timber and non-timber forest products maintains the forest's biodiversity, productivity and ecological processes.

Socially beneficial forest management helps both local people and society at large to enjoy long-term benefits and also provides strong incentives to local people to sustain the forest resources and adhere to long-term management plans.

Economically viable forest management means that forest operations are structured and managed so as to be sufficiently profitable, without generating financial profit at the expense of the forest resource, the ecosystem, or affected communities. The tension between the need to generate adequate financial returns and the principles of responsible forest operations can be reduced through efforts to market forest products for their best value.

biological level, adequate technical information may not be available to be confident of continued levels of production, especially concerning non-timber forest products. In some circumstances, management systems may be more a 'best guess' prescription than a plan based on proven experience. Economic predictions can only be as accurate as current market trends and predictions allow. Sudden unexpected market changes can alter results drastically. The long-term viability of local people's organisations or sustained political support can be fostered, but only time will demonstrate success or failure. Perhaps in recognition of these difficulties, the Forest Stewardship Council (see Section 1.3) tends to avoid the term sustainable, instead stating its mission to be the promotion of good forest management. It defines this broadly, as management that is environmentally appropriate, socially beneficial, and economically viable. Certainly all three aspects are included in the concept of sustainable forest management as used in this book.

At best, forestry operations that are both participatory and sustainable imply that:

- Local people are committed to maintaining the forest resource, have an active role in forest management decisions, and have (or are developing) the necessary skills for this.

- Tenure of the forest is secure, ideally (but not always) being vested in the local people themselves.

- Forest product harvesting is at levels that do not damage the productive potential of the resource, and can be maintained indefinitely.

- The economic aspects of production have been carefully assessed and appear viable for the foreseeable future, with a fair share of the benefits accruing to the local population.

- Institutional structures support a participatory approach to forest management. This is necessary both at the local level (for example, forest management committees that are properly representative of the local population) and nationally (committed forest department staff, appropriate government policies and legislation, etc.).

In most situations, one or more of these criteria will only be met partially. However, all should have been considered, and addressed as far as possible, in a detailed forest management plan. Sustainable management is perhaps best viewed as a long-term goal, rather than an objective that can be achieved in the immediate future. It is within this cautionary framework that the term is used in the study guide.

1.3 Why Assess the Forest Resource?

Resource assessment can be a sensitive issue in participatory forestry, especially if the need is suggested by outsiders. Local people may not see the necessity for detailed information and its collection, particularly if their role as forest management decision-makers is a new one. They may even be hostile to, or suspicious of, any form of forest measurement, as discussed in Section 1.5. In other cases, local people may initiate forest assessment themselves, sometimes without professional assistance (the East Kalimantan case study, described in Chapter 7, provides several examples).

This section addresses some of the main purposes for which forests are assessed, discussing the extent to which these may reflect local people's priorities.

Securing Tenure and Rights to Resources

In many parts of the world, local people are attempting to establish their rights to manage and enjoy the products of lands which they have viewed traditionally as belonging to them, but which may not be legally defined as such under national law. Often this entails two separate rights: the right to tenure of the land concerned, and the right to exploit the resources on that land. One does not necessarily imply the other. Establishing such rights can be a complicated, extremely difficult and sometimes violent process, with opposition from a variety of powerful interests including new settlers, logging or development companies, and even national governments. Elsewhere, national governments may actively support and encourage local communities to gain legal tenure and usufruct of forest resources that they wish to manage.

Where tenure or usufruct rights are uncertain or open to challenge, forest assessment can represent an important first step in making a legal claim to land and resources. Forms of participatory mapping, in particular, are being used increasingly to enable indigenous communities to delineate the boundaries of their territory in the face of outside threat. A number of examples are reported in *Cultural Survival Quarterly* (Winter 1995) 18(4). They include work with the Nunavik Inuit of Canada (Kemp and Brooke, 1995); the Darién of Panama (González, Herrera and Chapin, 1995); the Miskito reef communities of Nicaragua (Nietschmann, 1995); the Ye'kuanas of Southern Venezuela (Arvelo-Jiménez and Conn, 1995); and the Yucqui of Bolivia (Jarvis and Stearman, 1995). Whilst almost all these examples come from Latin America, experience is far from being concentrated on this continent. A case study in this book reports on the use of mapping with local communities in East Kalimantan, Indonesia.

The information required for establishing claims of tenure and usufruct, and the way in which it is collected, will vary considerably according to circumstances. What represents adequate

One observer has noted that 'More indigenous territory has been claimed by maps than by guns' and that, furthermore, more 'can be reclaimed and defended by maps than by guns'.
(Nietschmann, 1995)

information may not even be legally defined, at least in detail. Thus in the East Kalimantan case study, information for supporting tenure and usufruct claims has been gathered pro-actively through territory mapping, resource mapping, and resource inventory, but it is as yet uncertain whether this will be acceptable to the national government. By contrast, the governments of a number of countries have supported local participation in the definition and delimitation of indigenous territories. Reported examples of such support include initiatives in Ecuador and Peru (Davis and Wali, 1994), and among the Yucqui in Bolivia and the Darién of Panama (both cited above).

The granting of tenure and usufruct rights by government agencies to a community is often dependent on resource assessment and an appropriate management plan. The case study from Nepal (Chapter 6) describes this in detail. A further and quite different example is provided from Bolivia in Box 1.3.

Irrespective of land ownership, a forest management plan which includes some form of forest survey or inventory is often required by government authorities before permission to harvest an area of forest can be granted. In both the Latin American case studies described in this book, forest inventory was a legal requirement to gain permission for forest exploitation. Indeed, legislative requirements may often be a major reason behind local people initially accepting the need for an inventory. However, such requirements can act as a catalyst for far more detailed forest resource assessment. As this Study Guide illustrates, once local people participate in inventories and other forms of forest resource assessment and see how such information can be used, they often become interested in using such methods to greater effect.

Box 1.3 The Lomerío Forest Management Project in Eastern Bolivia

When this project began operations in 1984, the only way to obtain legal title to the forest of the indigenous territory was to prepare a forestry project based on the commercial use of the existing timber. At the time, Bolivian law did not recognise communal land titles (legislation on this matter has now changed). Thus effectively a forest inventory and management plan was necessary to obtain legal title. The initial inventory was of a very low sampling intensity (0.25%), and was conducted largely as a formality. As its results were put into use, it was found to have been highly inaccurate (vastly over-estimating feasible timber exploitation levels), and a more detailed inventory was initiated. This was time-consuming and costly but, after the experience of the early inventory, the need for it was accepted by the local community (who in this case did not have to bear the cost). Despite many problems (largely of an institutional nature), the project is now well established, has considerable potential for further development, and provides many lessons for similar initiatives elsewhere in Bolivia.

Source: Chase-Smith (1993); Lawrence (1994)

Compensation

Where there is conflict over land utilisation, and decisions are made against the interests of local people, there may be the possibility to claim compensation. Although this is often linked with claims for tenure, claims for compensation require additional and different resource assessment techniques since the objective is to place a value on the resource under threat. Quantifying tangible forest products may be the least complicated part of such an assessment, which ideally should also set a value on intangible aspects of the resource such as soil stabilisation, the safeguarding of water supplies, and the cultural or religious significance of the forest to the people concerned.

An example of forest resource assessment being used for compensation claims is provided in the East Kalimantan case study in Chapter 7. Although in this case there is no guarantee that claims will be met, it is notable that local people themselves instigated an assessment of the value of the forest resources for the purpose of claiming compensation.

Good/Sustainable Forest Management

Local people often express a desire to manage their forest in a 'good', 'wise' or 'responsible' manner, so that it will be available for future generations. At the same time, they wish to be able to harvest some products, either for subsistence or to gain an income. This implies sustainable management, even if not expressly defined as such by the people concerned. As noted earlier, sustainable forest management is a difficult management goal but one which in all cases demands a sound management plan. What this comprises is outlined briefly below.

A management plan for an area of forest generally takes the form of a description of the forest, a statement of management objectives, and then an outline of how these objectives will be achieved. If the forest is to be managed by local people, it should ideally also contain a section setting out how the people will organise themselves in their responsibilities – relating these to the achievement of management objectives. Obviously in participatory forest management, the entire plan of management should be drawn up by, or in close collaboration with, the people concerned.

Description of the forest

This should begin with a general description giving, at minimum, the following information:

- forest name, location, broad topography, area and boundaries
- forest ownership
- forest type and main species
- history of management (if any)

A more detailed description of the forest should follow. For this, it is often convenient to divide the forest into management blocks, although a small, fairly uniform area of forest might be treated as a single block. The description of each management block should contain information such as:

- species composition (frequency, pattern of distribution)
- forest condition – including age, canopy density, occurrence of regeneration
- soil, topography and access (particularly where this will influence harvesting operations)

Forest assessment is essential for preparing such a description, which usually includes at least one map of the forest showing its location, area and boundaries. More detailed maps showing the forest management blocks may also be necessary. A description of species composition and forest condition can be drawn from a survey or inventory – the choice between the two depending partly on the level of statistical accuracy and precision required (see Section 1.4).

Management objectives

These are often phrased in both broad and specific terms. Indeed, specific management objectives may often vary by management block whilst conforming to one or more overall management objective(s) for the forest as a whole. For example, a broad management objective might be the sustainable production of diverse forest products. A specific management objective in one management block rich in species considered to provide good fuelwood might be the sustainable production of fuelwood from species x, y and z. In another block, the focus might be on the harvesting of other species for other products. The nature of forest resource assessment will clearly depend on the management objectives – both broad and specific. These may dictate, for example, which species are included in a survey or inventory, and the level of detail recorded.

Achievement of management objectives

This should contain an outline of the forest operations to achieve the specific management objectives. Examples of regular forestry operations include selective felling, coppicing, thinning, and enrichment planting; examples of other operations that might be envisaged for NTFP harvesting include the establishment and maintenance of bee hives, hunting, and the gathering of fruits from certain species. Detail on the harvesting regime and cycle for all products should be included. For example, if strip felling is planned, the width of the strips and the method of harvesting within them (selective/complete/according to species, etc.) should be stated, as well as the number of years between harvests. If hunting is to occur, the plan might specify which species may be hunted, how (by shooting, traps, etc.), and the timing of a hunting season. A maximum kill per year might also be specified, with a clear statement about who will be permitted to hunt. The monitoring of forest operations forms an important part of resource assessment as the implementation of the management plan progresses.

The section of the plan on achieving management objectives should also cover financial aspects. These might include, where relevant, local or international market demand for the products, distribution of benefits (in kind or in money), banking arrangements, etc. Financial considerations may have considerable influence on the detailed planning of forest resource assessment. This is both in terms of what information is needed to make sound economic and environmental decisions, and in terms of affordability. Forest assessment is not cheap.

A particular issue that local people may wish to consider when investigating markets for their forest products is that of *certification*. This is most likely to be pertinent if production is focused on timber for an export market. Forest certification was developed as a mechanism providing a 'guarantee' to the consumer of sustainable production, certification only being granted where a forest is being managed demonstrably according to an appropriate management plan. Consumers in the North are, at least in some cases, prepared to pay a premium for products from such forests. This (in principle) increases profits for the producer and provides an incentive to continue sustainable production. Whether in practice it is a desirable option will depend on individual circumstances.

A major dilemma in drawing up plans for sustainable forest management is that current knowledge about harvesting regimes and cycles for different species and products is inadequate. Sustainable yield assessment, that is, determining how much of a given product can be harvested without jeopardising future production, is only at an early stage of investigation for all but a number of well known commercial timber species. Long-term forest monitoring and specific studies are needed in this regard, a matter discussed further in Chapter 10.

Monitoring Biodiversity and Species of Particular Conservation Value

A growing number of forestry projects, usually at least partially funded by donor agencies, are seeking to combine conservation objectives with a participatory approach to development. Of the case studies documented in this book, those from Uganda (Chapter 8) have overt conservation objectives, but a number of others (in particular those from Nigeria, Chapter 2, Ecuador, Chapter 3 and East Kalimantan, Chapter 7) have received external funding for conservation reasons. Much has been written on the extent to which conservation coincides with local people's needs and priorities, or can be organised in such a way as to do so (for example, West and Brechin, 1990; Wells and Brandon, 1992; Dunn, 1995; Fairhead and Leach, 1995). As Wells (1995) has noted, despite numerous initiatives in recent years, it remains difficult to find successful and convincing examples where local people's development needs have been reconciled with biodiversity conservation. Nevertheless, there are sound reasons for making the attempt – the overriding one being the need to find a working compromise between international, national, and local priorities and interests.

Where forests are being managed for conservation purposes, the monitoring of species composition over time is a necessary part of good management. Exactly what is recorded will depend on the given management objectives and the resources available. Thus where the conservation of biodiversity is the main objective, the ideal will be to record all species of the flora and fauna at regular intervals over time. This is being attempted under the national biodiversity inventory in Costa Rica, where an element of local participation is claimed through the employment of specially trained local 'parataxonomists'. Most parataxonomists come from a rural background, are educated to below university level, and have had a particular interest in biology prior to recruitment. Many are reported to have become extremely efficient collectors and identifiers of local flora and fauna (Janzen, Hallwachs, Jimenez and Gámez, 1993).

In many cases, the detailed recording of all species occurring in a given area of forest may not be feasible, or even necessary. The careful choice of certain indicator species for monitoring may be sufficient to determine any changes in the status of the forest. This is the approach being adopted, for example, in the Bwindi Impenetrable National Park (BINP) in Uganda, as described in Chapter 8. Where the conservation of certain rare or endangered species is the main management objective, monitoring activities will often focus on these. Thus again in the BINP, a key endangered species is the gorilla, the general health and population of which is being very closely monitored by both professional outside experts and skilled local people.

Under the International Convention on biological diversity, the term (which is commonly shortened to *biodiversity*) is defined as 'the variability among living organisms from all sources including, *inter alia*, terrestrial, marine and other aquatic ecosystems and the ecological complexes of which they are a part; this includes diversity within species, between species and of ecosystems'.

Local people often value the tropical forests in or around which they live for the variety of products that they provide, and may recognise a need to conserve them. They may also have concepts about the richness of nature and diversity of life (Darrell Posey, 1995, pers. comm.). However, the term *biodiversity* originated in the North, and the need to conserve it is frequently considered to be a Northern concept. Biodiversity conservation has considerable popular and political support in the North, and substantial funding commitments to it have been made by development agencies. At the United Nations Conference on Environment and Development (the 'Earth Summit') held at Rio de Janeiro in 1992, the importance of community-based biodiversity conservation was stressed. An international convention on Biological Diversity was agreed, which came into force on 29 December 1993 after ratification from the minimum 30 countries required (more have since followed). The convention, signatories to which are bound by international law, includes a requirement for each country to monitor its biodiversity. Brief details are given in Box 1.4. All the countries from which the case studies for this book are taken – Ecuador, Ghana, Indonesia, Mexico, Nigeria, Nepal, and Uganda – are signatories. To date there have been few real tests of the commitment of countries which have signed the convention. However, increasingly government- and NGO-supported initiatives in natural resource management may need to demonstrate such a commitment to secure any international support or funding. How this will be reflected in work with local communities remains to be seen.

Box 1.4 The International Convention on Biological Diversity: Commitments to Identification and Monitoring

The objectives of the convention are 'the conservation of biological diversity, the sustainable use of its components and the fair and equitable sharing of the benefits arising out of the utilisation of genetic resources, including by appropriate access to genetic resources and by appropriate transfer of relevant technologies, taking into account all rights over those resources and to technologies, and by appropriate funding.'

Under Article 7, on identification and monitoring, each signatory country is required to:

- Identify components of biological diversity important for its conservation and sustainable use.

- Monitor these components, through sampling and other techniques, paying particular attention to those requiring urgent conservation and those with greatest potential for sustainable use.

- Identify and monitor processes and activities which are having, or are likely to have, a significant adverse impact on the conservation and sustainable use of biodiversity.

- Maintain and organise data derived from identification and monitoring activities for the above three purposes.

Source: UNEP (1992)

1.4 Participatory Forest Resource Assessment Methods

This section outlines some of the main methods and tools that may be used in participatory forest resource assessment. The focus is on working with local people to quantify or measure the extent, composition and worth (to them and possibly to outside parties) of a forest owned or used by them. Prior to starting such forest-centred activities, or in tandem with them, data collection about the local population itself may be necessary. This might include a population census, a household survey on resource use patterns, and village meetings to discuss resource use and management planning. Some of the case studies in this book mention such activities, but they are not covered in any detail.

As indicated in the discussion in Section 1.3, participatory forest resource assessment may serve a variety of purposes. Different methods will be appropriate in different circumstances. Detailed decisions over the method used will further depend on factors such as the capabilities of local people, and the time, finances, and professional expertise available for the task. In addition, different forms of forest assessment may be appropriate over time, according to changing information needs. For example, in the early stages of management, the main focus may be on settling territorial boundaries, gaining a broad indication of the resources present in the forest, and building on traditional knowledge and patterns of resource use. Later on, there may be a need for more detailed information on certain species to facilitate their management and possible marketing. The establishment of a procedure for regular surveys or inventories for long-term monitoring may then be considered. In the long term, such monitoring activities may be the only form of assessment conducted. The case studies in this book are largely concerned with addressing information needs in the early or medium-term stages of project development.

Mapping

Maps are powerful information tools, which have long been used by governments to facilitate surveillance and control. They also tend to promote a standard scientific and largely European model of knowledge and cognition, which may not necessarily be readily accessible to people of other cultures (Harley, 1989). However, in many parts of the world mapping is now being used for community-based action (Poole, 1995a; Aberley, 1993). Uses in this respect include the following:

- territorial mapping
- current resource location and/or land-use mapping
- tracing historical developments, e.g. perceived changes in resource use over time
- as a tool in investigating processes of land-use change, e.g. locating hazard zones in landscapes where there is a substantial risk of earth-slides and land-slips
- planning and/or predicting future resource management, or related activities

This book focuses mainly on the first two applications.

Territorial mapping is often an essential part of forest resource assessment, whether for establishing legal title over an area of forest, seeking compensation for a forest area under threat, or as part of a description of a forest in a forest management plan.

Resource and/or land-use mapping may be used for establishing claims of tenure and usufruct. It can also be a very useful method of forest assessment for collaborative or co-learning approaches to the drawing up of forest management plans.

The degree of accuracy needed in participatory mapping will vary according to the precise purpose of the exercise. There is scope for considerable flexibility in this respect. The map produced can range, according to the methods and tools employed, from a sketch to a highly accurate piece of work.

Participatory sketch mapping as used in PRA/RRA

As a key RRA/PRA tool, participatory maps have become a popular means of information collection in natural resource management. The usual procedure is for small groups of local people to be brought together, and asked to draw a map of their village and its surrounding resources, perhaps focusing on an aspect of particular interest to the facilitator(s), such as the use of forest products, water supplies, or livestock grazing patterns. A number of groups, divided on the basis of gender, age, and (if appropriate) ethnic group or caste, may be asked to draw such a map for comparative purposes. The map is commonly drawn on the ground, using materials which come to hand (stones, leaves, ash, twigs, etc.) to mark key features. The results are then copied onto paper for discussion and future reference, although where local people are comfortable with the use of coloured pens and paper, these media may be used to create the map.

As developed in this context, participatory mapping has been used (often more for research purposes than as a precursor to development activities) to gain a deeper understanding of local people's perceptions of their environment (case examples include Campbell, Clarke, Luckert, Matose, Musvoto, and Scoones, 1994; Mayers, Peutalo, and Shah, 1994). The geographical accuracy of the map does not matter – indeed, it is of particular interest to the facilitators to note what features of their environment local people emphasise, making larger than reality, and what they consider unimportant – perhaps forgetting to mark onto the map altogether. It is common for wide differences to become apparent between men's and women's perceptions of their surroundings, and the importance they attach to different natural resources. Differences between old and younger members of the community may also be revealed, and between members of different ethnic groups or castes. These can serve as interesting issues to raise in subsequent village/community discussions over resource management.

Modified RRA/PRA mapping exercises

The mapping exercises described in this Study Guide draw on

RRA/PRA work, but have a greater emphasis on geographical accuracy. The form of participatory mapping used in community forestry in Nepal comes closest to the procedure described above, but here too the aim is to gain a reasonably accurate map of forest use by local people, rather than to investigate the perceptions of different users *per se*. Various users from different nearby settlements are consulted, with the aim of producing a 'best fit' map that represents the situation on the ground, and local use patterns, most closely. Problems may arise when this procedure is not followed, as indicated in Box 1.5.

Box 1.5   An Evaluation of Participatory Maps used for Range Post Planning in Bhajhang District, Far Western Nepal: the Question of Accuracy

Range Post Planning (see Chapter 6), employing participatory mapping as the key tool, was introduced to Bhajang District in late 1993. Following training, Rangers used participatory maps to collect planning information throughout all but one of the district's 47 VDCs (Village Development Committees, defined in Chapter 6). In order to assess the accuracy of the data collected, a follow-up study was conducted in late 1994 in three randomly selected VDCs. The study used exactly the same techniques (principally participatory mapping), and revealed the following:

- Of those forests identified in the follow-up study, only 44% could be correlated (according to the given name, approximate number of user households, and ward number) with those forests identified in the original data gathering exercise.

- Overall, the basic geographical features of the VDCs as determined in the original and follow-up exercise were quite similar.

- Forest use patterns indicated in the participatory maps prepared in the original and follow-up exercises varied considerably. Particular discrepancies were found in the numbers of user households, in the ward numbers of these users, and in information on relative forest use (indicated on the maps in the form of arrows showing primary and secondary use).

It was concluded that the original data collection exercise was useful, as it provided the Rangers with a general impression of the forests and the people using them in their area. The information was also possibly adequate for broad annual work planning. However, its inaccuracy was a cause of concern. One simple method for improving the reliability of information collection was identified. This was for field staff to make greater use of maps already available, such as a recently distributed series of 1:50,000 Community Forestry Block maps (which include VDC boundaries). Consulting secondary information before going to the field is of course a fundamental part of Rapid Rural Appraisal. The study recommended that it was given appropriate emphasis in training for Range Post Planning.

Source: Poudyal and Edwards (1994)

Increasing the accuracy of participatory maps through the use of conventional maps and aerial photographs

Greater accuracy may be achieved by consulting, and incorporating information from, alternative sources such as existing maps (as suggested in the box) or aerial photographs, if available. Aerial photographs, if of a large enough scale, have potential to be an extremely useful tool for working with local people, who often interpret them readily (Whittome, 1994, working amongst rural communities in Western Nigeria; Carter, pers. obs. amongst villagers in Central Nepal). Several studies have independently concluded that, for discussions with local people, the optimal scale of aerial photographs is 1:5,000 (Poole, 1995b). In practice, photographs of this scale are often not available. Those of a much smaller scale can only be interpreted by trained professionals, in what is a skilled and often complicated task (Avery and Berlin, 1992). Thus in Nepal, where the most recent aerial photographs (taken in 1992) are of a scale of 1:50,000, it was found that even forest identification by type, as conducted by office-based professionals, was subject to unacceptable inaccuracy (Kleinn, 1994). The use of aerial photography is further limited by the difficulty of obtaining any photographs at all in many areas. Reasons include almost permanent low cloud cover, or a very limited flying season; expense; and sometimes political sensitivity.

Increasing the accuracy of participatory maps through the use of GPS (Global Positioning Systems) and GIS (Geographical Information Systems)

Perhaps the most exciting development in producing geographically accurate maps with local communities is the use of Global Positioning Systems (GPS). GPS positioning enables the operator to plot his/her position on the ground to within an accuracy of anything between some 2 and 100 m, depending mainly on the sophistication (and cost) of the equipment used (see Appendix A). Thus by moving through a territory with local people, establishing boundaries and then plotting them using GPS, it is possible to draw a very accurate boundary map. As described in the East Kalimantan case study, accuracy is improved if good reference maps are also available. If the original territory map is elaborated upon to show, for example, the position of different resources and important local uses of the area, GPS can also be used to locate these. Indeed, new possibilities for the use of this technology, sometimes in combination with other technologies, are in a dynamic and rapid state of development, as outlined in Appendix A. The term *geomatics*, or *geomatic technology*, is increasingly being used as an overall term referring to all these possibilities. The ultimate use is in computer-based imagery, or GIS (Geographic Information Systems). This ranges from relatively simple image creation and map production from geocoded data (that is, data with geographic co-ordinates) to the manipulation of extremely complex information, using highly expensive equipment that can only be operated by experts. Although it is already widely used in planning at a national or regional scale, there are few examples of GIS being pertinent to local-level needs (Haase, 1992; Simonett, 1992).

Mapping using conventional land survey methods

Conventional land survey methods, using a compass and chain or tape, may also be used by local people for producing forest maps. Although this method may not have the potential to produce maps that are quite as accurate as those using GPS, it has the major advantage of requiring only cheap, simple tools. Local people may require intensive initial training in land survey and mapping, but once they have acquired such skills, they may be able to put them to future use without external assistance. Furthermore, the production of a base map through a conventional land survey may provide a logical first step for more detailed resource surveys by local people, as outlined below.

Surveys

The word survey can be used to cover a wide range of activities, and products of such activities. According to the Concise Oxford English Dictionary, a survey may be a

> General view, casting of eyes or mind over something; inspection of the condition, amount, etc., of something, account given as a result of this; department carrying on, operations constituting, piece of, surveying of land, etc., map or plan setting forth results of such.

The act of land surveying itself is defined as

> [to] collect by measurement all facts needed for determining the boundaries, size, position, shape, contour, ownership, value, etc.

Clearly, according to this definition, a survey may range from a description based purely on observation to an accurate account based on measurements. Both are valid in participatory forest resource assessment. Furthermore, the term survey is used in a variety of subject areas; thus it may be relevant to conduct botanical, zoological, ecological, social, economic, or anthropological surveys, or to focus on the interface between some of these topics, such as ethno-botanical or socio-economic aspects. There is a tendency for such subject-defined surveys to be conducted by experts, and although they may be necessary to provide background information for participatory forest management projects, they often entail limited local participation.

One type of forest survey, sometimes described as an inventory, is a cruise. Cruises are commonly used in initial assessments of large forest areas, providing crude estimates of quantities and locations. A logging company would then use such data to determine the most lucrative concession areas, prioritise its activities, etc. This type of assessment has some, but limited, application in participatory forestry. Since the forest areas in question are often quite small, more detailed assessment is often immediately appropriate.

The type of forest resource surveys on which this book focuses are those in which local people are actively involved from the start, defining – or at least being involved in decisions over – the information needed, and then taking part in its collection. Invariably information collection for such surveys takes place within the forest, although both preliminary and collation activities may be more conveniently based in nearby settlements. Experience to date has largely involved the quantification of (usually selected) resources present, and the recording, or ranking, of their value to local people. In conservation-based projects, an externally-introduced system of ranking species or resource types according to rarity or potential for sustainable management may also be important. Strict valuations of resources in economic terms appear to be mainly used for compensation claims (see Chapter 7, in particular Box 7.5).

Inventories

For the purpose of this text, a forest inventory is defined as a quantitative assessment of the forest resource which may be distinguished from a survey by its statistical accuracy. In most cases, it should be possible to calculate a standard error from inventory data, whereas this is not appropriate for surveys.

Inventory techniques assessing forests for timber production are very well established, with increasingly refined and statistically intricate designs. Inventories are the basis of traditional forest management planning, and their development dates back to the end of the Middle Ages in Central Europe (Loetsch and Haller, 1964). Using the definition given above, the early forest inventories were more a form of survey, since they had no real statistical basis. Assessments were based simply on the total growing stock, which was satisfactory because the main demand at the time was for fuelwood rather than timber. Total growing stock was visually estimated by units of area, and then checked by the yield from felled sample areas (Schreuder, Gregoire and Wood, 1993). By the 19th century, the shift from fuelwood to timber production as the main focus of forest management meant that growing stock estimation was no longer adequate. There was a need for more detailed assessment of tree production in terms of the volume of quality timber available per unit area. Tree volume tables were compiled for individual species based on diameter at breast height (dbh), tree height, and form factor – a system still used today. The possibility of minimising the cost of inventories through sampling was recognised early on, at a time when statistical theory was in its infancy. Linear strip sampling and random sampling are reported to have already been in use in Scandinavia in the first part of the 19th century, whilst in tropical forestry, D. Brandis introduced strip sampling at 5% intensity for managing teak forests in Burma in around 1850 (*ibid.*). Strip sampling is still used, in modified forms, in the management of tropical forests in many countries (an example is provided in Chapter 3). It may be noted that even at the turn of the 20th century, theoretical statisticians were still having to convince sceptics of the value of sampling in obtaining a reliable estimate of the characteristics of a population. As Schreuder *et al.* (1993:10) remarked:

> Statistics should be an aid to common sense and it is therefore not surprising that practitioners sometimes develop sound and reasonable methods before theoreticians do.

Statistical theory has developed enormously over this century, and a variety of sampling schemes have been put to practical use in forestry. For further details, the reader is referred to texts such as Philip (1994), Schreuder *et al.* (1993) and Loetsch, Zohrer and Haller (1973). The instruments available for conducting inventories have also become more sophisticated. An important development in forest sampling in North America was the use of aerial photography as a basis for stratification and sample selection, a technique also sometimes used in tropical forestry. More recently, the wide availability of powerful computers and GIS software has introduced a whole new range of possibilities for manipulating inventory data.

Forest inventories may be used for a wide range of purposes in regional and national planning, as well as the planning of forest management at local level. This book considers only the latter use. The challenge in participatory forest inventories is to develop a system of quantifying the resource that is both statistically appropriate and simple to implement. This is vastly complicated if non-timber products are to be included as well as timber. In practice, most experience in participatory forest inventories to date has been in situations where timber production is still the main objective. For this, data collection must at minimum address the following key questions:

- What is the current growing stock? How is it distributed through the forest (by volume and by species)? What is the harvestable volume?

- How is the forest changing over time – what are the growth, mortality and regeneration rates of different species? In other words, what are its population dynamics?

The first type of data are static, measured at one point in time. Nevertheless, they require two separate sets of information – one the inventory that gives species and tree size, and the other that provides the data from which tables to convert simple parameters of tree size (e.g. diameter) to volume or value are prepared.

The second type of data, on forest change, are dynamic and should be measured at regular intervals over a long period (possibly many decades). Although rational forest management demands both types of data, in reality harvesting usually begins based on static measurements, and is then modified as appropriate when the results of dynamic inventory become available.

Static (single) inventories

These may take two main forms, notably:

- sampling at a pre-determined intensity
- 100% enumeration

Sampling at a pre-determined intensity (usually below 10%, and often far lower) is commonly used where the area of forest to be assessed is too large for a full enumeration to be feasible. Properly conducted, such inventories can provide accurate assessments of the resource. They are commonly used to gain a broad impression of the forest that is sufficiently detailed to inform management planning. Sampling may also be used in certain circumstances prior to harvest to determine the harvestable volume. If sampling is systematic, it can be used to generate crude maps.

In inventory, data are collected from sample plots laid out in the forest. Usually they are not permanently marked, and may thus be referred to as temporary sample plots (TSPs). The purpose of data collection will determine which trees within the plot are measured. TSPs are often split into sub-plots, with more detailed, time-consuming data only being collected in part of the plot. This is best illustrated by an actual example, provided in Box 1.6 by the TSP design and layout used in Ghana's national forest inventory. Here two data sets were collected; one on standing volume (sampled throughout each plot), and the other on regeneration (sampled in only part of each plot).

Sampling may be conducted according to a variety of designs, in plots of varying shapes and sizes. Examples of designs include random, systematic, and cluster; plots may be square, linear, circular, etc. More details may be found in texts such as Freese (1984); Loetsch *et al.* (1973); Schreuder *et al.* (1993); and Philip (1994).

Full (100%) enumeration entails the sampling of all specimens conforming with pre-determined criteria (i.e. the population) within the entire forest area. It is analogous to an inventory of a warehouse, although not all the goods in store may be included. Usually a minimum dbh is set, and depending on circumstances, only certain species may be included. For example, where a forest is being managed primarily for commercial timber production, the inventory might include only tree species of marketable quality above a dbh determined by market demand. Full enumeration is particularly appropriate where:

- The area of forest in question is relatively small.

- Labour is not a limiting factor.

- The tree population is highly heterogeneous and unevenly distributed (meaning that variation is difficult to capture through low intensity sampling).

The most common use of 100% enumerations is prior to harvest to determine harvestable volume, or to facilitate the selection of individual trees for harvest. The latter is exemplified by the stock survey, described in several case studies in this book (see, in particular, Chapter 2, Box 2.3). In a stock survey, each tree is given an individual number, and mapped by species and dbh on a stock survey map. This map can be used to decide exactly which individuals will be felled and even the direction of felling and extraction. Full enumerations may also be used in drawing up management plans, in which case a lower dbh is set (with the intention of incorporating trees that may be ready for harvest in the future).

Box 1.6 Temporary Sample Plot (TSP) Design and Layout, as used in Ghana's National Forest Inventory

The data required from the inventory were estimates of reserve and national standing timber volume, and levels of regeneration.

Standing volume was estimated from the measurement of all trees in the sample plot over 30 cm dbh (a volume sampling exercise was later used to generate volume equations).

Regeneration was estimated using a sub-sample of all trees of 5–29 cm dbh. Sampling used 1 hectare rectangular plots at a 0.25% sampling intensity, plots being located systematically by laying a 2 x 2 km grid over a (1:50,000) map of each forest reserve.

A key feature of the sampling design was the use of 20 x 500 m plots, as illustrated below, which was found to increase fieldwork efficiency by facilitating supervision. (The increase in the number of edge trees was compensated for by the ease with which they could be checked.)

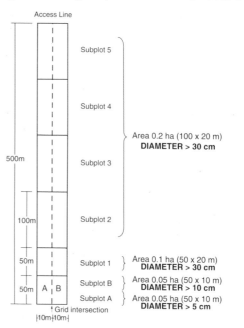

Dynamic (recurrent) inventories

As noted above, the purpose of dynamic inventories is to gain information on the changes taking place in forests over time. To do this, it is necessary to lay out permanent sample plots (PSPs) in the forest, and to repeat measurements within them on a regular basis (usually at 5–10 year intervals). Typically, they are square 1 ha plots (although note that this is not the case in the case study from Mexico, described in Chapter 4), the position of which is marked and recorded in such a way as to facilitate re-locating them in the future.

PSP sampling designs vary, as discussed in Alder and Synnott (1992). What is measured within the plots may also vary. Usually all trees of 10 cm dbh or over are measured, with a sub-sample which includes smaller saplings and seedlings sometimes also being taken. PSP measurements are not normally limited to certain species; at minimum, all those that have the capacity to become trees (normally reaching over 20 cm dbh) are included. This often results in very large data sets. Indeed, the processing and analysis of PSP data is a complex task which is now invariably computerised.

Many tropical forests are currently managed without adequate growth and yield data, and it may be argued that PSP establishment and monitoring is an expensive luxury which may not be feasible. However, the rich and accurate data that potentially they can provide may be crucial for making factually-based decisions on sustainable management. PSP monitoring is not the only means of assessing growth potential, or monitoring forest condition. Less costly (although also less accurate) surveys can also perform this function (particularly with regard to monitoring forest condition). Ultimately, decisions over long-term forest monitoring must depend on individual circumstances – both with regard to the given forest, and the interests of the local people and other stakeholders.

1.5 Local Hesitance over Forest Resource Assessment

The key feature in working with local people to dispel their hesitance or hostility to forest assessment should be openness. It is essential that all concerned are clear from the outset about the purpose of the planned assessment, and what is entailed (especially in terms of their own involvement).

Although forest resource assessment may be instigated by local people, it is more common for initiatives to be at least partly led by outsiders. There are a variety of circumstances under which local people may be hesitant to participate in any form of forest resource assessment, and suspicious of the motives of outsiders who wish to do so. Some of these are outlined below. It should be stressed that where difficulties are met, the first step should be to reconsider the approach being adopted under the given project, and whether the concerns or local people are in fact justified.

Time and Expense

Whatever form of forest assessment seems appropriate to the given circumstances – mapping, resource surveys, or more detailed inventories – it will take time. If local people are to participate fully in the process, a large amount of their time may be taken up, especially early on, when they are probably unfamiliar with the tasks suggested. For this reason, it may be possible to work only with certain communities who have a particular interest in, and demonstrated commitment to, forest management. Even in countries such as Nepal, where there is strong government support for community forestry and a substantial area of forest already under local people's management, it is recognised that some communities are more interested in forest management than others. Accordingly, it is on these interested communities that community forest management activities are focused.

Suspicion of Government Motives

In many countries, governments and their agents, notably forest departments, have a long history of policing forests, actively preventing local people from their use. Sometimes long-standing hostilities have been generated between forest department or other government staff and local communities. Even if policies have changed or are changing to a more participatory approach, such hostilities cannot be overcome without time and effort. Local people may have good reason to be suspicious or even fearful of government motives. Conducting measurements in forests used and/or owned by local people can be perceived as particularly threatening, as illustrated in Box 1.7 by an example from Papua New Guinea. Although in this example the intended level of local people's participation was low (no more than co-operation), it provides a good indication of the difficulties that foresters instigating a participatory approach may face. Suspicions may of course be reciprocal, with government officials distrusting local people and fearing ridicule in adopting a non-authoritarian approach.

Fear of Information Being Used for Unintended Purposes

Following on from the above point, local people may suspect, or in some cases be correct in realising, that forest resource assessment will be used to fulfil purposes or specific objectives that are not necessarily in their interest. One possibility that may be envisaged in the future, for example, is the use of data collected for community forestry purposes in biodiversity monitoring (Ingles, 1994; Jackson and Ingles, 1994; see also Box 1.4). This could have positive consequences for local people, emphasising the value of local control over resources, or negatives ones, if biodiversity was found to decrease. As in all the situations discussed in this section, openness in relations with local people is essential. If they are unwilling to have data collected from their forests used for purposes other than what they intended, there is a strong moral argument for respecting this view. At the same time, it is to be hoped that participatory approaches to forest management will generate an interest and commitment on the part of local people to take appropriate action or seek assistance if future forest monitoring data reveal worrying trends.

Box 1.7 Local Suspicions over PSP Establishment in the Community Forests of Papua New Guinea

Under the land tenure system in Papua New Guinea (PNG), land and forest ownership is customary, and vested in local clans or village groups. Current forest legislation allows for the exploitation of timber and other forest use through the granting of permits under a Timber Rights Purchase (TRP). To obtain such a permit, the customary landowners, or logging companies who have entered into an agreement with them, must produce a Forest Working Plan and apply to the government. Permits may be granted for periods of 15 to 40 years.

A recent Forest Act introduced the establishment of PSPs as a compulsory requirement in the Forest Working Plans of all logging operations. However, this legislation has yet to be implemented in the field. As a separate initiative, PSPs are being established in logged-over forest areas under a growth and yield studies programme supported by the International Tropical Timber Organisation (ITTO). Under this project, 50 PSPs have been established since 1993. Forest researchers assisting in PSP establishment have needed to interact with both the customary landowners and Forestry Department officials. They have found local people to be suspicious of PSP establishment for a variety of reasons. Suspicions include that:

- Forestry officials are marking trees to be secretly removed.

- A portion of the community forest is being taken over by the government for exploitation.

- Officials are using community forests to make money, to the community's loss, by removing non-timber forest products such as orchids, seeds, etc.

General hostility to all Forest Department staff is not uncommon, as a result of the past behaviour of certain individuals (including sexual harassment, demanding bribes, and making false promises). These feelings apart, a few local people take the opportunity to demand payment for the use of their forest, sometimes indicating that they have planned the use of the area demarcated as a PSP for another purpose. They are then disappointed and frustrated that no payment is forthcoming. Overall, customary landowners tend to distrust the government and its representatives. In locations provided with few services, they also see any government presence as an opportunity to gain some form of benefit.

PSP establishment has proceeded despite these constraints. This is due in a large part to the attitude adopted by the PSP teams, which take time to call meetings with the customary landowners in each area they visit, and to discuss with them the purpose of their work. They also try to hire local labourers, thus creating a small amount of employment and increasing the transparency of their operations. Landowners invariably support PSP establishment if the purpose of them is understood, since they are anxious to ensure that their forests are managed on a sustainable basis. In recognition of the importance of involving landowners in forestry decisions, the PNG National Authority has developed a landowner awareness programme. However, field operations under this programme are at an early stage.

Source: Forova Oakiva (1995, pers. comm.)

Maps created through local community participation as a means of claiming indigenous territories also have the potential to be used for exactly the opposite purpose (Darrell Posey, 1995, pers. comm.). There is also potential for forest resource maps, surveys and inventories to be used by outside individuals or companies to facilitate their own extractive operations (a concern expressed in the East Kalimantan case study, Chapter 7). As a result, considerable caution may need to be exercised with regard to who is permitted access to forest resource assessments conducted by and with local communities.

1.6 The Contents of this Study Guide

This study guide is not intended as a reference book on recommended practice, nor is it a collection of success stories. The case studies are provided as a means of learning from the experience of particular projects, set in the context of their own particular bio-physical, socio-economic, political and institutional circumstances. The reasons for the general approach to forest assessment adopted, as well as the specific methods used in each case, can only be thoroughly appreciated with this background. As far as possible, each chapter is set out in sections that facilitate comparison, discussing key issues in turn. It is hoped that readers will be able to compare their own experience with that of the case studies, and to reflect constructively on differences and similarities. Comments throughout the text, as well as this introduction and two final discussion chapters, are provided to catalyse such thought. In addition, a number of study questions are provided in Appendix B.

The case study chapters are ordered according to the methods they have used, beginning with fairly conventional inventories and moving to other forms of forest assessment. The first three case studies, of the Ekuri initiative in Nigeria, the Awá Sustainable Forest Management Project in Ecuador, and the Quintana Roo Forestry Project in Mexico, are all primarily concerned with timber production to provide income for the local communities concerned. They have thus used timber inventories, modified to a certain extent as was felt appropriate for local participation. The Ekuri initiative is at the earliest stage of development, having yet to harvest any timber for sale following the stock survey that was conducted in part of the forest. The Awá Sustainable Forest Management Project, which provides an example of a slightly wider range of simple inventory methods, is somewhat further advanced, with a small amount of timber having been harvested. Both projects have been delayed by funding difficulties. In contrast, the Quintana Roo Forestry Project is a far better established project with an interesting history of technical development.

Later chapters describe projects with more diverse purposes, and management objectives that are not primarily concerned with timber harvesting. In these case studies, mapping and/or resource survey exercises have been used to record a wide variety of forest products. In Chapter 5 the activities of the large Forest Inventory and Management Project in Ghana are briefly described. The chapter focuses on a recent initiative under the Collaborative Forest Management Unit, which is investigating methods of working more closely with local people in forest management. It describes how a forest resource survey has been conducted by local people to provide information for the collaborative management of two community forest reserves. In Chapter 6, the use of participatory mapping and simple forest inventories for planning community forest management in Nepal is described, taking the Nepal-Australia and the Nepal-UK Community Forestry Projects as examples. The chapter also discusses early attempts at establishing long-term monitoring procedures for community forests.

Chapter 7 documents recent work in East Kalimantan, where people of the Kayan Mentarang Nature Reserve have been assisted by NGOs (notably the World Wide Fund for Nature, WWF) to draw territorial and resource maps. The accuracy of these has been enhanced through the use of GPS, to try to secure land tenure. In a separate initiative, a method for a participatory inventory of rattans and other important NTFPs is being developed, to collect data in support of compensation claims. The final case study chapter considers forest resource assessment primarily for conservation purposes, examining the different approaches being adopted in three National Parks in Uganda – the Bwindi Impenetrable National Park (BINP), the Mount Elgon National Park, and the Rwenzori Mountains National Park. Activities in each are supported by projects partially funded through donor agencies, and partly by Uganda National Parks. In all three, the level of local people's participation has been limited by the overriding conservation objectives. A variety of information gathering techniques have been used by the projects, and field-based resource use assessment has been closely linked to information gathering at village and household level. Of perhaps greatest interest is the way in which species/resource vulnerability is assessed, and the monitoring of selected NTFP harvesting is being attempted.

The last two chapters in this book provide a discussion of various key issues that have arisen in the process of its compilation. Chapter 9 focuses on lessons and themes that may be drawn from the case studies, as well as wider experience in participatory forest resource assessment. Chapter 10 briefly examines a number of important aspects that either did not feature in the case studies, or are only at a very early stage of development. Some of the issues discussed in Chapter 9 that the reader may wish to consider particularly when going through the case study chapters are the following:

- Recognising local people's strengths and weaknesses.

- The extent to which data collection was systematically planned.

- Limitations in silvicultural knowledge, and how this influences data collection.

- The cost of forest resource assessment.

- The influence of markets.

- The degree of local people's participation in each of the initiatives described.

References

Aberley, D. (ed.) (1993) *Boundaries of Home Mapping for Local Empowerment.* The New Catalyst Bioregional Series, New Society Publishers, Gabriola Island, BC, Canada or Philadelphia, PA, USA.

Alder, D. and **Synnott, T. S.** (1992) *Permanent Sample Plot Techniques for Mixed Tropical Forest.* Tropical Forestry Paper No. 25, Oxford Forestry Institute, Oxford.

Arvelo-Jiménez, N. and **Conn, K.** (1995) 'The Ye'kuana Self-demarcation Process', *Cultural Survival Quarterly* 18(4): 40–42.

Avery, T. E. and **Berlin, G. L.** (1992) *Fundamentals of Remote Sensing and Airphoto Interpretation.* Macmillan, Basingstoke, UK.

Biggs, S. (1989) *Resource-poor Farmers' Participation in Research: A Synthesis of Experience from Nine National Agricultural Research Systems.* Project Study 3, ISNAR, The Hague.

Campbell, B., Clarke, J., Luckert, M., Matose, F., Musvoto, C. and **Scoones, I.** (1994) 'Local-level economic valuation of savanna woodlot resources: Village cases from Zimbabwe Hot Springs', Working Group unpublished document available from IIED, London.

Chambers, R. (1994a) 'The Origins and Practice of Participatory Rural Appraisal', *World Development* 22(7): 953–69.

Chambers, R. (1994b) 'Participatory Rural Appraisal (PRA): Analysis of Experience', *World Development* 22(9): 1253–68.

Chambers, R. and **Guijt, I.** (1995) 'PRA – five years later. Where are we now?', *Forests, Trees and People Newsletter*, No. 26/27 April: 4–14.

Chase-Smith, R. (1993) 'Indians, Forest Rights, and Lumber Mills', *Cultural Survival Quarterly*, Spring 1993: 52–5.

Cornwall, A. (1995) 'Towards Participatory Practice: PRA and the Participatory Process' in de Koning, K., (ed.) *Participation and Health*, Zed Books, London.

Davis, S. H. and **Wali, A.** (1994) 'Indigenous Land Tenure and Tropical Forest Management in Latin America', *Ambio* 23 (8): 485–90.

Davis-Case, D. (1990) 'The Community's Toolbox: The Idea, Methods and Tools for Participatory Assessment, Monitoring and Evaluation', *Community Forestry Field Manual*, FAO, Bangkok.

Dunn, A. (1995) 'Summaries of Some Recent Project Approaches to Conservation and Development'. *ODI Rural Development Forestry Network Paper 18d*, ODI, London.

Fairhead, J and **Leach, M.** (1995) 'Whose Forest? Modern Conservation and Historical Land Use in Guinea's Ziama Reserve'. *ODI Rural Development Forestry Network Paper 18c*, ODI, London.

Freese, F. (1984) *Statistics for Land Managers: an Introduction to Sampling Methods for Foresters, Farmers and Environmental Biologists*. Paeony, Jedburgh, UK.

Freudenberger, K. S. (1994) 'Trees and Land Tenure: Rapid Appraisal Tools', *Community Forestry Field Manual 4*, FAO, Rome.

FSC (1994) *Forest Stewardship Principles and Criteria for Natural Forest Management*. Forest Stewardship Council, Oaxaca, Mexico, June.

Gilmour, D. A. and **Fisher, R. J.** (1991) *Villagers, Forests and Foresters: The Philosophy, Process and Practice of Community Forestry in Nepal*. Sahayogi Press, Kathmandu.

González, N., Herrera, F. and **Chapin, M.** (1995) 'Ethnocartography in the Darién', *Cultural Survival Quarterly* 18(4): 31–3.

Haase, S. (1992) 'Geographic Information Systems and Community Resource Management for Sub-Saharan Africa: Opportunity Lost?' A report submitted to the Department of Engineering and Policy of Washington University in partial fulfilment of the requirements for the degree of Master of Science in Technology and Human Affairs. Washington University, USA.

Harley, J. B. (1989) 'Deconstructing the Map', *Cartographica* 26(2): 1–20.

Ingles, A. W. (1994) 'Conserving the Biological Diversity of Nepal's Forests: Some Opportunities Provided by Community Forestry'. Nepal-Australia Community Forestry Project Discussion Paper presented to the IUCN Workshop on Biological Diversity Conservation Outside Protected Areas, Madrid, 11–14 April.

Jackson, W. J. and **Ingles, A. W.** (1994) 'Developing Rural Communities and Conserving the Biodiversity of Nepal's Forests through Community Forestry'. Nepal-Australia Community Forestry Project Discussion Paper presented at a Seminar on Community Development and Conservation of Forest Biodiversity through Community Forestry, Bangkok, 26–28 October.

Janzen, D. H., Hallwachs, W., Jimenez, J. and **Gámez, R.** (1993) 'The Role of the Parataxonomists, Inventory Managers, and Taxonomists in Costa Rica's National Biodiversity Inventory' in Reid, W. E., Laird, S. A., Meyer, C. A., Gámez, R., Sittenfield, A., Janzen, D. H., Gollin, M. A. and Juma, C. (eds) *Biodiversity Prospecting: Using Genetic Resources for Sustainable Development*. World Resources Institute, Washington DC.

Jarvis, K. A. and **Stearman, A. M.** (1995) 'Geomatics and Political Empowerment: The Yuquí', *Cultural Survival Quarterly* 18(4): 58–61.

Kemp, W. B. and **Brooke, L. F.** (1995) 'Towards Information Self-Sufficiency: Nunavik Inuit Gather Information on Ecology and Land Use', *Cultural Survival Quarterly* 18(4): 25–8.

Kleinn, C. (1994) 'Forest Resources Inventories' in *Nepal Status Quo, Needs and Recommendations*. Forest Resource Information System Project (FRISP) His Majesty's Government of Nepal/Finnida Finnish Forest and Park Service. FRISP, Kathmandu.

Lawrence, A. (1994) 'Short Report on the Lomerío Forest Management Project, Eastern Bolivia' in 'The Role of Inventory in Communal Forest Management, The Awá Sustainable Forest Management Project, North-West Ecuador with short reports on projects in Bolivia, Guatemala and Ecuador'. ODI Internal Report, London.

Loetsch, F. and **Haller, K. E.** (1964) *Forest Inventory* Vol. I BLV Verlagsgesellschaft, Munich.

Loetsch, F., Zohrer, F. and **Haller, K. E.** (1973) *Forest Inventory* Vol. II BLV Verlagsgesellschaft, Munich.

Mayers, J., Peutalo, B. and **Shah, M. K.** (eds) (1994) *Adapting Tools for Local Forest Management. Report of an Introductory Workshop on Participatory Rural Appraisal for Community-led Forest Conservation and Development in Papua New Guinea.* IIED, London.

Messerschmidt, D. A. (1995) *Rapid Appraisal for Community Forestry: The RA Process and Rapid Diagnostic Tools.* IIED, London.

Molnar, A. (1990) 'Rapid Appraisal', *Community Forestry Notes* 3, FAO, Rome.

Nietschmann, B. (1995) 'Defending the Miskito Reefs with Maps and GPS', *Cultural Survival Quarterly* 18(4): 34–37.

Philip, M. S. (1994) *Measuring Trees and Forests* (2nd edn). CAB International, Wallingford, UK.

Poudyal, A. S. and **Edwards, S. L.** (1994) 'Evaluation of Range Level Planning in Bajhang District Bajhang District Forest Office, Chainpur, Bhajang, Far Western Development Region, Nepal'. Unpublished paper submitted to Community and Private Forestry Division, Kathmandu.

Poole, P. (1995a) 'Geomatics: Who Needs It?', (guest editorial) *Cultural Survival Quarterly* 18(4): 1.

Poole, P. (1995b) 'Guide to the Technology', *Cultural Survival Quarterly* 18(4): 16–18.

Pretty, J. (1995) 'Participatory Learning for Sustainable Agriculture', *World Development* 23(8): 1247–63.

Schreuder, H. T., Gregoire, T. G. and **Wood, G. B.** (1993) *Sampling Methods for Multiresource Forest Inventory.* John Wiley and Sons, Inc. New York, Chichester, Brisbane, Toronto and Singapore.

Simonett, O. (1992) 'Geographic Information Systems for Environment and Development'. Summary paper, UNEP/GRID, 6, rue de la Gabrielle, 1227 Carouge, Switzerland.

Sussman, R. W., Green, G. M. and **Sussman, L.** (1992) 'The Use of Satellite Imagery and Anthropology to Assess the Causes of Deforestation in Madagascar'. Unpublished paper, Department of Anthropology, Washington University, St Louis, USA.

UNEP (1992) *Convention on Biological Diversity* 5 June.

Wells, M. (1995) 'Biodiversity Conservation and Local Peoples' Development Aspirations: New Priorities for the 1990s', *Rural Development Forestry Network Paper 18a*. ODI, London.

Wells, M. and **Brandon, K.** with **Hannah, L.** (1992) *People and Parks: Linking Protected Area Management with Local Communities.* World Bank, World Wildlife Fund and US Agency for International Development, Washington DC.

West, P. C. and **Brechin, S. R.** (eds) (1990) *Resident Peoples and National Parks: Social Dilemmas and Strategies in International Conservation.* University of Arizona Press, Tuscon, Arizona.

Westoby, J. (1987) *The Purpose of Forests. Follies of Development.* Basil Blackwell Ltd, Oxford.

Whittome, M. (1994) 'The Adoption of Alley Farming in Nigeria and Benin: The On-farm Experience of IITA and ILCA'. PhD. Thesis, Department of Geography, University of Cambridge, UK.

World Commission on Environment and Development (1987) *Our Common Future.* Oxford University Press, Oxford/New York.

2 A Community Forest Inventory for Productive Forest Management in Cross River State, Nigeria

Robert Dunn and Daniel Otu

This case study describes why and how a forest inventory was conducted by the people of Old and New Ekuri villages in Cross River State, in south-eastern Nigeria (see Figure 2.1). It is of interest as a case study in which a stock survey was successfully conducted by highly motivated villagers who had no previous experience of such work. It also illustrates the precarious situation in which communities with control over valuable forest resources often find themselves – caught between persuasive logging companies and a wish for sustainable development. There are many aspects to compare and contrast between this case study and that of the Awá Sustainable Forest Management Project in Ecuador, described in Chapter 3. Superficial similarities include the fact that the initiative involves remote forest-dwelling communities and is only in the early stages of development. In this case, the harvesting of timber for sale by the community has not even begun. Unlike the Ecuador example, there appears to be a good local market for a variety of timber species. The Ekuri initiative does not hinge on the foreign export market, although the community would like to exploit this in future. An additional similarity is that both case studies are located in areas of high biodiversity, in which there is an international conservation interest.

The Ekuri forests are largely undisturbed and are part of the Korup-Oban Hills forest, an area of high biodiversity with some 6,000 plant species and many rare primate species. The villagers of Old and New Ekuri have received assistance to manage the forest under their control on a sustainable basis from a variety of sources. These include one member of staff, in particular, of the Cross River National Park (CRNP) (at the time through funding from the World Wide Fund for Nature, WWF-UK); many members of the ODA-assisted Cross River State Forestry Project (CRSFP); other members of the Cross River State Forest Department (CRS FD); and, more recently, the British High Commission and several Nigerian-based companies.

Figure 2.1 Cross River State and the Ekuri Community Forest, Nigeria

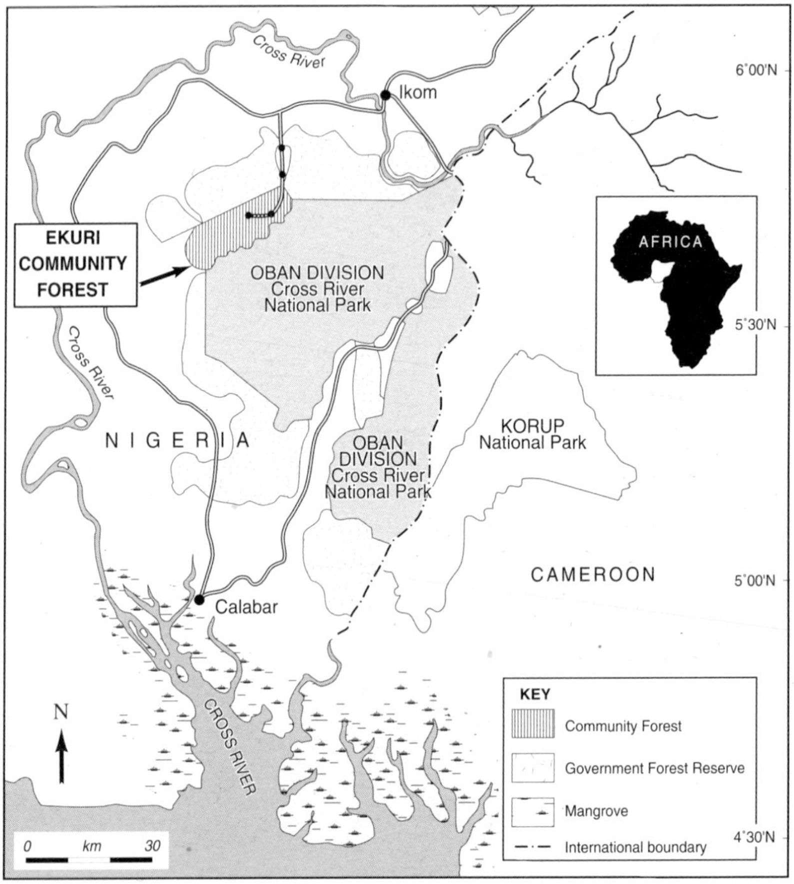

Source: Morakinyo (1993)

2.1 Forest Legislation and the Role of the State Government in Forest Management

Nigeria is a federation of 30 States, each of which has its own government. National forest policy is of course set at federal level, but each State has its own forest rules and regulations as appropriate to its particular circumstances. State legislation is implemented by State Forest Departments, which have overall responsibility for all forest reserves, trees and forest products lying within State borders. The exception to this is forest land within

National Parks, which are under direct federal control. In this chapter, all comments on forest policy and legislation refer explicitly to Cross River State, unless otherwise indicated.

Forest Policy

Until recently forest policy focused almost entirely on the exploitation of the State's forests as a source of State revenue. Accordingly, the CRS FD was primarily concerned with generating income from the harvesting of forest products, and the establishment of fast-growing exotic species in forest reserves to provide raw materials for a pulp mill in what is now a neighbouring State. This was in line with federal policies and funding, and at the expense of high forest (as is well illustrated by the example given in Box 2.1). In theory the CRS FD controls high forest exploitation by issuing logging concessions and individual tree felling permits to recognised companies and individuals who are registered with the Department. In practice, there are many difficulties in implementing this.

Box 2.1 Past Forest Policy and Forest Clearance in Cross River State: A Practical Example

Ekinta, an 11,000 ha forest reserve in the south-east of the State, provides a good example of accelerated high forest loss as a consequence of forest policy that favoured forest exploitation and the establishment of fast-growing exotic species. The reserve was good quality high forest until the late 1970s. The government-owned logging company Seromwood cleared much of the forest in a salvage cut and opened up the entire reserve with a network of roads. A large number of farmers (from the then south-west of CRS, now the neighbouring State of Akwa Ibom) were permitted to move into the area to establish plantations of *Gmelina arborea* using the *taungya* system. However, due to a shortage of funds for seedlings and supervision, virtually no plantations were established. In less than a decade 90% of the forest reserve had become cassava farms instead of forest plantations, with hardly a tree standing.

The policy of high forest clearance for plantation establishment within forest reserves was reversed in Cross River State in 1991, after discussions between the pulp mill, the CRSFP, CRS FD, and CRNP. Now new plantations are only permitted in forest reserves where the forest has already been illegally cleared by farmers. (Most of these farmers come from the neighbouring state of Akwa Ibom, where the population density is approximately seven times that of Cross River State, and farmland is extremely difficult to acquire.)

Forest Ownership

Land tenure in Cross River State, as in many parts of Africa, reflects the superimposition of modern law on traditional (customary) law. Under customary law, land ownership in most parts of the State is vested in the village/town head on behalf of the local community. However, there are tracts of land owned and controlled by family heads who allocate areas to family members for farming/development. Although generally allocated on an annual basis, some areas are granted for permanent use. Virgin land or forest land owned and controlled by the village head can be acquired by any member of the community who first clears or cultivates it. This results in more forest being cleared than is currently required as people anticipate future shortages of farmland and clear for their children. The land, once cleared, is always controlled by the family responsible for the original clearing. Therefore, with sharply rising populations, families are understandably anxious to safeguard their future by clearing forest land.

Under modern law, all forest land outside National Parks is subject to State legislation. That outside National Parks is divided into two major legal categories:

- Forest Reserve, the management of which is entirely the responsibility of the CRS FD.

- 'Protected Forest'. This comprises all non-reserved forest, including community forests. CRS FD responsibility in these areas is restricted to the monitoring of harvesting and the levying of tariffs on commercially extracted forest produce.

With the creation of CRNP in 1991, a forest area of 330,000 ha (nearly half the State's high forest area of 731,000 ha) came under federal jurisdiction, prohibiting any form of forest product harvesting. This places a great strain on forest resources outside the Park. Just over half (214,000 ha) the high forest outside the Park is owned and controlled by local communities. The wise management of community forests, to produce income for local people and forest products for local and national consumption, is thus essential for the health of the entire forest resource of Cross River State.

The Cross River State Forest Department (CRS FD)

The CRS FD falls under the Ministry of Agriculture, Fisheries and Rural Development, and is entirely funded by the State government. (Particular projects to be implemented by State Forest Departments may be funded by the federal government, but there is no funding from this source at present.) In common with many State Forest Departments, it suffers from low levels of staffing, limited training opportunities, and inadequate funding. From 1991 to 1994 the CRS FD was supported by the ODA-assisted Cross River State Forestry Project (CRSFP), which focused on institutional strengthening and capacity building. Unfortunately, due to political difficulties, the continuation of the project is in doubt. However, enthusiasm generated by the CRSFP for assisting the Ekuri villagers in their forest management activities is such that the CRS FD continues to provide support to the villagers where possible (Forestry Development Department, 1994).

The Cross River National Park (CRNP)

The CRNP was created in recognition of the outstanding conservation value of the forest in the area (as noted earlier, it has exceptional species diversity – one of the highest levels in Africa). Financial assistance for Park activities was initially provided by WWF-UK, a role subsequently taken over by the Commission of the European Union. As part of the planning of Park management, a 'Support Zone' comprising the land and 105 villages immediately around the borders of the Park was identified. This zone was designed to provide rural development assistance to the people living within it, and is not a legally classified area. The rationale for the support provided is to compensate the inhabitants for income lost as a result of the curtailment of access to the Park, and to enlist their support for its protection. The Ekuri villages which form the focus of this case study lie within the 'Support Zone'. As described in Section 2.4, much of the initial outsider interest in their plans for forest management may be attributed to one particular member of the CRNP staff.

2.2 Past and Present Forest Utilisation in Cross River State

The forest resource base of Cross River State cuts across four eco-zones. In the south lies mangrove and swamp forest; moving northwards, the vegetation changes to high forest and then guinea savanna. The State covers an area of 21,265 km², with approximately 7,310 km² of this area being high forest. This represents about one third of the high forest remaining in Nigeria. The forest in Cross River State comprises a few very large blocks (Dunn, Otu and Wong, 1994). The relative inaccessibility of much of it probably explains why, despite the huge demand for timber and agricultural land in Nigeria, the State's forests have only been cleared at a rate of about 1% per annum since the early 1970s.

Throughout this century, the forests of Cross River State have contributed significantly to the economy of both rural areas and the State. Although the value of financial and economic benefits is difficult to estimate, the forest provides medicines, fuelwood, building materials, food, sources of employment and income to rural and urban communities. Many of these benefits are felt elsewhere in Nigeria where the forest products of Cross River State are processed, traded and consumed. Some of the most valuable forest products found in the State's forests are indicated in Box 2.2. (They may be compared with a similar list given for Ghana in Chapter 5, Box 5.1.)

Box 2.2 Some of the Most Valuable Forest Products Found in Cross River State, Nigeria

Gnetum africanum	A leafy climber, known locally as **afang**. The leaves are used in soup.
Irvingia gabonensis	A large forest tree, known locally as **bush mango**. The nuts are used to thicken soup, and, despite being a valuable timber tree, it is almost never felled.
Elaeis guineensis	Oil palm – the leaves, fruits and kernels of which are all widely used and valued. Most oil palm is exploited on farms and from fallow land.
Raphia vinifera	Raphia palm. Tapped for palm wine; the leaves are used for roofing. Most raphia palm is exploited from swamp forest.
Raphia hookeri	The sap of this palm is often distilled for local 'gin'.
Garcinia spp., *Randia* spp.	Chewing sticks, used for oral hygiene throughout southern Nigeria. The species used are only found in forest areas.
Timber	Over thirty species are harvested, processed and traded within the State, with perhaps 80% 'exported' outside the State.
Bush meat	Most wild animals are caught and consumed or traded, providing valuable protein and income throughout the State.

Timber and Non-Timber Forest Product (NTFP) Extraction

The extraction of timber from the high forest over recent decades has been conducted unsustainably – both outside and within forest reserves. Stock estimates within forest reserves, using temporary sample plots (TSPs), were occasionally carried out prior to exploitation. However, such inventories only gave estimates of timber volumes available, leaving the issue of sustainability

The situation in Cross River State may be compared with Ghana (see Chapter 5), where there is a strong history of relating extraction to growth rates and planning harvesting cycles.

unaddressed. Until as recently as 1992, concession agreements stated that all desirable trees above 56 cm dbh and all the remaining species above 33 cm dbh *must* be felled. If carried out as instructed, a virtual clear-cut would have resulted, from which the forest would take a long time to recover. Fortunately these rules were not enforced, the companies taking only the species and sizes that they required.

Prior to 1992, the CRS FD's management role was confined to monitoring the number of trees harvested for revenue generation, not regulating the harvest itself. Some of the most destructive logging has been conducted by small, private sawyers and dealers. The larger, State-owned logging companies had less direct effect on the extent and quality of the forest resource, as they operate relatively uncompetitively. However, the opening up of forest areas previously inaccessible to farmers by these large timber companies, combined with the CRS FD's inability to patrol the forest reserves effectively, has led to accelerated encroachment in many areas.

Major timber companies currently account for about 10% of the timber harvest in the State. This may change in the future, as the large plywood factory being established in Ikom, if ever fully operational, will require a vast supply of raw material. At the time of going to press, a court injunction was being sought to halt the factory. Most of the timber currently harvested by large companies is either processed to add value (e.g. veneer or plywood) and/or exported. The domestic market is supplied by local timber dealers, who convert trees to lumber at the stump site using chainsaws, and move it to lorries using a mixture of head-loading and tractors. Unlike the large companies, the smaller operators utilise cheap labour and keep equipment to a minimum. This method produces roughly hewn planks that are relatively inexpensive and are in strong demand throughout Nigeria for furniture and construction. The only restriction to 'exporting' timber out of the State is an 'Interstate Fee' attached to large planks. This encourages processing into smaller pieces within the State.

Although by law the timber dealers have to be indigenous to Cross River State, they are often front men for wealthy dealers based in neighbouring States. The head of the Cross River State Timber Dealers Association recently estimated that fewer than 5% of the chainsaws felling and converting trees within the State were owned by Cross Riverians. Most of the sawing and carrying is also conducted by non-Cross Riverians. The result is that most of the material and economic benefits of the State's forests are being enjoyed by people outside the State. This greatly frustrates and angers local people who own the resources but lack the capital required to start such businesses. Other forest products are also purchased in the State and processed elsewhere. For example, Cross Riverians often buy chewing sticks originating from their State, after they have been processed outside it.

The harvesting of NTFPs for domestic purposes is conducted freely in all forest areas, including forest reserves. One exception concerns the fruit of the **bush mango** tree, *Irvingia gabonensis*, which on farm land usually belongs to the individual controlling the land. Commercial NTFP harvesting inside forest reserves requires payment of a specified tariff, and, like lumber, most of the profits from harvesting and trade are made by non-Cross Riverians. Timber and NTFP tariffs have always been shared between the CRS FD and the traditional owners of the land, both for forest reserves and 'protected forest'. Until recently the portion of the tariff paid to the indigenous people (royalty) was 20% within forest reserves and 50% outside reserves. As tariff rates were extremely low this resulted in a relatively small income for both the Cross River State government and the local people. For example, in 1993 the royalty accruing to the local owners of a forest reserve from the removal of a mature Class 1 tree, such as mahogany, was only ₦50 (worth about £1.00 at the time). Recent changes in tariff rates and royalty proportions have increased the community royalty share for the same tree to approximately ₦1,250. This has resulted in greater co-operation between the CRS FD and local people, many of whom are eager to confirm that all the timber removed from their forest has had the tariff paid. Local people are even setting up check points to confirm that timber lorries have their correct papers, and often fine offenders before passing them on to the CRS FD.

Forest Clearance for Agriculture

Apart from selling the rights to the products in their forests, some communities also permit farmers from neighbouring States to lease forest land which is then cleared for farms. As indicated above, forest land outside forest reserves remains communally owned until it is cleared (or crops are planted on it) by a member of the community.

There appears to be no lack of appreciation amongst local people of the environmental value of the forest or the economic benefits derived from it. When the present authors and their colleagues conducted PRA exercises on forest issues, many participants commented on the immense value of the forest and how they were concerned that it was taking longer to reach it in order to collect the numerous forest products they rely on. However, they also expressed their need to eat and said that farmland had to be the priority.

2.3 The People of Cross River State

The population of Cross River State is ethnically diverse. Indigenous tribes include the **Efik, Qua, Ekoi, Yakurr, Ejagham** and **Boki**, whilst 'immigrants' from other States mainly belong to the **Ibibio, Hausa/Fulani, Yoruba** and **Igbo** tribes. The State is split into 14 Local Government Areas (LGAs), each of which has an elected assembly. The government recognises paramount rulers (the traditional ruler of each LGA), clan heads and village heads/head chiefs. Within families there are also locally recognised family heads. In each chief's court there is often a council of elders that is the decision-making body. It often also includes a youth leader and a women's leader. Village issues that relate to women are generally left to them to discuss and take decisions on. Decisions in council are mostly reached by consensus, except when a chief is autocratic.

Problems including family disputes about issues of land ownership and land distribution and allocation amongst family members are handled initially by the immediate chiefs. When these issues cannot be settled by them, they are referred to the higher chiefs up to the village head and even to Customary Courts if necessary. In most cases decisions handed down in Customary Courts confirm decisions reached in the chief's court. A variety of societies help to bind the village communities together, emphasising discipline, peace, orderliness and the maintenance of a cultural identity.

2.4 The Development of the Ekuri Community Forest Management Initiative

The communities of Old and New Ekuri lie about 7 km apart, deep within primary moist high forest (see Figure 2.2) and surrounded on three sides by forest reserves and the CRNP. Although much of their original land is now under the jurisdiction of the State or Federal government, they still own and control approximately 30,000 ha of unspoilt primary high forest. Unusually, the two communities share forest ownership. This is a result of individuals from Old Ekuri founding New Ekuri during the 1930s, long after the boundaries between Old Ekuri and neighbouring communities had been established.

The Ekuri community forest is probably the largest single area of community-owned and -controlled high forest in Nigeria.

The people of the **Ekuri** ethnic group (known to themselves as **Nkukole**) live in a total of five villages (the other three are Ekuri Eyeying, Okokori and Edondon, two of which are marked on Figure 2.2). They have one clan head, and speak their own language, **Lokole** (Morakinyo, 1993). The combined resident population of the villages of Old and New Ekuri is about 1,500; it is these people to whom all subsequent reference to the 'Ekuri villagers' applies. Many more Ekuri people are occasional village residents, mainly living outside because of employment opportunities or attending secondary/higher education. Very few non-Ekuri people live in either village and respect for traditional systems of law and authority is still intact.

The Ekuri villagers are ruled by village heads, assisted by other village elders. The village 'youth' (males younger than about 40 years) also have great influence and are always represented in important village meetings. The population is divided into age-grades which comprise people born during the same years, each of

The relative social cohesion of the Ekuri people is not the case in many villages elsewhere in the State, particularly in the southern third, where recent migrants often comprise the majority of the population. In such villages, the youth commonly display little respect for the decisions made by the village chiefs or heads.

which has a name chosen by the members. Age-grade members have a strong affiliation to each other and will always give help, if possible, during times of need.

Until 1989, members of both villages had a four-hour walk to the nearest motorable road. Prior to this, both villages tried separately to make agreements with logging companies – in effect swapping their rich forest resources for a road. However, in every case the other village vetoed the agreement. These disagreements have been a primary reason for the villages' continued isolation (see Box 2.7, below). It was the people of Old Ekuri, led by a dynamic city-based villager, Oliver Enuor, who eventually organised and subsidised the construction of a road to their village. They also set up a village Co-operative to facilitate the harvesting and marketing of forest products. Both activities were entirely village-based, and not a response to outside intervention. As a result of the initiative that they demonstrated, the CRNP became interested in assisting the villagers to manage their forest, which lies within the 'Support Zone' of the Park.

Figure 2.2   Ekuri Community Forest

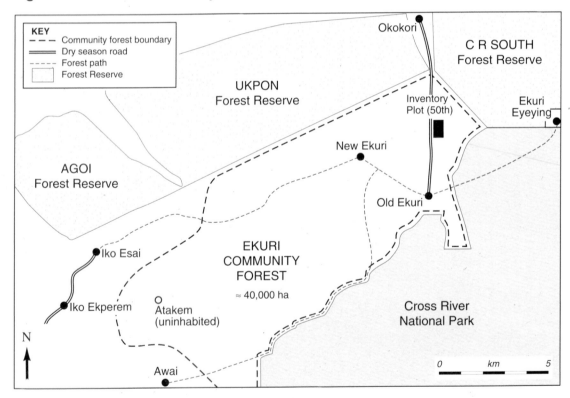

Source: Morakinyo (1993)

The length of time spent by the CRNP Community Forester in the villages was extremely important for developing rapport with the Ekuri people. There is no doubt that this helped to develop a course of action that was supported by all concerned.

The CRNP Community Forester concluded that assisting the villagers in road and bridge construction / improvement was a prerequisite to sustainable forest management. As a result, since mid-1992 the main effort of the villagers and their supporters, primarily the CRS FD and CRSFP, has been to improve access.

The need for a stock survey was clearly identified by CRSFP staff rather than the villagers. However, the villagers had asked for technical advice – specifically on timber harvesting, and training to make them independent of outsiders. They were therefore highly willing to test the system suggested.

In 1992, the CRNP Community Forester was dispatched to the villages to determine a possible course of action (Morakinyo, 1993). Whilst living in the villages for eight months, he liaised with the CRS FD from the outset, which laid the foundation for co-operation between the two organisations. Although his main task was to encourage sustainable forest management practices, he spent time listening to the villagers and found that an improved road, with bridges across the main rivers, was their top priority. Without it, they claimed, they would not have access to markets for their forest products and therefore there would be no point in worrying about sustainable forest management. The people of New Ekuri, who still had only footpath access up to Old Ekuri and other villages, gave a new road even higher priority. Many were unwilling to give full support to any new initiatives until a road reached their village (see Box 2.7).

The commitment shown by individuals outside their community to road improvement encouraged the villagers to express great interest in the productive but sustainable management of their forest resources, particularly timber. Although there were potential improvements to be made in the harvesting and, particularly, marketing of NTFPs, the villagers had been selling most of the more valuable ones (such as bush meat, *Irvingia gabonensis*, and *Gnetum africanum*) for many years. However, timber remained an undeveloped resource, due to the costs and difficulties associated with processing and transporting. It was on timber that discussions focused when, during a meeting in Old Ekuri to which the CRS FD had been invited in mid-1992, the villagers asked the CRS FD to assist them in managing their forests 'wisely'.

2.5 The Need for Forest Resource Assessment

Members of the Cross River State Forestry Project responded to the villagers' request for assistance by suggesting that a useful first step towards sustainable forest management would be to select a small area and carry out a 100% enumeration within it. This would enable the villagers, assisted by the CRS FD, to determine what would be a reasonably sustainable harvest and felling cycle. Project members recommended using the stock survey system that they had seen in the high forests of Ghana during a study tour (see Box 2.3). The survey would result in all trees above a chosen diameter being identified, measured, numbered and located within the plot. The information would then be used to produce a stock map which would allow those planning the extraction to determine which trees should be removed. The map was also to record streams and steep slopes which would assist in planning the few tractor routes required and could even indicate optimum felling directions.

Whilst the Ghanaian system was suggested to the Ekuri people as a model, it was always anticipated that it would be adjusted or rejected by the villagers depending on how useful they found it as a tool. The minimum diameter for sampling was subject to particular scrutiny, under the expectation that it might be altered after trial. In the context of timber exploitation in the rest of Cross River State, even if the Ekuri villagers eventually decided that enumeration was unnecessary and imposed a judicious minimum felling diameter (of, perhaps, 90 cm dbh), this would still be far less damaging to the forest than timber harvesting elsewhere.

Box 2.3   The Value of the Stock Survey System

As noted in Chapter 5, the Ghana FD uses the stock survey system to allow staff to dictate exactly which trees should be removed by a logging company working a particular concession. Recently updated growth rate data, collected over the last thirty years from a network of Permanent Sample Plots, enable extraction rates to be set. The system is implemented by District Forest Officers who produce yield maps after studying the stock survey map for a particular compartment due for harvesting. As all trees above 50 cm dbh are numbered it is a relatively simple system to monitor and over-cutting can be easily detected.

The stock survey is an indispensable tool that permits planning and control at the individual tree level during harvesting. The enumeration is relatively cheap and straightforward, does not require high levels of accuracy, and the results do not have to be processed by computer. Therefore relascopes and tripods or ladders can be replaced by the extremely quick and simple tangent stick. Even tree identification is relatively straightforward as there is an exponential reduction in species diversity as minimum diameter is increased (relatively few tree species reach very large sizes). Species identification is more important and difficult in permanent and temporary sample plot enumerations, where a lower minimum diameter for sampling is often set, and results are used to extrapolate over large areas. Such surveys commonly identify many more species than is usual in a stock survey.

2.6   The Forest Assessment Process

Demarcation and Enumeration

An area of 50 ha was suggested as being reasonable for training villagers in how to conduct a stock survey (Dunn, 1992). This would contain a large number of valuable trees but be small enough to demarcate and enumerate within a month. The villagers selected an area north of Old Ekuri, close to the road. Village heads chose six individuals from each village to carry out the inventory. It had been suggested that at least a third of those selected should be women, but only one woman from each village was chosen initially.

Most of the trainees sent by the chiefs had passed through secondary education, although a few were illiterate. Amongst the latter group were people with specialist skills, such as tree

Involving women in the process was not easy, even though many depend on NTFP collection for their livelihoods. However, it was found that women were more willing to attend meetings if a female member of CRSFP staff was present. This indicated a need for greater numbers of women, who are at present a small minority of CRS FD staff.

All parties concerned agreed that one of the most important aspects of the inventory would be the participation and training of villagers, the intention being that they would eventually form the core of a forest management group.

identification. One day was spent by the trainees (who, after two additions, numbered fourteen) learning about the stock survey before they began operations. This is detailed in the sub-section on training.

The demarcation of the plot proved harder than the actual enumeration, due to the difficulty of accurately demarcating the internal access lines (transects) required by the enumeration team. The plot measured 1.0 by 0.5 km and was aligned North-South. Concrete corner pillars marked with EF (Ekuri Forest) and plot and corner numbers were buried, the first of which formed part of a village-led pillar burying ceremony. This was well attended by chiefs of both communities and many other highly placed villagers. Prayers were said, libations poured and photographs taken with all the chiefs with a hand on the pillar and everyone else around them. It was a happy occasion and the only question asked by the Head Chief was how would they get more pillars for plots in the future. With the official blessing of the chiefs, it is considered extremely unlikely that the plot will be cleared for farmland, even during the long interval (forty years or more) between felling cycles.

Demarcation was conducted by the fourteen trained villagers, with supervisory assistance from CRS FD staff. Supervision was spread between external and internal line cutting, with individuals cutting the internal lines (which ran North-South) being given a bearing on which to make a thin access line. To ensure that these lines followed the bearing exactly, without continual use of a compass, poles made from forest saplings were aligned with each other approximately 6 m apart. When the line passed through any obstruction obscuring the line of sight (even a small tree), a compass man had to be called and a new bearing given.

The method of demarcation is shown in Figure 2.3. The initial plan entailed the cutting of internal lines at 20 m intervals throughout the plot, and the enumeration of strips 40 m wide at a time. This would provide a central line for the record-keeper (booker)/chain person, and two boundary lines for the enumeration (20 m either side of the booker's line). This plan was followed in the western half of the plot, but was not very satisfactory, because of the amount of time taken. The importance of aligning the poles exactly was not understood at first by the villagers. As a result, the lines (that should have been parallel to each other) started crossing, and many had to be re-cut. It also became clear that more poles had to be used on slopes than on flat ground. Eventually it was decided that fewer lines, further apart, would be more appropriate. Accordingly, an interval of 40 m was used in the eastern part of the plot. This proved to be more efficient. Each line was cut by two men, one to clear the line and the other to cut and align the poles. With this arrangement a 1 km line could be cut in two days by two people. The compass person kept a check on the direction of a certain number of cut-lines, re-establishing the bearing where necessary. The ratio of compasses to cut lines was vital, with the optimum ratio being about one compass person for every three internal lines.

Figure 2.3   Layout of the Stock Survey Plot in Ekuri Community Forest

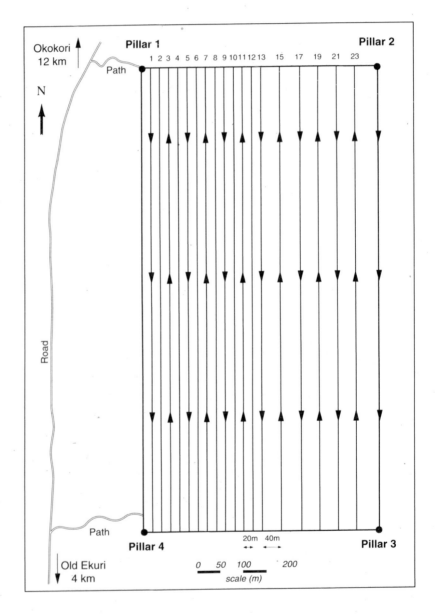

Once demarcation had been completed, the enumeration team followed the internal cut-lines (in the western part of the plot, only alternate lines) enumerating the trees 20 m either side of the lines.

All trees greater than 50 cm dbh were measured to the nearest 5 cm. The diameter was determined by a diameter tape when no buttress was present. For buttressed trees, the method detailed in Box 2.4 was used. Each tree was given a number, unique to that plot. The numbers followed consecutively and were given by the booker. The number was carved onto the bole of the tree using a locally made scribing knife. These numbers remain visible for a number of years, depending on the tree species.

Box 2.4   Measurement of Buttressed Trees

A simple, home-made calibrated tangent board was used to measure buttressed trees. The board was marked with 5 cm graduations between 50 cm and 110 cm (any measurement over this was recorded as 110 +). It was mounted on a pole and held up to rest against the bole of the tree, about 30 cm above the convergence of the buttress. A second person stood 6 m away from the base of the tree, holding the end of a 6 m piece of string attached to the board. This person gave directions to the pole man so that the left edge of the board matched the left of the bole and the size could then be read from the right side of the board.

The trees were identified by the team using the local names. At the same time a botanical species list was compiled so that these names could be matched with local names. This list was improved two years later when a team of experienced FD 'tree spotters' visited the area as part of a State-wide TSP inventory.

The team was co-ordinated by the booker who stayed on the cut-line marking the centre of the 40-m wide strip being enumerated. A chain was used to determine the distance down the cut-line. A single person had responsibility for moving the chain and holding an umbrella over the booker when it was raining. The distance from the chain to any tree was estimated by the booker. After allotting each enumerated tree a number, the booker then noted its location, size, number and local name on an enumeration form.

Enumeration training proved to be much easier than the very precise demarcation work. After initial instruction, all the tasks, including recording, were carried out by the villagers. They were circulated within the team, so that everyone had an opportunity to try most of the different tasks. The two women participating had major roles; one was the most efficient booker, and the other was an excellent tree identifier. The speed with which the skills were learnt was most impressive. All the FD members involved in the exercise commented on the enthusiasm and high spirits of the local inventory team and the speed with which they learned new ideas and techniques. The optimum number for such a team was found to be about 8–10, as detailed in Box 2.5, which also indicates the equipment needed by each team.

No great difficulties in species identification have arisen so far from using local names. A major reason for this is that the important commercial timber species are all well known to villagers. Furthermore, relatively few species were enumerated (since only large trees were recorded). Should the villagers ever require a more comprehensive enumeration of all the tree (or other) species in their forest, they would probably require professional assistance in species identification.

Box 2.5 The Team and Equipment Needed for the Pilot Ekuri Forest Enumeration

The team was made up of the following persons:

- 1   Record-keeper (Booker)
- 1   Chain person
- 6–8   Enumerators (for scribing, measuring and identification),
  3–4   on each side of the central cut-line

The team required the following equipment:

- 1   20 m chain (or, failing that, a tape)
- 1   Clip board and enumeration forms
- 4–6   Scribing knives (made locally)
- 2   Tangent boards (made locally)
- 4–6   Diameter tapes
- 1   Umbrella (during the rainy season)

The entire plot enumeration was completed within about ten days. The villagers were paid a daily stipend, approximately half of the normal daily wage for a labourer, to compensate them for their time. However, it was made clear that the Co-operative would have to bear such costs when future plots were inventoried.

Some members of the village inventory team visited local timber markets and talked to dealers to find out which of the species found in the plot were marketable. The villagers decided that it was these species that they wished to put on the stock map. The list of marketable species and their stocking in the plot is shown in Box 2.6. Within the 50 ha plot 1,460 trees of over 50 cm dbh were enumerated, which indicates that the forest was relatively undisturbed.

Preparing the Stock Survey Map

A month after the inventory, four members of the team and a member of the local CRS FD office who had assisted with the inventory, spent a week at the CRS FD headquarters planning and drawing the stock map. The team members were the four village youths who had been most closely involved in the inventory work and had a clear understanding, although no former experience, of the process. In drawing their stock survey map, they used a Ghanaian stock survey map for reference and were provided with suggestions from CRSFP staff. However, there was no formal training session.

Small circles indicated tree locations and tree numbers, with the species code, number and diameter being written within each circle. Each species was given a colour code so that the distribution of various species could be assessed at a glance. Initially the team wanted to illustrate all trees above 50 cm dbh on the 1:1,000 scale map. However, after experimenting with a randomly selected strip and finding that there just was not sufficient room for all the trees, they decided to include only species of 70 cm dbh and above. This reduced the number of trees illustrated on the map to 471, which proved more manageable (see Box 2.6).

Box 2.6   Marketable Species of Diameter Greater than 70 cm dbh in the 50 ha Enumerated Plot of Ekuri Forest

Local name	Botanical name	Total number of stems
Ukpienche	Pycnanthus angolensis	136
Akukuba	Parkia bicolor	54
Ewai	Piptadeniastrum africanum	47
Obolo	Khaya ivorensis	30
Lutuche	Pterocarpus osun	27
Ijemolokol	Afzelia bipindensis	24
Nymchikpai	Erythrophleum ivorense	19
Ikyil	Terminalia ivorensis	19
Itail	Albizia spp.	17
Ebong	Brachystegia eurycoma	13
Kpai-kpai	Albizia spp.	13
Owal	Canarium schweinfurthii	12
Ekobi	Nauclea diderrichii	11
Achimagbo	Distemonanthus benthamianus	9
Others (12 species)		40
TOTAL		471

The map was successfully produced on tracing paper which could easily be reproduced on the CRS FD's dye-line printer. Species codes were hand coloured on the prints. Laminated copies were presented to the village chiefs by the inventory teams, with lengthy explanations concerning what the map represented and how it might be used when the Co-operative was ready to start harvesting lumber. The copies are given pride of place on the walls of the respective chiefs' palaces. There is no question that, by carrying out the enumeration and producing the stock survey map themselves, the villagers gained great confidence in their ability to manage their timber resources, even though it was only the beginning of the process.

Training

Although a number of specific training sessions were held for selected individuals, in many ways training extended to the whole community. The reasons for conducting forest assessment prior to harvesting were discussed extensively in village meetings, as were the methods used. All villagers were encouraged to visit the 50 ha plot when it was being enumerated, and to see what was being done and why. The fact that the stock survey maps are displayed in the chiefs' palaces has also generated further awareness and comment.

Stock survey training

A one-day training session covered the purpose of stock surveys, and how one should be conducted. It was divided into a morning theoretical session, held in a classroom of the local school, and an afternoon practical session held on the village football pitch. The main trainer was an expatriate CRSFP officer with experience in stock surveys. He was assisted by four CRS FD staff and the CRNP Community Forester. None of the latter had stock survey experience, so they found the session useful and learned sufficient to be able to conduct a similar training programme themselves in the future.

The morning session began with a discussion on forest inventories in general, and their use in decision-making and management. The tool of stock survey was explained particularly with regard to sustainable forest management, and how much easier it would be to plan what, when and where to harvest, once basic information about the largest trees in a particular area was already known. This was followed by an explanation of the two major field tasks involved: the surveying and demarcation of the chosen area, and the enumeration of the larger trees within it.

In surveying and demarcation, the way in which external and internal lines should be cut was explained, as was the use of the necessary equipment (poles and compasses). Enumeration covered tree identification, measurement, numbering and location, again with an explanation of the equipment to be used. Questions were encouraged, and many were forthcoming. It was stressed that all trainees would have the opportunity to learn all the skills involved, by rotating tasks amongst them.

The afternoon practical session concentrated on pole alignment (crucial in inexpensive forest demarcation work) and the use of prismatic compasses. The following day, and most of the next week, these new skills were put into practice in the forest as demarcation work began. Close supervision was needed, but by the time the plot had been demarcated and enumerated most team members had practised and were reasonably confident in the following:

- Tree measuring – diameter at breast height – using a diameter tape for trees without buttresses, or a simple tangent stick for trees with buttresses.

- Tree identification – this was something that participants could not learn quickly, but many were very familiar with all the main tree species. Training identified those with particular knowledge, and encouraged others to learn from them.

- Tree marking – carving numbers onto trees.

- Booking – recording tree species, diameter, number and location on the enumeration form and co-ordinating the team's work.

- Ground measurements – measuring the distance along the cut-line using a 20 m chain.

- Survey techniques required to demarcate straight lines on a bearing in the forest.

The villagers were highly motivated to learn and often spontaneously practised aligning poles and reading the compass on the village football pitch after working in the forest all day. This is a very positive sign for future inventory work.

Chainsaw training

In preparation for timber harvesting, a chainsaw training course was sponsored by the British High Commission for six members of the village youth (three from each village). This course lasted approximately three months, starting in September/October 1994 and continuing until early 1995. The course was initially run by an expatriate working in the area, and was continued by a local sawyer experienced in log conversion (who is also a young chief of New Ekuri). It covered chainsaw operation and maintenance as well as felling and conversion procedures.

Further training is planned, initially through general workshops on the establishment of a joint Co-operative. It is hoped that, at these, villagers will identify their own training needs. Amongst those envisaged are accounting, Co-operative management, forest management, harvesting, extraction and marketing; however, the choice should lie with the villagers themselves (Dunn, Otu and Thornber, 1994).

Ekuri villagers participating in the chainsaw training course
Photograph: Robert Dunn

The Next Step: Planning the Harvest

The inventory team discussed how many trees might be felled in the plot during an initial harvest. They agreed to try a 40-year felling cycle, again copying the current Ghanaian system. Since very few reliable growth data are available for Cross River State, the generally accepted figure for the growth of commercially desirable species in a reasonably well stocked tropical high forest, 1 m^3/ha/yr, was assumed. It was decided that perhaps 50% of this volume would represent an acceptable harvest because of damage caused to the stand during felling. Taking a 40-year felling cycle, this would result in a volume of 1,000 m^2 or approximately 100 large trees per harvest. This estimate probably errs on the cautious side, since:

- The method of extraction to be used – converting logs at the stump-site and then head-loading the planks to a small tractor road – is amongst the least destructive timber harvesting methods possible.

- A wide variety of species are acceptable to local markets, meaning that the harvest can probably be fairly evenly spread.

- Given the dense nature of the forest, opening up the canopy could even be beneficial by promoting the growth of younger trees and saplings.

Speculation on the effect of harvesting on the relatively undisturbed Ekuri forest should be related to the gap theory – see Chapter 9, Section 9.3.

Probably even a harvest of 150 trees (i.e. 75% of the volume assumed available) would be sustainable. The harvest could be limited to trees of 90 cm dbh and above, still leaving over 50 trees as seed trees above this size. As the number of marketable trees in the 70–90 cm dbh size class is around 240, this provides optimism for a high value second harvest.

2.7 Current and Future Developments

The people of Ekuri are fortunate in that the forest area available to them is so vast that they are extremely unlikely to come close to the potential sustainable harvest. Crude calculations indicate that this may be as much as 8–10 huge trees per day. However, it is likely to be many years before the Co-operative is able to harvest, transport and sell even one tree per day. Therefore the CRS FD's main concerns focus less on sustainability and more on encouraging the development of the Co-operative and training its members. The potential difficulties in this are acknowledged. Since, until recently, Old and New Ekuri have often had major disagreements, it will be extremely difficult to build a democratic institution that is trusted by both communities. It should also be managed by villagers, not dominated by urban-based elites. Nevertheless, urban-based educated elites of village origin can be extremely influential in village affairs both directly and indirectly through their urban contacts. It is therefore important to enlist their support.

This change in the State Forest Law and Regulations represents a significant shift in the attitude of the CRS FD to local communities. Through it the Department officially recognises the capabilities of local people in managing the forests that they control themselves.

Prompted by the Ekuri initiative, the CRS FD inserted a new clause in the Cross River State Forest Laws and Regulations during a recent review (Cross River State, 1994). Any village or individual harvesting timber from communally controlled areas ('Protected Forest') in a sustainable manner, as approved by the CRS FD, is entitled to a 50% reduction in the tariff that has to be paid to the CRS FD for each tree. This was designed to encourage communities throughout the State to seek assistance from the CRS FD when they wish to harvest their timber resources sustainably.

Since the stock survey was undertaken in 1992, progress has been slow. This was partly because of disagreements between the Chief and the youth of New Ekuri concerning the best method of obtaining a road to the village (see Box 2.7), and partly because of a lack of funds for most of the period. The villagers of Old Ekuri raised sufficient funds to make some progress on the road, but were unable to complete it. However, in April 1994 some funds were made available by the British High Commission for both road-building and a chainsaw training course (including the purchase of two chainsaws). This has also stimulated donations by several Nigerian-based companies.

Although the first phase of the CRSFP ended in December 1994, the CRS FD continues to assist the Ekuri villages as it can, particularly with the support and development of the Ekuri Project.

Assistance is also being provided through Voluntary Service Overseas (VSO), which is helping to organise Co-operative organisation and training, road, bridge and guesthouse construction, and market development. The bridges have now been completed, using decking and mouldings cut during the chainsaw training course.

In time, it is hoped that the Co-operative might attempt to export their most valuable lumber with a 'sustainably managed' label, attracting premium prices. This would earn valuable foreign exchange for the community. Continuing with stock surveys would almost certainly be essential for achieving certification as a sustainable producer. Members of the community are also considering attracting local and passing 'overlander' tourists to their forest as another source of income – although this is unlikely in the near future. Once the road is completed, their area will be the most accessible high.quality tropical forest anywhere in Cross River State.

Box 2.7 Recent Events in New Ekuri: Improved Prospects for Continued Joint Co-operation between the Two Communities

One of the major difficulties experienced by all those involved with the Ekuri project was the attitude of the Chief of New Ekuri. He hoped to attract a logging company to build a road to the village from the nearby village of Iyamitet, in exchange for the rights to all 'New Ekuri's' forest resources. However, all of Old Ekuri and most of New Ekuri agreed that the forest was jointly owned and neither village could sell a portion unilaterally, without the consent of the other. The sustainable management of the forest as a co-operative venture by both villages meant that the company would not be permitted to build a road or log the forest. This resulted in the Chief being unco-operative, at best, and openly hostile at worst.

The Chief was nevertheless successful in his negotiations with the company, which began building the road from Iyamitet in early 1995. Shortly after the Chief had celebrated this, the youth of New Ekuri banded together and decided to remove his title. He has now been de-throned, and the company informed that they are unwelcome in the Ekuri forests. A criterion in appointing the new Chief will be that he wants to form a successful co-operative with Old Ekuri. The old Chief has continued his efforts towards road construction, as a result of which court charges are being brought against both him and the company.

2.8 Conclusion

The attempts of the villagers of Old and New Ekuri to manage their forest on a sustainable basis are only at a very early stage. However, the villagers have demonstrated both commitment and ability in what they have achieved so far. As long as they continue to receive some external support (both financial and technical) in setting up their Co-operative, there is good reason to be optimistic that they will succeed. Access is the crucial factor. Although the remoteness of the Ekuri forest has protected it from exploitation in the past, its future depends on the villagers having an incentive to manage it on a sustainable basis. Access to markets and a generally improved standard of living should provide such an incentive.

References

Cross River State (1994) Forest Law and Regulations: Cap. 55 Regulations for marketing and transportation of forest products. Forest Department, Calabar, Cross River State, Nigeria.

Dunn, R. (1992) 'A Report on the Recent Inventory Work Carried Out in the Communally Owned Ekuri Forest'. Internal document, Cross River State Forestry Project, Forest Department, Calabar, Cross River State, Nigeria.

Dunn, R., Otu, D. and **Thornber, K.** (1994) 'The Old and New Ekuri Community Forest Management Initiative: Workplan and Funding Proposal for K. Thornber and G. Allan'. Internal document, VSO Field Office, Nigeria.

Dunn, R., Otu, D. and **Wong, J.** (1994) 'Report on the Reconnaissance Inventory of High Forest and Swamp Forest Areas in Cross River State, Nigeria'. Cross River State Forestry Project, Forest Department, Calabar, Cross River State, Nigeria.

Forestry Development Department, Cross River State (1994) 'A Strategy for Sustainable development, Conservation and Management of the Forests of Cross River State, Nigeria'. Calabar, Nigeria.

Morakinyo, T. (1993) *Ekuri Community Forestry Project Project Report and Recommendations* (and report on Okwangwo Division Community Forestry). Prepared by WWF-CRNP Community Forestry Officer for Old Ekuri and New Ekuri, Cross River National Park WWF-UK.

Acronyms specific to this chapter
CRNP   Cross River National Park
CRSFP   Cross River State Forestry Project (ODA-assisted)
CRS FD   Cross River State Forest Department

3

Forest Inventory in the Awá Sustainable Forest Management Project, Ecuador

Anna Lawrence and Mario Godoy
with contributions from Jim Bampton and Leonel Quiñónez

This chapter describes how a number of small communities in the Awá region of north-west Ecuador are attempting to manage their forests on a sustainable and productive basis, whilst facing an immediate need for cash to survive. Timber companies are carrying out selective and destructive timber extraction in neighbouring forest areas, for which they offer immediate cash payment. The communities have been supported in their forest management activities by a number of external agencies, including the CIBT (Centro de Información de los Bosques Tropicales – originally the Rainforest Information Centre) and the ODA (Overseas Development Administration of the British Government). Support initially focused on the pilot communities of El Pan and Arenales, but is now being expanded to others. The project is only in a very early stage of development, but is an interesting case study for a number of reasons. It demonstrates the importance of markets (in this case international markets) in productive forest management, and raises questions over the extent to which local people, at least in the circumstances described, can become involved in the details of forest inventory. It also illustrates the difficulties often faced by similar projects in balancing appropriate action against the immediate urgency of disappearing forests. The communities in this case study are remote, and financially and politically vulnerable. Project success is by no means guaranteed.

As indicated in Figure 3.1, the project area lies in the Pacific lowlands of north-west Ecuador, along the border with Colombia. It is part of the Chocó phytogeographical zone, an area markedly distinct from the Amazon basin, with very high biodiversity (Orejula, 1992). More than 6,000 species of vascular plants are found within this zone, of which 20% are endemic – many to very restricted areas (ODA, 1991). There is thus national and international interest in preventing its widespread destruction. However, logging operations in the area are significant. Logging in Ecuador in fact began in the coastal region, because of the ease of access for timber extraction provided by rivers and the sea. Under current national policy, the nearby port of Esmeraldas has been identified as the main port servicing the country's entire timber exports.

Figure 3.1   The Awá Sustainable Forest Management Project, Ecuador

3.1 Forest Legislation and the Role of the Federal Government in Forest Management

Forest Policy and Legislation

In general, the Ecuadorian forestry sector is characterised by a lack of information on policy and legal aspects, and a scarcity of trained Ecuadorian professionals. The latter is largely due to poor remuneration, salaries being much higher in the commercial forestry sector. The former difficulties are being addressed to a certain extent by two externally funded projects (one supported by the German Government through GTZ, and the other by FAO, as described below). The country's forest policy and related legislation have undergone considerable change in the recent past, but the extent to which this has influenced activities on the ground is difficult to ascertain.

Ecuador is a participating country in the Tropical Forestry Action Programme co-ordinated through the FAO (Food and Agriculture Organisation). A **Plan de Accion Forestal Ecuador** (PAFE) was approved in 1991 after some three years of work supported by the FAO, but was not implemented due to the changes in the organisation of the forestry service outlined below. However, it is now in the process of review and implementation with support from FAO and the Netherlands Government. A feature of note is that the Plan does not make specific mention of indigenous rights with regard to forest use.

In 1992, a new National Forestry, Natural Areas and Wildlife Institute, INEFAN (**Instituto Ecatoriano Forestal y de Areas Naturales y Vida Silvestre**) was established by decree, to replace the Sub-secretariat of Forestry and Renewable Natural Resources. INEFAN has the remit of implementing a strategy for forest management along guidelines established by the International Timber Trade Organisation (ITTO). These guidelines aim to address present and future forest needs, taking into account economic, social, cultural and ecological aspects. INEFAN's objectives include 'overseeing the conservation and rational exploitation of the existing natural and forestry resources'. In this regard, an INEFAN policy statement of particular note is that

> the success of the management plans depends largely on their compatibility with the interests of the local communities. All sustainable forest management programmes should consider a process of consultation with the communities which inhabit the forest regions, with the aim of formulating the actions which conform with their interests. (INEFAN, 1993:5)

However, this statement represents a recommendation rather than a requirement.

About 13% of Ecuador's territory is designated as either national parks or forest reserves. As long as the latter are not specifically protected, they may be commercially harvested. Permission for harvesting non-protected forests is granted on submission of a management plan, including a professional forest inventory. To assist in management plan preparation, INEFAN provides models of such plans according to forest size. In most cases, a 5% inventory of the area to be harvested is required, providing an error of less than 20%. (Under current law a lower sampling intensity is acceptable for forest areas greater than 5,000 ha.) Responsibility for checking inventories and reviewing management plans is vested in INEFAN. This work is assigned to **peritos extensionistas**, or technical extensionists, who report to more senior officials. Permission for exploitation may be granted by different officials, depending on the size of the forest. The relevant official may be the Zonal Forestry Chief (for forests of up to 100 ha), the District Forestry Chief (up to 200 ha), or the Executive Director of the National Forest Programme (200–500 ha).

The system of management plans and permits for exploitation does not always work in practice. Indeed, there appears to be widespread disregard of such legal requirements by both the logging companies and local people carrying out most of the timber extraction in the case study region. A further significant fact is that, since 1982, there has been a government-imposed ban on logging concessions. Southgate (1990) has made the observation that the ban 'makes the forest products industry in north-western Ecuador almost entirely dependent on agricultural colonists, whose rudimentary harvesting and log transport techniques cause significant damage to commercial timber...' In many cases, however, it is not the colonists or other local people who conduct the logging operations, but companies which buy the standing trees or the land from them. In the project area itself, a new road is resulting in increasing pressure on the surrounding forests by the timber companies. This is already affecting the forests of communities which might become involved in the project in the future.

Forest Ownership

Land tenure is a particularly sensitive issue in Ecuador, and has also been subject to recent change, in a programme of land reform. This has had significant implications for the case study project in its attempts to secure legal security of land tenure for the communities concerned. This has not yet been achieved in either El Pan or Arenales, but has always been considered by project staff to be of the highest priority. Under former legislation, community or individual title to land had to be established by purchase from the state. Accordingly, the project paid 18,000 sucres (US$9) per hectare to commence the land legislation process in El Pan. In total, the two communities were loaned 9 million sucres (US$4,500) as the first payment for establishing title to their land. It was expected that this would be repaid from timber sales into a rotating fund for the

the timber enterprise. The loan was seen as an important benefit to the communities, many of whose neighbours could not afford the costs of title establishment.

Under the new legislation, indigenous and Afro-Ecuadorian communities are not required to pay for establishing legal title. This raises a question over the sum already paid for this purpose. Institutional change has caused further confusion. A National Institute of Agrarian Development (INDA – **Instituto Nacional de Desarrollo Agrario**) has replaced the organisation previously responsible for land tenure issues, IERAC (National Institute of Agrarian Reform and Colonisation – **Instituto Ecuatoriano de Reforma Agraria y Colonización**). INDA has a remit to provide land title to those occupying land without current title, as long as they can prove an uninterrupted tenancy of at least five years (excepting if the land in question is state forest or under INEFAN control). Unfortunately for the project activities, INDA has been slow to start operating and it is unclear exactly how and when the legal position of the communities' land will be resolved.

One possibility open to communities in Ecuador is to adopt the legal status of **comuna**. The communities of El Pan and Arenales both have this status. Under it, the community (which must number at least 50 residents) is bound by common ownership of forest resources and individual non-transferable ownership of cultivated land. The boundaries between cultivated and common land are well established. Following recent legislative changes, individual members are allowed to sell their cultivated land, but such a person thereby loses the right to live in the community. The buyer, in turn, has to agree to live by the rules and decisions of the community. A **comuna** can also take the collective decision to divide its land among members, if this is approved by a two-thirds majority of its general assembly. However, the communities with which the project is working seem unlikely to take such action in the foreseeable future.

Legislation on Timber Exports

Since the project is based on timber extraction for export, legislation on timber exports is of potential significance to activities – although in practice control over timber exports is minimal. A list of species which may not be exported is determined periodically by the Ministry of Agriculture and Livestock, as is the minimum level of timber processing prior to export, and the exportation of non-timber forest products, wildlife and botanical specimens. One problem encountered by the project to date has concerned the export of *Humiriastrum procerum* (**Chanul**), one of the species of most potential interest to the international timber market, which it did not receive permission to export in a 1995 trial consignment.

3.2 Past and Present Forest Utilisation in the Awá Region

The forest of the Awá region may be broadly categorised as lowland tropical moist forest. As noted in the introduction, it is a forest of exceptional biodiversity. The mean annual rainfall is about 3,000 mm, with rain falling in every month. The dryest period occurs in December to February. Temperatures do not fluctuate greatly through the year, the mean annual temperature being 23–25.5°C.

The topography and soils of El Pan and Arenales differ in certain respects, as do the forests themselves. El Pan lies on hilly terrain, with slopes of up to 40%, whereas the topography of Arenales is more undulating, with slopes of around 25%. The soils of the area are generally deep, clayey and acidic; in Arenales there are frequent rocky outcrops. The forest of El Pan is in a more advanced state of succession, the trees having greater diameters and the understorey less ground cover than in Arenales. As far as the commercial timber species are concerned, the most common are *Brosimum utile* (**Sande**), *Dialyanthera* sp. (**Cuangare**), and *Humiriastrum procerum*, with *Carapa guianensis* (**Tangare**), *Pouteria* sp. (**Cartagena**), *Trattinnickia barbourii* (**Pulgande**) *Pseudolmedia eggersii* (**Guion**) and *Virola* sp. (**Chalbinde**) occurring at a lower frequency. Other common tree species include *Ficus spp.* and *Inga spp.* in more open areas, and *Cordia alliodora* along the river banks. 77 tree species were recorded in the El Pan forest in one study (Pleydell, 1992) although the total number of species recorded in the CIBT inventory (see Section 3.5) was over 150. The forest of Arenales has less well defined strata, and a somewhat different species composition. One species, *Brosimum utile*, forms nearly 50% of the harvestable volume. The other important commercial timber species found are *Humiriastrum procerum*, *Virola* sp. and *Persea rigens* (**Amarillo**).

Logging operations in the area began on a significant scale about 30 years ago. Extraction has been highly destructive, and it is estimated that only about 5% of the original forest area remains undisturbed by logging activities. This is in very fragmented pieces. Initially exploitation was carried out through government concessions, but the system was complicated by colonisers settling on the same land and often clearing it to obtain title. Following the end of the concession system in 1982, logging companies now either buy timber from farmers and communities, or buy the land themselves. Timber is usually purchased standing, for as little as US$3 per tree, but even where the companies buy the land, there is no attempt at resource management. Timber extraction is selective (for example, some companies are exploiting only four species), with heavy machinery causing great damage to soil, forest and water resources.

Surprisingly little information is available on the use of the forest by local communities beyond its commercial exploitation for

Economic valuations of NTFPs occurring in Ecuadorian forests of the Amazon basin have resulted in claims that NTFPs have a far higher value than timber (Grimes, Loomis, Jahnige, *et al.*, 1994). The forests of the Awá region are botanically distinct from such forests, and their economic potential in NTFPs remains largely undocumented. Markets are a key factor. The communities of El Pan and Arenales are very remote, and no ready markets for NTFPs currently exist.

Timber extraction by loggers from an area of Forest Reserve near El Pan
Photograph: Anna Lawrence

timber. The main timber species used by local people themselves appear to be *Brosimum utile* and *Dialyanthera* sp. for the construction of houses, and *Laetia procera*, *Trattinnickia barbourii* and *Tetragastris varians* for canoes. Certain sub-storey plants, mostly of the family Gesneriaceae, are reported to be consumed, whilst some are used for the preparation of medicines against snakebite and intestinal problems. One clearly important product is bush meat for domestic consumption. In addition, some forest fruits are eaten, but none are marketed. To date, the project has done little to investigate the current use and potential of non-timber forest products. Attention has focused on timber extraction because this is considered to have the most viable and lucrative market. However, interesting work promoting the cultivation of fruit trees is being conducted in the area under a completely separate initiative (co-ordinated by an American Peace Corps Volunteer).

The remoteness of the communities is also a constraint on agricultural marketing (although the potential for agricultural production in the area is in any case poor). El Pan produces few cash crops except cacao, which is carried out on foot (a six-hour walk) or by canoe, and then truck if available. This distance is considered by community members to be too far to carry most products. Arenales is connected to markets by river, so transport is less arduous although slow. It takes two days to take a canoe full of plantain to the nearest town, Borbón, and two days to return. Travelling shopkeepers pass by the community in canoes, selling basic foodstuffs.

The Awá Forest Reserve

In 1988 an area close to the two communities with whom the project is working was declared the Awá Forest Reserve. The stated objective of the reserve is to protect and preserve the culture of the Awá population and the territory in which they live, under policies of eco-development. Adjacent zones are included in this objective, given that they are closely associated with the indigenous territory. The total area thus covered is estimated at 586,000 ha, of which 101,000 belong to the Awá Reserve and the rest to a buffer zone. El Pan lies within this buffer zone; Arenales falls outside it. A Management Plan for the reserve notes that the inclusion of the buffer zone obeys two important principles, notably:

- The idea of managing the reserve not as an island but as an integral part of a whole in which are included other communities, and maintaining and reinforcing their interrelations.

- The protection and sustainable exploitation of the genetic resources and ecosystems for the maintenance of the biological diversity of north-west Ecuador.

The existence of the reserve is significant in that it provides part of the rationale for the project's operations in the area. To date reserve management has had little practical influence on project activities, although this is likely to change as the number of communities participating in the project increases, with a corresponding expansion in its area of operations.

In recognition of the international importance of the Awá Region, its inclusion in UNESCO's Man and Biosphere (MAB) programme was also proposed in 1988 (Orejula, 1992). The proposed reserve would be bi-national, straddling the Ecuador-Colombian border, but it has yet to be ratified.

3.3 The People of the Awá Region

There are three types of community in the Awá region: indigenous peoples, traditional settlers (non-indigenous but long-established), and **colonos** or colonisers. Both the communities currently participating in the project are traditional settlers. Others identified as potential participants include indigenous communities. The **colonos** are considered to be a more challenging group with which to work as they have tended to establish title to their new lands individually by clearing the forest, and still tend to sell or burn their timber to cultivate the land.

The people of El Pan are of native origin (although they are not true indigenous peoples). Those of Arenales are almost all ethnically Black Africans, descended from early slaves. They are both very small communities, in El Pan forming one extended family numbering only 162 people in 27 households, in Arenales some 111 people living in 43 households. Of the communities that have become involved with the project more recently, La Ceiba numbers some 105 people living in 25 households, but unlike El Pan and Arenales comprises a group of indigenous people, the Chachi. A fourth small community of about 90 people, Guadalito, is in advanced negotiations to join the project, and discussions have started with two others. The members of Guadalito are indigenous Awá and their land lies within a satellite part (physically separated from the main block) of the Awá Reserve.

> The decision over whether individuals should be paid for their labour was a community one. The people of El Pan decided that they wanted to be paid (the money coming out of profits made on the sale of timber), whilst the people of Arenales decided to contribute their labour on a voluntary basis.

As noted above, the communities currently working with the project have the legal status of **comunas** (although that of Guadalito differs in being an indigenous Awá community, bound by strong traditional codes of practice and organisation). The **comunas** have elected leaders who change every year, and are always men. The president, vice-president, treasurer and two others form the **cabildo** which makes decisions regarding the use of communal land and the organisation of labour. Every community member is expected to contribute equally to communal labour needs, although how this works in practice may vary. In Arenales, it has not been a contentious issue, but in El Pan it was thought advisable to pay those who participated in the timber harvest of 1991, to 'ease any arguments about community members not doing their share of the work' (ODA, 1991).

3.4 The Development of the Awá Sustainable Forest Management Project

Historical Development

The present project has developed from activities initiated in 1989 by UTEPA (**Unidad Técnica Ecuatoriana para al Ecodesarrollo de la Amazonia y la Región Awá**) and CIBT. UTEPA is a government organisation responsible for the co-ordination of a development programme for the Awá region under the Ministry of Foreign Affairs (UTEPA, 1990a and b). CIBT is a non-governmental organisation working on rainforest conservation, staffed by biologists (mainly of non-Ecuadorian nationality). CIBT initiated biodiversity research in the area, and at the same time investigated ways of working with local people both to protect the forest biodiversity and to improve their standard of living. CIBT staff describe the origins of the project as 'buying time while studies of the forest progressed'.

The community of El Pan had already sold their timber to a logging company when UTEPA and CIBT persuaded them to reverse the decision. They did this partly by utilising the legal argument that the community did not have legal title to the land and so did not actually have the right to sell the forest. With the collaboration of the director of the Ecological Trading Company (ETC – at the time based in Newcastle, UK) who had come to Ecuador to identify sources of sustainably produced timber, CIBT staff convinced the community of the value of attempting sustainable forest management. They argued that by harvesting only a proportion of their timber, processing it *in situ* and selling directly to the ETC, they would be able to command premium prices for 'sustainably produced timber'. To this end, CIBT conducted an inventory of the El Pan primary forest area in 1990, and together with the community designated a 100 ha area as the trial first 'forest management block'.

The ETC sent a portable sawmill ('Trekkasaw') to be used by the community and placed an order for 70 m^3 of sawn planks of eight species (see Box 3.1). In 1991 the timber was selected, felled and sawn, and carried (mostly manually) 2 km to the nearest forest road. Community members took part, and were paid for their labour. The operation provided a net income of nearly US$12,000 to the community. This represented more than five times the usual rate of return that communities could expect from forest exploitation in the area, and generated huge enthusiasm for the project. However, the sale was not entirely successful as the quality of most of the timber on arrival in the UK was too poor for it to be marketed. This was partly due to poor storage and drying arrangements, exacerbated by delays caused in transport which resulted in warping and splitting on arrival.

Box 3.1 Species Harvested in El Pan

The species requested by the ETC from the El Pan harvest were as follows:

Local name	Botanical name	Frequency of occurrence	Comments
Sande	*Brosimum utile*	8%	Well known as an export timber, especially for plywood
Tangare	*Carapa guianensis*	5%	Well known internationally for sawn timber
Cuangare	*Dialyanthera* sp.	9%	Unknown on international markets
Chanul	*Humiriastrum procerum*	3%	Heavy hardwood; good potential on international markets
Cartagena	*Pouteria* sp.	low	Unknown on international markets
Cucharillo	*Talauma* sp.	low	Heavy hardwood; good potential on international markets
Pulgande	*Trattinnickia barbourii*	low	Unknown on international markets
Chalbinde	*Virola* sp.	2%	Well known internationally for sawn timber.

Following the first harvest, ETC and CIBT sought funding to continue and expand the experiment. An ODA project was approved in 1991 but was not implemented until January 1994, when ODA began work with UTEPA. There have thus been considerable delays in fulfilling the community's aspirations.

The objectives of the project are 'to develop the ability of communities in the region to manage, harvest and sell their own timber resources.' It is further hoped that by 'developing the communities' ability to realise the full value of their forests in a sustainable way the project will give them the incentive to protect their forest lands, as well as providing the members of the communities with increased income' (ODA, 1991). The current project team comprises six individuals. The two coordinators (an expatriate and his UTEPA counterpart) are based in Quito. Based in the field (in the town of San Lorenzo) are a forest engineer, a forest technician, an expatriate forester, and a social communicator (who works for the project on a part-time basis). An additional expatriate forester has been based in San Lorenzo since September 1995. The project has also received a significant input of expertise from consultancy visits.

The preliminary work of CIBT biologists in physically identifying and marking the traditional boundaries of the land belonging to the communities of El Pan and Arenales was important in creating a suitable context for permanent forest management. Each community has a maximum of about 600 ha of primary forest available for management, and the idea is that they should designate blocks as Permanent Forest Areas which will be managed on a sustainable basis and not be converted to any other use. Relatively small blocks have been designated forest management areas to date, the rest being held as buffer zones of unharvested forest. Some of these areas are never intended for exploitation, being left as they are for watershed protection and species conservation. Following from the 100 ha identified for productive management by the people of El Pan, the community of Arenales has designated 96 ha as its first 'forest management block'. It is expected that each pilot community will expand the area under management by adding further blocks in due course.

Awareness Raising and Attitudes to Sustainability

UTEPA field staff have contributed significantly over the last three years to promoting an awareness of the value of the forest and the benefits of sustainable management amongst the two project communities. This has been an important factor in creating current community attitudes.

Community members in both Arenales and El Pan are concerned to maintain their forests and avoid the destructive results of logging seen in neighbouring communities. Individuals in Arenales describe the forest as 'the inheritance of our grandchildren' and state that 'we have always lived on this land, the land belongs to us, that's why we want to manage the forest.' Comments from El Pan, which has experienced more frustration, are more mixed. Some community members are wholly in favour of the project; one community leader, representing this view, stated that 'nobody will touch our forest, only us'. However, a number of community members (notably those with an interest in the local timber companies) are less confident about the project, and want to reduce the area which has been provisionally set aside as Permanent Forest Area.

It is clear that a major motivation for forest management is the income expected from the timber sales, and it seems likely that the enthusiasm will wane if the timber harvest is further delayed. At the time of writing, harvesting was scheduled to start again shortly.

Both communities are financially vulnerable. The benefits of selling sustainably harvested timber at a premium are clear to them. The El Pan community received gross prices of US$410/m^3 for the sawn timber that they produced for the ETC. They compare this with the few dollars per tree for standing timber paid by timber companies to communities in the surrounding area. The logging companies are now operating up to the boundaries of El Pan and Arenales land, and have even extracted timber from parts of community land which is outside the designated management block (by felling and sawing *in situ*). Although this is not a profitable system for the communities, for many individuals a few dollars in the hand are worth more for immediate and urgent needs, than hundreds of dollars in a distant and increasingly uncertain future. The project itself is thus vulnerable to failure if its activities are delayed.

3.5 The Need for Forest Resource Assessment

The initial need for forest resource assessment followed partly from the legal requirement for an inventory, but was based primarily on CIBT's desire to implement a system that was ecologically sustainable and would cause minimal damage to the forest. It was also recognised by CIBT staff as an essential part of gaining credibility with the ETC, and thus access to the sustainably harvested timber market. The involvement of the community at this stage was limited to providing free labour in opening up paths in the forest and identifying trees by their local names. The inventory was merely explained to them as a necessary part of the project, to which they agreed.

CIBT prepared the requisite management plan in 1990, and obtained official permission to extract 70 m^3 annually from the forests of each community. The inventory was conducted by CIBT in two stages; the general floristic survey, and the systematic inventory. The first part, the general floristic survey, was carried out by taking a walk through a randomly selected sample of forest, identifying trees, estimating volume and gaining a general impression of species richness and variability.

Blocks of forest for the first stage of the project were then selected. These were chosen largely for logistical reasons, the

The inventory method adopted was guided by a need to determine the commercial exploitability of the forest as well as an interest in its botanical composition. It was considered to fulfil both criteria at the time, although it was more of a qualitative than a quantitative assessment. The harvesting regime subsequently introduced by CIBT staff was designed to be so low, and to cause so little forest disturbance, as to be almost certainly sustainable.

management block (of 100 ha) in El Pan being the nearest area to the forest road (although still 2 km away). In Arenales the block (of 96 ha) was the nearest to the village (and also the river for transport). The systematic survey, which provided volume estimates for subsequent exploitation, was carried out on a single transect 20 m wide and of sufficient length to give the 5% sampling density required by law. Enumeration was conducted in 10 m^2 blocks. The inventory has been criticised by professional foresters on a number of grounds, including the following:

- No maps are available with the original plan, so it is not known where the sample transect was located.

- There is no explanation of any of the calculations in the plan (it is simply stated that they were designed to be as conservative as possible). However, it is recorded that they were based on estimated commercial heights, without the aid of a clinometer. Their accuracy has thus been questioned, although the forester who conducted them was a Professor of Forestry from Cali University, Colombia with many years of experience.

- The lack of replicated sampling means that no estimation of variation or error was made. No indication of the distribution of species and volumes throughout the forest management blocks can be determined from the data collected because of the lack of replication or stratification.

CIBT states that it used certain aspects of the Palcazú project in Peru as a model for its forest management system, although the method of extraction is very different (see Box 3.2). On the basis of the Peruvian model, CIBT chose a 40-year rotation which seemed a reasonable estimate for sustainable production (Mondragón, 1990).

Under the CIBT management plan, the forest was divided on the basis of area rather than volume. Each block was marked in sections 50 m wide, with extraction (on a selective basis) beginning in the first section. The plan was for it to continue in subsequent years in alternate sections, leaving untouched sections between exploited sections. These untouched sections will be exploited approximately 20 years later when the end of the first set of sections has been reached. The length of section allocated for exploitation in one year is one-fortieth of the total length of the sections. Clearly, until an inventory of the whole area has been carried out showing tree species distribution and density, an equal distribution of timber volumes between years cannot be guaranteed. Extraction within the sections is to be kept low; in the first harvest, it was intended to fell 40 m^3/ha (giving an overall extraction rate of 1 m^3/ha/year). In fact, only 70 m^3 was cut from 2.5 ha (ODA, 1991) – considerably less than was originally planned. In this exploited section at El Pan, many large diameter good quality trees have been left standing. This was a deliberate part of

The management system based on sections was chosen by the biologists concerned in accordance with the gap theory of forest dynamics (see Chapter 9, Section 9.3). Key features were considered to be that:

• it ensures that no two adjacent areas are exploited in sequential years; and
• the extraction rate is very low and selective, leaving very small gaps which would imitate natural gap formation in the forest.

Insufficient information is currently available on the growth and regeneration of the tree species concerned to be certain that the system (or indeed any other) is ideal.

the management plan, which stated that not all mature trees should be harvested (particular attention being paid to leaving seed trees).

According to CIBT staff, the management plan was always intended as a preliminary measure, with much follow-up inventory work and regeneration studies. They note that it was not possible to conduct these without further funding. Following the start of ODA assistance for forestry activities, there have been significant changes in the inventory procedure. The instigation of long-term regeneration work is also intended.

Box 3.2 The Palcazú Project, Peru

The Palcazú forest project of eastern Peru is working with the native Amazonian people, the Yanesha, to manage their forest resources on a sustainable basis and provide them with an economic return. It is thus a project with similar overall objectives to the Awá project. Most of the Palcazú valley floor, in which forestry development activities are focused, is classified as tropical wet forest. Some 75% of the land area is still primary forest, characterised by great species richness (at least 1,000 tree species are estimated to occur in the valley).

The forest is managed on a strip-shelterbelt system, under which narrow strips (30–40 m wide) are harvested completely. This is reported to promote vigorous regeneration of shade-intolerant tree species. The length of the narrow strips is determined by logistics or physiography. In successive years, new strips will be located at least 100 m from recently cut strips. Through this careful rotation of strip harvesting within production blocks, primary forest is left on one or both sides to ensure a ready seed supply from suitable seed trees to felled areas. A 40-year rotation is planned; thus if a production block has 120 ha of harvestable forest, 3 ha are scheduled for harvest each year.

Despite the wide variety of tree species in the forest, almost all the timber harvested from the strip is utilised. One way in which this is achieved is through the on-site longitudinal impregnation with preservative of small-dimensional roundwood. This produces preserved posts and poles of any length between 5 and 38 cm diameter. On average, about 35% of the harvest is processed in this way, whilst 60% is processed for sawnwood. Most of the remaining timber is converted to charcoal.

There are clear differences between what has been achieved under the Palcazú project and the potential of the Awá project in the foreseeable future. One is the far more highly developed markets in Palcazú, and the availability of technology facilitating the utilisation of small diameter timber. In Awá, complete harvesting of strips would be pointless because of the limited market. In fact, under the current extraction regime, harvesting is selective with the removal of only small volumes per hectare. There is also a far greater area of forest available for production forestry (about 44,000 ha) in the Palcazú valley than under the Awá project, which itself has obvious market implications.

Source of information on the Palcazú Project: Stocks and Hartshorn (1993); Hartshorn (1990)

3.6   The Current Forest Assessment Process

The CIBT inventories provided useful information for the proposed exploitation of the initial forest management blocks at El Pan and Arenales. However, they were insufficient in both scope and information for the drawing up of management plans for the sustainable management of the entire Permanent Forest Area set aside by each community. Inventory data for this purpose had to be collected before any further exploitation could take place. Given the growing impatience of the pilot communities, they had to be collected quickly. A new method for a baseline inventory was required that

- was simple and could be standardised through all communities (including those newly joining the project); and,
- could be conducted rapidly to obtain all the information needed for economic feasibility studies, guiding commercial decisions.

The design selected as most appropriate for the baseline inventory was suggested by a project consultant, Dennis Alder, during a visit to Ecuador in February 1995. His recommendations were based on experience gained from the Quintana Roo Forestry Project in Mexico (see Chapter 4). The basic design involves the systematic layout of a large number of small circular plots at a relatively low intensity. As in Quintana Roo, these temporary sample plots (TSPs) are 500 m^2, but the design differs in being laid out on a 200 m x 200 m grid, giving one plot for every 4 ha – a sampling intensity of 1.25%.

   The first inventory using this design was carried out in an area of 430 ha that was recently designated as Permanent Forest Area by the Chachi community of La Ceiba. As shown in Figure 3.2, their Permanent Forest Area is approximately rectangular, 4 km by 1 km.

A Base Map

Prior to conducting the inventory, project staff required a map of the area. Unlike the communities of El Pan and Arenales, La Ceiba has legal tenure of its land. When this was formalised, a government topographer visited the area to supervise the boundary demarcation. The physical cutting of the boundary lines was carried out by the community members. As a result of this demarcation, survey figures for boundary distances and bearings were available to project staff. However, there was no record of the position of the major landmark in the area – a river which cuts across the community's land. By following the course of the river in canoes and taking appropriate bearings, project staff were able to use the boundary distances and bearings to position the river. A number of community members accompanied them in this task. Project staff then drew up a map of the community's land, which they presented to the community, marking two possible boundaries for the Permanent Forest Area, one 800 m and the other 1,000 m from the river. The community chose the latter option, giving as the reason that the area closest to the river is the best for plantain cultivation (which they wished to have room to expand in future).

Efforts are being made to verify the map of the community's land against the most detailed government topography map available, which is of a scale 1:25,000. One boundary corner is clear, as it represents the confluence of two rivers. Project staff plan to use a Global Positioning System to verify the position of the other boundary corners.

Figure 3.2   Layout of the Baseline Inventory Conducted in the Permanent Forest Area of La Ceiba under the Awá Sustainable Forest Management Project

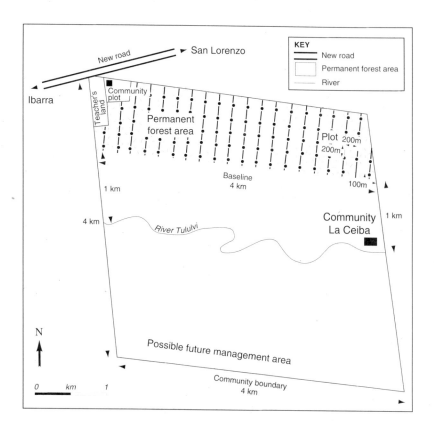

The Method for the Baseline Inventory

One long straight boundary separates La Ceiba's Permanent Forest Area from the rest of the community's territory. This boundary was used as the baseline for the inventory. Prior to fieldwork, transects into the forest at right angles to the baseline and 200 m apart were drawn on the map produced by the project. All plots were then marked on the map, the first plot centre being at 100 m from the baseline and subsequent plot centres being marked every 200 m (see Figure 3.2). Plots were numbered using co-ordinates according to their position on the grid. This means that re-locating them should be simple.

The first step of fieldwork was then to cut the transects into the forest, following compass bearings. Horizontal distances were calculated in the field using simple trigonometry, by measuring distances with a tape and slope with a clinometer. The data recorded in this way not only allowed the accurate marking of plot centres but will also be extremely useful for enhancing topographic maps. Stakes were used to mark plot centres.

Within each plot, the dbh of all trees of diameter over 20 cm was measured. Where trees with giant buttresses occurred, they were marked for later measurement using a relascope. Trees were identified using local names since it is these that community members will use in managing the forest. Full botanical accuracy was not deemed necessary, as the inventory is primarily concerned with well known commercial species and volume. Nevertheless, the botanical verification of species is an issue which will need to be addressed in the future (see Box 3.3). Estimates of commercial timber availability were improved by scoring each tree for health/defects using a three-point score, as follows:

- A – Free from defects (at least two 3.5 m logs of commercial timber).

- B – Defective, but one 3.5 m log of commercial timber.

- C – Completely defective; useless for commercial purposes.

The choice of 3.5 m as the log length reflects the length to which logs are processed by the 'Trekkasaw'.

To save time, not all trees were measured for height, but four trees in each plot were selected (according to basal area through a sweep with a relascope, freedom from defects, and visibility) for measurement. This will form the basis for the calculation of volume equations and tables, and form factors. Measurements of height to crown-break were taken in addition to diameters at crown-break, mid-point and breast height to permit the use of Newton's equation for volume calculation.[1]

Box 3.3 Species Identification in the Awá Region

Although local people are proficient in tree identification, the use of local names without botanical cross-checking has caused some confusion. Members of the same community sometimes have different names for the same species. This was in fact an issue which the CIBT biologists addressed in some detail, drawing up a list of local names and checking their botanical identity. However, the list is long and complicated, limiting its use in the field. Current project staff do not have detailed botanical knowledge, which means that giving priority to botanical identification would be extremely time-consuming. They therefore decided that it should be addressed at a later date – especially since the identity of most of the trees of commercial interest is not in question, and local people will always use their own names for tree species when making future management decisions.

The potential significance of the mis-identification of species is illustrated by experience in the initial forest inventory of La Ceiba. Here confusion between two tree species of the same family (Burseraceae) was significant, as they have very different timber quality. One, *Trattinnickia barbourii* (**Pulgande**), has a white colour, is more susceptible to blue stain, and has a low commercial value. The other, probably *Dacryodes cupularis* (**Anime**), is a red coloured medium hardwood with good market potential, mainly limited by the fact that it occurs in very low volumes per hectare.

The verification of the botanical identity of uncertain species will be checked in future, one possibility being for samples to be checked at the national herbarium in Quito.

Labour for the Baseline Inventory

Fieldwork was undertaken by male community members with the assistance of six students and their teacher from a local technical school in San Lorenzo, and was supervised by two professional foresters from the project team. The assistance of students was welcomed as La Ceiba has only a small adult male population, and all concerned wished to complete the work rapidly. Work was accordingly divided into four stages, with separate teams specialising in and performing different tasks, as follows:

Team 1:
Transect cutting

- 1 student (compass operator)
- 2 community members (cutting)

Team 2:
Transect measuring

- 1 student (data recording and calculations)
- 1 student (clinometer operator)
- 2 community members (tape measurements and stake placement)

Team 3:
Diameter measurement
- 1 forester (data recording and supervision)
- 1 community member (plot demarcation and tree cleaning)
- 1 community member (tree identification and diameter measurements)

Team 4:
Volume measurements
- 1 forester (relascope operator, data recording and supervision)
- 2 community members (tape measure operators, plot clearing and tree identification)

Teams 1 and 2 were duplicated to save time, allowing the inventory to be completed within ten days. Usually 20 people worked each day. During this time, approximately 17 km of transect lines were cleared and measured, together with the trees occurring in some 110 plots. Direct costs were kept to about US$400 for form printing, transport, payment of the students and their teacher, and food for all involved. The community members elected not to pay themselves, as all who were able participated. The direct costs do not, of course, include the salaries of the professional foresters or the time spent in planning and analysis. Nevertheless, the method appears to be very cost-effective.

Lessons Learned

The data collected are yet to be analysed. However, a number of practical lessons were learned from the fieldwork.

- The advantages of the design, in terms of using small circular plots, are consistent with those reported in Chapter 4.

- The use of small plots facilitates slope correction measurements. This is important in the project area, which covers some very abrupt topography.

- A disadvantage of the use of small plots is that they frequently contain fewer than ten trees with a dbh over 20 cm. This means that any mistakes over the inclusion or exclusion of border trees can alter plot totals significantly.

The same inventory method will be used for obtaining the information needed for drawing up management plans with all participating communities. However, they are unlikely to be repeated in the same area of forest in the near future. Instead, 100% stock surveys will be conducted prior to harvest in each management block, as described in Section 3.7.

Training

All data recording and mapping is currently the responsibility of the project team working with the communities. The eventual aim is for the community to conduct all the inventory and mapping work. However, this is a long way off. Educational levels are very basic in both communities (especially in El Pan where many of the older members are illiterate). This problem is exacerbated in the newer communities joining the project by the fact that Spanish is a second language. Much basic training has to be carried out before community members will be capable of recording data accurately. It is intended that training in data analysis will then follow.

For the early inventory using the CIBT design, training began with a two-day course held by UTEPA in Arenales. It covered basic forest mensuration techniques, including the use of compass, measuring tape and clinometer. The course was attended by twelve community members, and taught by the project forester. It was followed by a practical test, and further practice in the forest. None of the participants had any previous experience of this type of work, and it was necessary to start the training with an explanation of basic principles. For example, none knew that there are 360° in a circle – a fundamental piece of knowledge for using a compass.

The level of education in these communities, where few individuals possess even a secondary school education, may be compared with that of the communities in Quintana Roo (Chapter 4), where some community members are studying forestry at university.

Members of the Arenales community learning some basic forest mensuration theory. This formed part of the first inventory training course.
Photograph: Leonel Quiñónez

The nine best participants were selected to continue as inventory specialists. Most of them are young men, although two are in their forties. The group works as a team, assisted by non-specialist community members who clear paths into the forest. They have not yet reached the stage at which the inventory can be conducted without the supervision of the project forester, but those involved are enthusiastic about the work and express interest in further courses.

Training in the techniques used in the baseline inventory was conducted *in situ*. It was found that community members quickly became proficient in the use of tape measures and diameter tapes. However, the use of compasses and clinometers proved difficult, and much further training in the field will be necessary before community members are able to conduct this type of work without assistance. The concepts of slope correction and the use of trigonometry for measuring transects and demarcating plots were also not readily understood. Even the students (who were specialising in forestry) and their teacher had difficulty in applying such principles in practice.

Despite the problems encountered, project staff are confident that, with more training and continued supervision (in the first stock surveys), community members will eventually be able to conduct inventory fieldwork on their own.

Women have not participated in forest inventory and management activities to date. Male community members consider that their role is fulfilled by providing food while the men are working in the field. Given that literacy levels amongst women are even lower than among men, it seems unlikely that women will play a more active role in the near future.

3.7 Current and Future Developments

The Use of Stock Surveys

The most important requirements for a species to be marketable internationally are:

- timber utility and quality
- regular supply
- sufficient quantity available.

It is recognised under the ODA project that the communities in the Awá region are extremely dependent on external markets for sustainably harvested timber. The system is entirely demand-led; any timber not sold to these markets is sold at a loss. The dependence of the project on external, limited (but probably expanding) markets is a clear risk, but one which is being addressed by aiming to maximise timber marketability.

Premium timber markets are very specific about the quality and regularity of supply of whatever volume of timber is negotiated. The communities therefore need to plan exactly how much timber, of which species, they will fell each year. Unlike larger forest management projects where a margin of uncertainty is acceptable in the annual timber harvest, the communities in this project, with their limited amount of land, should know the location, volume and species of each timber tree. A suitable method for obtaining this information is through 100% stock surveys of the area to be harvested in a given year. Apart from the detail of information provided through stock surveys, their simplicity means that they have the additional advantages of:

- facilitating the participation of members of the community in data collection, and
- not requiring complex data analysis.

Prior to every harvest, the commercial height and dbh of all harvestable trees of 50 cm dbh or over will be recorded, and their locations mapped at a scale of 1:500. In addition,

- defective trees will be identified for removal (as part of silvicultural treatment), and
- seed trees will be marked, in order to take particular care that they are preserved and not damaged during harvesting operations.

There will be no procedure for sub-sampling smaller size classes or regeneration.

In a provisional stock survey conducted in Arenales, a cut-off dbh of 20 cm rather than 50 cm was chosen, and all tree species were included. The purpose was to map all trees and to use this in planning the felling direction of trees to be harvested, bearing in mind not only seed trees but also the smaller commercial species which should be available for harvesting at the next felling cycle (30–40 years into the future). The practice of including in the inventory all trees of dbh over 20 cm will be continued for the baseline forest inventories described in the previous section. However, it is not practical for regular pre-harvest stock surveys. Not only does it involve considerable extra work, but it is of limited value in determining felling direction. This is better decided in the field, taking into consideration topography and general site conditions as well as the surrounding valuable trees.

In the dense forest, visibility is impeded and it is often difficult to measure the commercial height of a tree. A student has been invited to conduct a study relating commercial height to dbh, so that only the latter needs to be measured. The results of this study should be available in late 1995.

Immediate Priorities for Forest Inventory

Technical areas which project staff feel should receive immediate attention include the computerisation of data mapping and analysis, regeneration surveys and establishment of permanent sample plots (PSPs). All data were initially analysed and mapped by hand. With such small forest areas this is still feasible, although the utility of the data is limited. Simple computer programmes for

It may be debated whether or not it is realistic, or indeed appropriate, to expect that the communities of the Awá region will conduct inventory work and, in particular, computerised data management by themselves in the future.

The very limited involvement of community members in the establishment and measuring of PSPs is explained by there being very few members available who currently have the ability to conduct such work, particularly given that there is so much other inventory work to do. It is unfortunate that this opportunity for developing a deeper understanding of the process and purpose of inventory cannot be utilised to a greater extent.

the calculation of volume and the plotting of tree locations are now being introduced. Field staff consider this to be an urgent priority. Computerisation will need to be linked with training for technical staff, but this need not be to a complicated level. As noted above, the use of stock surveys means that there is no need for statistical data manipulation. It is therefore argued that it should be possible eventually for technical staff to train community members in using computers to enter and process inventory data.

So far no trees under 20 cm dbh have been measured in the community forests. Technical staff are aware of the need for regeneration studies and a system of PSPs. A three-month Ecuadorian consultancy was commissioned to establish a system of PSPs at 1% intensity (in four blocks of 0.25 ha each) according to the recommendations of Alder and Synnott (1992). This was completed by mid-1995, and involved limited participation by community members. Three young men from Arenales, all educated to secondary level, assisted in their establishment. PSP measurements will be taken both before and after harvest. It is not envisaged that community members will be involved in this data collection until other more immediate goals in communal forest management have been achieved.

Non-Inventory Activities

Following the first harvest, the El Pan community members have been taking a particular interest in the natural regeneration of the main timber species, which appears to be abundant. They also transplanted natural seedlings into the gaps left after the 1991 logging operations and have been informally observing their growth. The best ones are now reported to be 'taller than a man', but it is uncertain what percentage have survived.

The greater involvement of women in project activities is being encouraged by training them in handicrafts using non-timber forest products (NTFPs). The use of palm leaves for weaving mats has been promoted, and markets are being sought. However, this aspect of the project is still at an early stage. It has not been thought necessary to date to survey the NTFPs on which the handicrafts are based, since relatively small quantities are being used.

Ecological Sustainability of Forest Management

Project staff believe that the current forest management system is ecologically sustainable. However, it is not known what size of gap created in harvesting is ideal for the regeneration of the important timber species. Ecological studies are necessary to decide whether this system is the most appropriate for maximising the economic benefit to the community whilst maintaining the forest resource in a productive state.

The volume of timber that the project will be harvesting in the near future is small, and the project is confident that it can be marketed as sustainably produced timber without certification. However, it is possible that this will become more difficult in the future, assuming the certification system becomes more widely recognised.

The caution currently exercised in harvesting is necessary, particularly in the light of the small areas of forest involved, until further data are available. However, volumes of the better-known species must be increased to maintain income while more secure markets are sought for other species. Reliable inventory data and regeneration studies are needed urgently to allow increased extraction on an informed basis.

The project has considered certification of forest management by an accredited certification company, in accordance with the principles and criteria set by the Forest Stewardship Council. It is felt that management has not yet reached a stage at which this would be appropriate. However, certification of one of the community managed forests by the end of year three of project operations (1996) is a project objective.

Institutional Sustainability

The institutional sustainability of the project does not rest entirely on building sufficient capacity within the local communities to conduct inventory work themselves. The situation is much more complex than this. When the ODA drew up the project document in 1991, it expected the project to reach self-sufficiency by the end of the three-year period of co-operation. It was to have achieved this through the involvement of several communities in forming marketing co-operatives to spread the overheads of timber extraction. However, delays in implementation have been critical and it now appears very unlikely that self-sufficiency will be achieved in the near future. Indeed, opportunities for multiplying the number of participating communities are disappearing rapidly as timber companies continue their activities in the area. Until harvesting under the project begins, staff are unable to promote sustainable forest management in other communities because they have no results to demonstrate the value of such ideas. Furthermore, project staff are also having to deal with increasing disillusionment and scepticism amongst the pilot communities.

Economic Sustainability

The dependence of the project to date on one buyer and above-market prices is a clear concern. In addition to improving timber quality through better processing and timely export, it will be important to:

- broaden markets
- establish timber prices which are acceptable both to the communities and to buyers, and
- increase the number of species which can be sold on the international market.

The small forest areas and therefore small quantities of timber form an unstable basis for a long-term project. Even if four or five communities can be incorporated into the project, the total forest area will be unlikely to exceed 1,500 ha, with large differences in species composition between the forests of different communities. Thus large volumes of each species will not be guaranteed, and very specialist markets will need to be sought.

As a step towards broadening its market base, the project prepared a 20 m³ trial consignment of 10 species in early 1995. This arrived in the UK in good condition, and is being used to promote the timber and seek a variety of potential UK-based buyers.

Considerable work is necessary on incorporating the costs of forest management into the community enterprises. There is currently some misunderstanding on the part of community members over this issue. Realistically, the costs of carrying out an inventory have to be included in the cost of timber production. To date these have not been worked out by the project, partly because all labour is provided free by the communities (the project incurs the cost of providing them with food on work days). However, CIBT charged the El Pan community US$110/m³ for 'development costs', largely attributed to the cost of conducting the original inventory. CIBT has not made available details on how it calculated these costs, and opinions are divided as to whether they are reasonable or not. One significant expenditure was on technical expertise (notably the services of the Colombian Professor of Forestry), which was included in the charge to the community. The ODA project document (1991) accepted that the inventory costs were probably realistic, but the community cannot understand the reason for them and strongly resent the deduction from their expected total income. Whilst the charges levied by the CIBT may be high, clearly some inventory costs will have to be incorporated, if only gradually. This will require careful discussion with the communities. On the positive side, the low costs of the recent La Ceiba baseline forest inventory indicate that the incorporation of such costs into forest management should be feasible.

It is difficult to compare inventory costs between projects and countries, but the sum charged to the El Pan community does seem high. One reason may be that the cost of technical expertise (salaries and subsistence) is often covered by external agencies and budgeted separately, whereas here it was included in the inventory costs.

3.8 Conclusion

The first steps towards training the community in conducting a forest inventory have been achieved, and members participated with enthusiasm. All community members are very aware of the forestry project, with the men having a good grasp of the management plan and being particularly knowledgable about the results of the first timber harvest (including volumes and prices). They also have a clear understanding of the basic objective of inventory, and the reason for conducting one. Their attitudes towards the management and conservation of the forest are very positive and it is clear that through them there is good potential for achieving communal forest management. Nevertheless, there are still many obstacles to achieving even the preliminary goals of the project. These include marketing problems, weaknesses in institutional links, and continuing doubts about tenure and land-use definition. However, the greatest immediate threat to the project appears to be the four-year delay in harvesting operations since 1991, broken only by the small recent harvest for a trial consignment. A full-scale harvest, followed by the satisfactory marketing of the timber and appropriate remuneration to the communities, seems to be needed before other project difficulties can be properly addressed. Fortunately, this is likely to begin in the near future.

Note

1. Newton's equation is one of three different formulae which can be used to estimate log volume based on measurements of diameter and length. Further details may be found in Philip (1994: 56–8)

References

Alder, D. and Synnott, T. S. (1992) *Permanent Sample Plot Techniques for Mixed Topical Forest.* Tropical Forestry Paper No. 25, Oxford Forestry Institute, Oxford.

Grimes, A., Loomis, S., Jahnige P. *et al.,* (1994) 'Valuing the Rain Forest: The Economic Value of Nontimber Forest Products in Ecuador', *Ambio* 23(7): 405–9.

Hartshorn, G. S. (1990) 'Natural Forest Management by the Yanesha Forestry Cooperative in Peruvian Amazon' in Anderson A.B. (ed.) *Alternatives to Deforestation: Steps Toward Sustainable Use of the Amazon Rain Forest.* Columbia University Press, New York.

INEFAN (1993) *Plan Maestro de Forestacion, Instituto Ecatoriano Forestal y de Areas Naturales y Vida Silvestre,* Quito.

Mondragón, B. M. L. (1990) 'Propuesta de manejo forestal sostenido para el primer bloque de aprovechamiento en las comunidades de El Pan y Arenales – Región Noroccidental, zona de influencia de la reserva forestal de asentamiento comunal Awá'. Quito.

ODA (1991) 'Awá sustainable forestry management project'. Project memorandum. ODA, London.

Orejula, J. E. (1992) 'Traditional Productive Systems of the Awa (Cuaiquer) Indians of Southwestern Colombia and Neighbouring Ecuador' in Redford, K. H. and Padoch, C. (eds) *Conservation of Neotropical Forests Working from Traditional Resource Use.* Columbia University Press, New York.

Philip, M. S. (1994) *Measuring Trees and Forests* (2nd edn). CAB International, Wallingford, UK.

Pleydell, G. (1992) 'Report on Marketing Aspects of the Awá Sustainable Forest Management Project'. Consultancy report to Government of Ecuador under assignment from ODA.

Southgate, D. (1990) 'Policies Contributing to Agricultural Colonization of Latin America's Tropical Forests'. A Report to the World Bank's Agricultural Department. World Bank, Washington DC. 7 December (unpublished).

Stocks A. and Hartshorn G. (1993) 'The Palcazú Project: Forest Management and Native Yanesha Communities', *Journal of Sustainable Forestry* 1(1): 111–35.

UTEPA (1990a) 'Plan de conservación y desarrollo de la región Awá. I. Diagnóstico general de la región Awá'. UTEPA / WWF, Quito.

UTEPA (1990b) 'Plan de Conservación y desarrollo de la región Awá. II. Propuesta de manejo (estrategía de ecodesarrollo)'. UTEPA / WWF, Quito.

Acronyms specific to this chapter

CIBT	**Centro de Información de los Bosques Tropicales** (Rainforest Information Centre)
ETC	Ecological Trading Company
INDA	**Instituto Nacional de Desarrollo Agrario** (National Institute of Agrarian Development)
INEFAN	**Instituto Ecatoriano Forestal y de Areas Naturales y Vida Silvestre** (National Ecuadorian Forestry, Natural Areas and Wildlife Institute)
UTEPA	**Unidad Técnica Ecuatoriana para el Ecodesarrollo de la Amazonia y la Región Awá** (Ecuadorian government organisation responsible for the co-ordination of a development programme for the Awá region).

The Role of Inventory in the Communally Managed Forests of Quintana Roo, Mexico

4

Anna Lawrence and Felipe Sánchez Román

This chapter focuses on a twelve-year-old community forestry project in the state of Quintana Roo in south-east Mexico, on the Yucatan peninsula (see Figure 4.1). Of all the case studies, **Plan Piloto Forestal** (PPF), or the Quintana Roo Forestry Project, has the greatest experience in using forest inventory as a tool to achieve sustainable forest management by and for the local community. It is the most advanced in terms of technical implementation, and of particular interest because the development of the inventory system has been a dynamic process, which has responded to new information as it became available. The result is a communal forest management programme which has changed forest management from the destructive extraction of two high-value species to the rational planned extraction of fifteen species, with investment in research and enrichment planting. The PPF has been described as 'probably the largest, most important and successful forest management operation in Latin America' (Synnott, 1993) and has stimulated the development of similar management plans in neighbouring areas of the Yucatan Peninsula. However, as the case study details, it has also had its critics.

4.1 Forest Legislation and the Role of the Federal Government in Forest Management

Nearly 80% of Mexico's forest land is occupied by indigenous communities and **ejidos** (groups of farmers who share usufruct rights to specific areas of land). The aim of the PPF has been to work with a number of these **ejidos**, assisting them to manage the forest themselves. When the project was first conceived, its approach – which bypassed the federal forest service – was considered radical, with little legal precedent. However, the PPF's development has occurred in the context of rapidly and frequently changing federal legislation and a certain flexibility of interpretation at local level. Since the project began in 1983, significant changes in forestry legislation and the associated legal procedures have occurred twice. Forest legislation prior to the start of the project has also been important to its development.

Figure 4.1   The Quintana Roo Forestry Project, Mexico

Mexico's first major forest industries were established as state-owned corporations in the 1950s and 1960s. They were granted exclusive 25-year concessions on nearby **ejido** forests, an arrangement which gave little benefit to the **ejidos** (beyond limited employment opportunities) compared with the obvious profits being made from timber extraction. Since, according to the Mexican Constitution, the forest belonged to the nation, the **ejidos** were paid no compensation for logging operations. This generated considerable resentment, and conflict often arose between **ejidos** and the logging companies.

When the time came for the concessions to be renewed in the late 1970s, forest policy was revised to allow for a form of community forestry. This was seen as a more promising model that would both favour a regular supply of timber to local industries at a fair market price and contribute to overall rural development. A number of community forestry programmes were initiated in the late 1970s and early 1980s, the PPF being one of these projects. Unlike most, however, it received international donor support and has grown into a well known success story.

At the time the PPF began in 1983, forest management and utilisation was governed by the federal forest service, under the Secretariat of Agriculture and Water Resources (SARH). However, a loophole in the law allowed the Ministry to grant a forest concession outside the control of the federal forest service in certain circumstances. It was this which acted as a catalyst for the organisation of the **ejidos** into **Sociedades Civiles** (as detailed in Section 4.5), civil societies which had the legal authority to obtain timber concessions. It was only in 1988 that the legislation changed to recognise formally the rights of the **Sociedades Civiles** to receive concessions.

The legislation changed again in 1992, adopting a more liberal stance. The government now recognises the legal right of traditional communities and **ejidos** to own and manage their forests. **Ejidos** and private landowners have to provide their own technical services in this regard, with the government merely playing a supervisory role. Whilst it is no longer legally necessary for **ejidos** to be organised into SCs for the purpose of obtaining concessions, the SCs continue to be an important and convenient institution through which to channel forestry operations.

Permission to extract timber from a forest area can be granted only when a management plan, based on a full forest inventory, has been drawn up. This work has to be overseen by a professional forester authorised by SARH. In practice, such an inventory is often nothing more than a bureaucratic formality. Ironically, the system often impedes communal resource management because it discourages real assessment of the resources, and because **campesinos** (peasant farmers) rarely have the money or connections to obtain a management plan.

4.2 Past and Present Forest Utilisation in Quintana Roo

The forests of central and southern Quintana Roo are classified as sub-humid tropical forests, and are considered the most important forest type in Central America. They are seasonally deciduous, many species experiencing a brief leaf fall during the 5–7 month dry season. Annual rainfall is about 1,200 mm. Soils are derived from limestone, and are moderately fertile. The topography is flat or gently undulating, posing little problem for forest extraction during the dry season.

According to recent investigations, at least 150 tree species occur in the Quintana Roo forests. Of these, the most common is *Manilkara zapota*, the **chicozapote** or **sapodilla**. This tree is the source of chicle latex, used for making chewing gum, as well as bearing an edible fruit. *Swietenia macrophylla* (mahogany) is more common in this type of forest than any other, whilst another valued timber species (now relatively uncommon) is *Cedrela odorata* (**cedro**, or Spanish cedar).

The earliest settlers in Quintana Roo were indigenous Maya populations, who managed the forests under swidden cultivation systems (Edwards, 1986). Following the arrival of European colonisers from the sixteenth century onwards, the population declined until the middle of the present century. Valuable timber was extracted without control, in particular *Swietenia macrophylla*, *Cedrela odorata* and (to produce dye) *Haematoxylum campechianum*. From the end of the nineteenth century, chicle latex was also extracted, and became an important local industry. In the early 1950s, immigrants and existing Maya populations were encouraged to settle in farming groups sharing a common area of land. These are the **ejidos**. Initially they were formed with the aim of living from chicle extraction, so land was granted on the extensive basis of 420 ha per **ejido** member or **ejidatario**. This was calculated as the area necessary to sustain him and his family. Later settlements were for agriculture, and smaller areas of land were allocated on the basis of the area of forest that an **ejidatario** and his family could clear.

In the mid-1950s, a parastatal logging company, MIQRO (Maderas Industriales de Quintana Roo), established operations in the area with a veneer and plywood processing plant. In 1957 it was awarded a 25-year logging concession for 540,000 ha of Quintana Roo, much of which belonged to the **ejidatarios** (Richards, 1992). During this period, the first forest inventories were conducted and a network of logging roads established. Extraction focused entirely on the two 'precious woods', *Swietenia macrophylla* and *Cedrela odorata*. In accordance with the law at the time, harvesting was limited to trees above a minimum dbh (60 cm), and attempts were made at enrichment planting in logged areas. However, forestry operations were neither sustainable nor particularly beneficial to the local people. Although the company adhered to its legal requirements for reimbursing the **ejidos** and provided local employment through its logging operations, the net gain to the **ejidatarios** was relatively small. As a result, many preferred to clear the land for agriculture rather than retain it as forest. When the MIQRO concession expired in 1983, local and national circumstances favoured a move towards community forestry. This came about as the Plan Piloto Forestal (PPF).

4.3 The People of Quintana Roo

The present **ejidatarios** of Quintana Roo are descended both from indigenous Maya people and from immigrants. **Ejidos** are not a traditional form of community structure; they were formed in the 1930s under a socialist government. **Ejidos** consist of a fixed number of **ejidatarios** who each occupy an area of land within the **ejido**, and have the right to the products of that land, including the forest. Since the changes in the law in 1992, they now also have the legal right of forest ownership. **Ejido** rights are not transferable and are inherited by male offspring; the only women who can be **ejidatarios** are widows (about 4% of the total). Until 1992, only the products of the land could be sold, not the land itself. However, it is now possible for **ejidos** to change voluntarily from their present system of tenure, known as **propiedad ejidal**, to a system of private property, **propiedad privada**. This gives them the right to sell or mortgage their land, and may radically affect future forest management. As a recent change, its effects cannot be assessed as yet.

The board outside the ejido-run sawmill in Nohbec. It reads 'Here the forestry activity supports the economy of 200 families. Therefore we conserve the forest. Avoid fires'. Photograph: Anna Lawrence

The distinctive aspects of the **ejido** system of land tenure are that the boundaries and user group are well defined and that, within the **ejido**, there is no hierarchy. Leaders are elected every 4–5 years, and general communal organisation is good. This may be attributed in part to a history of co-operative working, in the form of chicle marketing co-operatives. There are, however, inequalities within the overall community, as women play a minor role in decision-making and non-**ejidatarios** can only be wage-workers, not landowners.

As a result of the mixed history of the **ejidos**, some occupy more forest than others. More remains, in particular, where the economy was based on chicle extraction. Forest extraction is most important in three **ejidos** where 60–80% of family income is derived from forest activities. In others, forestry is less developed and, as one of several income sources, represents only 25–40% of the family income.

4.4 The Development of the Plan Piloto Forestal (PPF)

The PPF was initiated in 1983, as a result of various favourable circumstances. These included:

- The change in forest policy in support of community forestry.

- The existence of a large forest area which still contained much valuable timber and a network of access roads.

- A fairly small local population with considerable internal cohesion and some experience in forestry operations.

- Strong local political support from the State Governor at the time.

- The offer of assistance from the **Acuerdo México-Alemania** (AMA), a programme of technical support to Mexican forestry funded by GTZ (the overseas development agency of the German Government).

A recent statement by the PPF summarises the twin objectives of forest management as being to produce an economic yield which is attractive to the **ejidos** but is at the same time sustainable in the long term.

In the first instance, a number of SARH foresters were recruited to collaborate on the PPF with AMA staff. The PPF team began by assisting **ejidos** to organise themselves into a commercial group to sell timber, and to obtain the equipment needed for logging operations. A key step was the definition by each **ejido** of a Permanent Forest Area, to be managed in perpetuity (or as long as can be foreseen) for timber production. The total Permanent Forest Area among the ten **ejidos** amounts to 120,000 ha.

In 1986 the ten **ejidos** formed the **Sociedad de Productores Forestales Ejidales de Quintana Roo** (SPFE). A **Sociedad Civil** (SC) is an organisation with commercial purposes recognised under mercantile law. The main objectives of the society were to:

- Provide technical forestry services to their members.

- Act in the political arena to obtain a concession and to establish dialogue with the government and the timber industry over timber prices.

The same objectives are maintained, although the second has clearly been partially fulfilled and it is now merely a matter of ensuring continued good relations. By the time the original SC was formed, funds were available from timber sales, and it was able to use these to contract two forest technicians to advise on forest management.

There are now five SCs in the state of Quintana Roo, each of which has organised a forestry service for its members. There is a technical director who must be a professional forester (forest engineer), and a variable number of forestry technicians. The money for their salaries and expenses originates from timber sales, but is usually insufficient so that additional funds have to be sought from outside sources.

Although an SC represents all its member **ejidos**, and uses their funds for forest management, decisions about resource use can only be taken by the particular **ejido** concerned. Each **ejido** has a technical council which assists in this process. It comprises a group of elected **ejidatarios** with relevant experience. In practice technical decisions made by the council are usually accepted by the **ejido**. Nevertheless, all such decisions must be approved by the entire **ejido** at regularly held assemblies.

Foreign assistance for the PPF has continued up to the present time, most notably through the AMA. This has provided somewhat exceptional support, in that virtually all the expatriate staff who have worked on the project have been based in Mexico for many years, and thus have a detailed knowledge of the local situation. Many observers point to the value of the long-standing technical support provided through the AMA in the development of the project (Scrase, 1992; Snook, 1993b). The project has also attracted financial assistance from organisations such as the Macarthur Foundation, and, more recently, the Overseas Development Administration of the British Government.

4.5 The Need for Forest Resource Assessment

The need for forest inventory was recognised and accepted by **ejidatarios** from the outset. Not only is it a legal requirement, but they were already familiar with inventory procedures from the period of forest exploitation by MIQRO. However, it is doubtful if at this stage the **ejidatarios** viewed forest inventory as more than a necessary formality.

Under the MIQRO concession, the inventory was subjective and included only the two most valuable species, *Swietenia macrophylla* and *Cedrela odorata*. When the PPF began forest management in 1983, the annual cutting areas were initially defined using the rough extraction records of cut volume available from MIQRO. A 25-year cutting cycle was introduced, based on an assumed 75-year growth cycle for *S. macrophylla*. The Permanent Forest Area of each **ejido** was then divided into five five-year cutting areas, based on general knowledge of the occurrence of *S. macrophylla* which was divided as equally as possible between them.

Technical staff quickly realised that the existing inventory data were unreliable. They therefore instigated an immediate inventory in the area designated for harvest in the first year, measuring only *S. macrophylla* and *Cedrela odorata*. The federal forest service permitted this temporary arrangement because no money was then available from timber revenues to finance a more thorough inventory.

A minimum dbh at harvesting of 60 cm was set for *S. macrophylla*, mainly because of sawmill requirements rather than any silvicultural prescriptions. The minimum has since been reduced to 55 cm for *S. macrophylla* and a few other species (notably *Pseudobombax ellipticum* [**Amapola**] and *Manilkara zapota*). For most of the less valuable species, the minimum dbh is 35 cm. The minimum dbh is not a legal requirement, but a local rule of the Ministry, enforced at local level, its purpose being to provide some form of logging control without forest inspection.

By 1986 discussions between **ejidatarios** and technicians had defined concerns about the forest stocking and how long it would last. Furthermore, the **ejidos** had built up enough capital to afford the costs of an inventory. A joint decision was therefore taken to carry out a full inventory of the Permanent Forest Areas, which would be used to draw up management plans for reliably sustainable harvesting.

4.6   The Forest Assessment Process

Forest Survey

In 1985, the state government paid for an aerial photographic survey (scale 1:32,000) of Quintana Roo. The **ejido** and Permanent Forestry Areas maps produced from this have been used by the PPF ever since. The legal formalities for surveying the Permanent Forest Areas have varied from year to year over the running of the project, with considerable local interpretation being involved.

The Inventory Design

The original design
During the period 1987–8, the entire Permanent Forest Area of the ten **ejidos** in the SPFE was inventoried at a 2% sampling intensity,

as well as that of other forest SCs. The area was divided into 1 km² blocks, within which sampling was conducted in two parallel transects of 1,000 m x 10 m. All trees over 30 cm dbh in these temporary sample plots (TSPs) were measured. Smaller diameters were measured within a subsample of each transect. For trees of 15–29 cm dbh, a 25% subsample was used; for trees of 5–14 cm dbh, a 10% subsample was taken.

Several features of this method caused difficulties, of both a practical and technical nature (Arguelles, Gutiérrez, Ramírez and Sánchez Román, 1992). These were as follows:

- The transects have a long perimeter. There is thus a high risk of bias because of uncertainty over including border trees.

- Long straight lines proved difficult to control in the forest.

- The entry points were chosen at random and were not marked. They therefore proved difficult or impossible to relocate.

- The **ejidatarios** found the use of subsamples confusing, and questioned the need for them.

These disadvantages were confirmed during data checking and analysis. Technical staff realised that the volumes extracted from the annual cutting areas were considerably lower than those predicted by the inventory. To make up the predicted volume, the **ejido** logging teams were cutting beyond the boundaries of the defined area. Staff calculated that, as a result, the available timber would be harvested in considerably less than the allocated 25 years. These problems, and the need to include forest dynamics in the data analysis, led to the redesign of the inventory methodology in 1990.

The revised design

The size of the TSPs was chosen from practical experience. It was the largest which allowed brigade members to maintain visual contact, thereby reducing errors. All the **ejido** inventory specialists are capable of demarcating plots and taking these measurements, and supervision by technical staff is no longer necessary.

Under the new model, sampling is conducted on a systematic basis in small circular plots. These are spaced at 100 m along lines running North-South, 250 m apart. The circular plots have a 12.6 m radius and cover 500 m² in area. All trees of 10 cm dbh and over are now included, with dbh, commercial height, vigour and form being recorded. Paths are cut along the transect lines, and the centre of the plot is marked permanently with short hardwood stakes and covered with stones. They are also numbered with grid co-ordinates. The lines are marked on the map, so plots can always be relocated.

PPF staff consider the present design to have the following advantages:

- The plot shape minimises border problems (although see Box 4.1), and is easy to demarcate in the forest, requiring only the centre point and a tape measure.

- The systematic design makes the establishment of each plot much simpler, and the lines which are cut form the boundaries of the extraction units so that the costs can be divided between the two. Because inventory and extraction use the same frame of reference, the predicted and actual volumes can be compared more easily.

- Measurements within the TSPs are simplified (although more arduous, since they include all trees down to 10 dbh).

- Plots can be relocated without difficulty if this is necessary for checking data.

A member of an ejido inventory team conducting measurements in a temporary sample plot. All trees over 10 cm dbh are included
Photograph:
Anna Lawrence

The design is radical in its use of such small plots (Alder, 1992). This has caused some experts to express reservations. Furthermore, many inventory specialists would argue that it is only with a 100% inventory of commercial species and a yield allocation based on their distribution that a low impact harvest can be guaranteed (Stewart Maginnis, 1995, pers. comm.; see also Chapter 1). Some of the potential disadvantages of the design are outlined in Box 4.1.

However, all inventory design is essentially a compromise between what is statistically ideal, simple to implement, appropriate for the given forest and management objectives, and cost effective. The inventory specialists working for the PPF, who know the local forest conditions well, are confident that the current inventory design is the best for the local circumstances. They argue that the quality of data collected from them has proved the appropriateness of the design.

There is also potential for error in the tree measurements taken by inventory teams. This is discussed further in a separate sub-section, as is the system of checking which has been institutionalised through the establishment of permanent sample plots (PSPs).

Box 4.1 Criticisms of the Present Inventory Design used by the PPF

The use of small circular sample plots
Some inventory specialists point out that certain statistical problems may arise from the use of exceptionally small circular sample plots. The most serious are as follows:

- In heterogeneous natural forest, plots must be large enough to capture the variation in the forest. With smaller plots the variation between plots will be greater. In order to maintain a low sampling error, the number of observations (plots) must be increased substantially. If a very much larger number of plots is needed, inventory costs will be increased.

- Small plots, whatever their shape, have a large perimeter in comparison to their area. This can increase bias if mistakes are made over the inclusion/exclusion of border trees.

However,

- The larger variation associated with smaller plots is virtually nullified by the number sampled in the PPF inventory, and costs are still low.

- The advantage of small plots in the field is that it is easy to check border trees, since there are not very many of them. In one plot containing, for example, ten trees, about eight will be definitely inside the plot, leaving only two to be checked.

Risks associated with the prescription of yield based on a low intensity inventory

These include the following:

- At a coarse-grained level, the inventory will highlight areas rich in *Swietenia macrophylla* or other valued species, but it will not serve to guard against localised over-logging or the preferential harvesting of all the finest trees.

- The inventory may provide useful information for determining the route of primary extraction roads, but it will not assist in planning secondary roads and skid trails to minimise forest damage.

Both these potential problems can, however, be addressed in the field by skilled field workers.

Not all the **ejidos** are undertaking the new inventory immediately. Two situations take priority. One is the inventory of areas targeted for harvesting within the next five years in the **ejidos** most affected by the earlier errors. The other is the first inventory of forests in **ejidos** which have increased their Permanent Forest Area since the first inventory.

Identification of tree species

A common problem encountered with the early data collection was the diversity of tree species and limited local plant knowledge. A local botanist now assists with the inventory, and at least 150 tree species have been identified in the **ejido** forests (compared with the 102 recognised in a 1968 inventory). Inventory workers can now recognise many of these species from bark, slash and leaves. They take botanical specimens when in doubt.

The approach to species identification may be compared with that in the case studies from Nigeria (Chapter 2) and Ecuador (Chapter 3). This project has been running far longer, and has therefore had more time to address species identification. Furthermore, far more species are being routinely recorded.

PSPs: Checking Inventory Data and Predicting Growth

Since 1990, a system of permanent sample plots (PSPs) has been established in some **ejidos**, selected to cover the range of ecological and edaphic conditions found in the **ejido** forests. The selection is conducted using the TSP inventory data. The plots are analysed to select a representative subsample (about 10%), which become PSPs. They are chosen to cover undisturbed forest, disturbed forest and logging trails in the different ecological zones, through cluster sampling over the systematic inventory sample.

Within the PSPs, every tree with a dbh of 10 cm or over is measured and its position recorded with polar co-ordinates so that individual trees can be located in subsequent evaluations. A subplot of 4 m diameter is sampled for regeneration, in which all plants over 1.3 m in height are recorded. A diagram of a PSP is shown in Figure 4.2. About 500 PSPs have now been established in the SPFE zone. A further 350 have been established in the Zona Maya, another SC to the north of the SPFE area. The PSPs established in 1990 and 1991 were measured a second time in 1995, making available the first dynamic inventory data. A system of regular measurements at five-year intervals has been designed for the next ten years.

The PSPs also have an important function in checking measurements made during the routine inventory. Since they represent a subsample of the TSPs which are relocated and remeasured within two months of the original inventory, they provide a control on the accuracy of the figures recorded.

Figure 4.2   Diagram of a Permament Sample Plot (PSP)

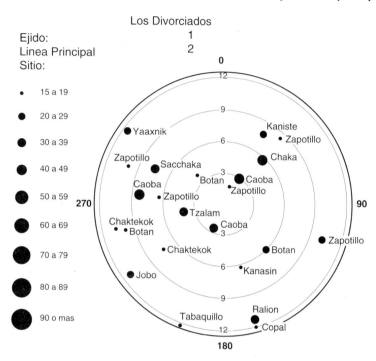

Participation of the Ejidos in Data Collection and Decision-making

At the start of the project, the PPF team presented the **ejidos** with a two-volume management plan. This was rejected by the **ejido** councils because they had not been involved in its preparation. The PPF team therefore re-commenced work by asking the **ejidatarios** what they wanted to do with the forest, and what assistance the foresters could provide. Their response was that they wanted the forest to last '**para toda la vida**' (for our whole lives) and the foresters to help them achieve this. Since then, participation has been fundamental to project activities. There was no thrust to produce quick results; instead, a process approach was adopted. A strategic objective was defined, of enabling forestry **ejidos** to take control of their forestry activities. The project then acted as necessary to achieve this, responding to circumstances as they arose.

The **ejidatarios** are more than project participants; it is they who have ultimate authority over all decisions, whether technical or non-technical. The technical staff are contracted by them, and are well aware that their advice will be assessed according to the priorities of the **ejidos**. Nevertheless, the technical staff express considerable job satisfaction and see their role as a very positive one.

Because of the previous history of forest exploitation, the **ejidatarios** were initially distrustful of the technical staff recruited to work with them (SPFE, 1988). Within the first year, however, these suspicions had faded. As a result, 'instead of a plan for the campesinos produced by the institutions, it was a plan of and with the campesinos who … were thus incorporated in the decision-making process' (Carreón, 1991, authors' translation).

Since the PPF began, the **ejidatarios** have been involved in inventory data collection. Inventory brigades comprise four **ejidatarios** and one forester. Initially the **ejidatarios** were assigned to this work on a rotating basis, often influenced by the availability of other employment in the **ejido**. As a result, participants did not gain much experience before being replaced by another novice, and work tended to be inefficient. In 1991 this system was changed, so that the inventory brigades now consist of specialists who have built up experience through working together with the foresters over a long period. Brigade leaders have been selected on the basis of their interest in the work, and their skill and reliability. There are about 20 such **jefes de brigadas** in the 10 **ejidos**. They work together, travelling between **ejidos**, and taking on the former role of the forestry technicians. Many are sons of **ejidatarios**, a younger generation which has undergone more formal education than their fathers. These specialists are now in demand for inventory work outside the **ejido** (as discussed in Section 4.6).

Most of the cost of inventory personnel is paid by the **ejido** concerned, or from a special budget for inventories in situations were the **ejido** has raised funding for the work (usually from government agencies which lend money at low interest rates). Two of the brigade leaders are trainees who, it is hoped, will be employed in the technical service and then be paid by the SC.

Crisis in Forest Management and How It Was Tackled

A report written shortly after the inventory problems had been recognised illustrates the mood of the PPF team. It states, 'a whole community has structured its economy and social organisation on the forestry activity based on false premises... The cost that this omission could have for the project is incalculable, what is certain is that the **ejidatarios** of Nohbec must now begin to pay it' (Ramírez and Sánchez, 1991, authors' translation).

The realisation that timber harvests in some **ejidos** were too high, and must be reduced on average by about 35%, presented difficulties for the foresters. The admission that forest management was not as profitable as they had predicted represented a potential economic crisis for the communities involved. Furthermore, since the 1986–7 inventory data could not be used, the expenditure on it represented a loss of money, with a further financial outlay being required for a new comprehensive and urgent inventory. PPF team morale fell, and the foresters began to feel that they had neglected the technical aspects of forest management in favour of the social ones.

However, the emphasis placed on the social aspects of the project was justified by the reaction of the **ejidatarios**. A meeting was held in Nohbec, the **ejido** worst affected because it is most heavily dependent on forest activities, which account for 80% of its revenue. The PPF team presented the revised volume forecasts to the **ejido** assembly, and suggested how and why the errors could have occurred. They also indicated what steps should be taken to correct them. It was a difficult meeting, but the members accepted that the reduction in extraction was necessary. They decided to conduct a survey of the logged areas to check for standing trees which had been missed in the selection procedure. They also agreed to begin a new forest inventory immediately.

The interest of the **ejido** in sustainable management is clearly demonstrated by this incident, in which they took a decision which they anticipated would reduce their income. (In fact, the expected shortfall was more than compensated by increased sales of other timbers.) Furthermore, their appreciation of the value of a good inventory is indicated by their commitment to a new assessment of the area in the remaining 17 years of the cutting cycle, which amounts to 11,400 ha.

Human Error in Participatory Inventory Work

It became apparent during the data analysis that human errors had occurred in inventory measurements made over the period 1984–91. In particular, some data had been repeated, and some were probably invented by tired inventory workers. There was evidently also a temptation to include trees just outside the plot border, especially when they were large and valuable.

The bias was quantified when sufficient data were available from the 1992 inventory in Nohbec to compare with the results of the 1987 inventory. It was found that in the earlier inventory:

- The smaller size classes were underestimated (40% of all trees of 15 cm dbh were not recorded in 1987).

- Unknown species and those thought to be commercially unimportant were underestimated (only 35% of 'others', that is, non-commercial species, were recorded).

- There was a slight tendency to overestimate the presence of *Swietenia macrophylla*.

The reasons for these biases and errors may be summarised as follows:

These errors are not necessarily associated with a participatory approach. They can occur in any inventory in which the personnel involved are inadequately trained or poorly motivated. Motivation was certainly not lacking in this case. The main problems were inadequate training and supervision, compounded by an unsatisfactory inventory design.

- Lack of training and comprehension of the different sampling intensities of different size classes.

- Lack of understanding of the need to avoid bias towards commercial trees, and of technical supervision to ensure this.

- Identification errors.

- Careless cartography and control of field operations so that sample areas could not be located again.

- Geographical gaps through missed sampling.

The revised inventory method aims to minimise bias and other errors through both its design (systematic sampling of small areas with minimised borders) and its implementation (by specialist, trained inventory brigades). Technical staff and **ejido** specialists alike are now far more conscious of the need for scrupulous accuracy. Inventory teams now check data sheets together, looking for gaps and obvious errors in data records, before delivering them to the computer specialist.

Training

The PPF has put most emphasis on the training of technicians in the field. Initially those in charge of data collection in the field were trained by AMA staff, as well as attending some courses at CATIE (**Centro Agronómico Tropical de Investigación y Enseñanza**, in Costa Rica). The most advanced brigade leaders now train others in the field. Training of a new recruit usually takes 1 to 2 months, although to a certain extent it is a continuous process. After three years experience with the new inventory design, the specialist inventory brigades are now extremely competent. The species-recognition skills of the brigade leaders have also been improved by the AMA botanist, who has worked with them in the field to this end.

There are various needs for training at a more specialist level, as indicated in Section 4.7. No training programme has yet been devised, although the need for this is recognised.

Analysis and Applications of the Inventory Data

The inventory data are analysed by computer. Volume tables (prepared by MIQRO) for the most important marketable species were found to be reliable, and have therefore been used. When volume tables for newer commercial species are needed, the PPF may employ undergraduate students to prepare them.

The AMA programming specialist has developed programmes which:

• Calculate the number of trees and the timber volume of each species within the five-year area.

• Calculate the map density contours for these data.

• Divide the five-year area into five annual cutting areas based on equal volumes of a given timber; currently *Swietenia macrophylla* is used as the 'guide' species in all **ejidos**.

The processed inventory data are entered into a model to predict the costs and income deriving from exploitation of the species available. The computer specialist prepares alternative options for extraction and budgets. This information is then discussed with the technical council of the **ejido**, and if necessary with the **ejido** assembly. In this way it is used as a decision-making tool, helping the **ejido** to choose where and what they will harvest in future years. It is also a planning tool which allows the **ejidos** to predict income and employment in each year, and to make contracts in advance based on reliable minimum estimates of volume.

The full use of the computer maps began in 1993, and has significantly improved the planning of forest operations. Density maps of commercial species help technicians to design forest road networks and plan the order of extraction operations.

The inventory data can also be used to predict the effect of more unusual management options. For example, when the **ejido** of Nohbec wanted to increase their area of agricultural land by moving back the boundary of the Permanent Forest Area, the computer specialist supplied them with information on the economic effect of three options. These were: leaving the boundary unaltered, moving the boundary by 500 m, or moving the boundary by 700 m. In the end the **ejido** decided not to clear the forest, and to buy more agricultural land elsewhere.

The Cost of Forest Inventory

Those working on the PPF feel that it is right for the **ejidos** to pay for the necessary technical services for timber extraction (including extraction-oriented inventories) and sawmill control, whether they do it directly or through their SC. However, collecting and analysing data related to the sustainability component of management should be financed externally, since it is of interest and benefit to a far wider audience than the **ejidatarios** alone.

The issue of cost and who pays is a crucial one for the PPF. At present, the costs of the inventory operation are divided between the data collection (paid for by the **ejidos**), supervision by the SC technicians (paid by the SC, and soon to be paid by other sources) and the data analysis by AMA staff (funded by GTZ). This assignment of costs is a delicate balance. Under existing circumstances the **ejidos** are willing to pay the substantial costs of data collection from the timber revenue, but any further costs to be borne by them would drastically affect profitability, and might contribute to the rapid conversion of forest to other land uses.

The costs of data collection in the first inventory were slightly over US$8 per hectare. The costs of the second inventory rose to US$10/ha in Nohbec **ejido**, as better data were collected. Since then, costs have fallen again to US$7/ha in the most recent inventory in Petcacab, as after training the **ejido** inventory specialists now require less supervision by the more expensive technicians.

Reducing the costs of inventory further is considered to be a priority. With the specialisation of **ejido** workers the work can be completed more efficiently than before, but even so the brigade was occupied for eight months of the year in 1993–4, completing the most recent inventory of 6,500 ha in Petcacab **ejido**. In future a limit of 4,000 ha per year is expected. Detailed inventory data are now available which can be analysed for patterns of variation and used to determine sampling intensity. Several parameters are used, notably:

- total area to be inventoried
- objectives of management (ranging from timber extraction using *S. macrophylla* as the 'guide' species to charcoal production)
- minimum sub-area for which meaningful results are required

The resulting sampling intensities have varied from 4.7% to 0.5%, averaging at 2%. Computer modelling will be used to minimise sampling intensity in the future. PPF staff consider, for example, that it may not be necessary to measure certain species, but merely to record their presence, as it is known that they reach only a small maximum diameter. Some also argue that the more evenly distributed species require less intensive sampling than clustered species such as *Swietenia macrophylla*.

The costs of the PSP evaluation are currently covered entirely by external funding. A reduction in the time and expense of data collection for this is also considered essential. Working from the large data base now available, advisers will soon produce a streamlined model suited to the forests of Quintana Roo.

PIQRO, the local factory producing parquet from tropical hardwoods. This has generated local employment opportunities.
Photograph: Anna Lawrence

Effect of Increasing Markets

Up to 1985 markets existed only for *Swietenia macrophylla* and *Cedrela odorata*. **Ejidatarios** pressed for markets to be opened, and in 1985 the Federal and State governments supported them by requiring timber enterprises to buy 2 m³ of less valuable species (combined under the term **corrientes tropicales**) for every 1 m³ of the valuable ones. Although originally MIQRO and other timber companies tended to leave the **corrientes tropicales** to rot, this acted as an incentive to the **ejidos** to include all tree species in the evaluation. However, as indicated above, their inclusion was sometimes more in theory than in practice, at least during the first inventory. The interest of international timber certification companies such as the Ecological Trading Company (UK) and the Green Cross Certification Company (USA), as well as the opening of PIQRO, a local factory producing parquet from tropical hardwoods, have stimulated the market for more species. With new openings in timber markets, the value of data on all species is now appreciated within the **ejidos** (see Box 4.2).

Box 4.2 Increasing Markets for Corrientes Tropicales

Currently up to 15 species (including the original two, *Swietenia macrophylla* and *Cedrela odorata*) are extracted from the Quintana Roo forests for timber. They include *Brosimum alicastrum* (**Ramón**), *Bucida buceras* (**Pukte**), *Bursera simaruba* (**Chaká**) *Caesalpinia platyloba* (**Chakte-viga**), *Calophyllum brasiliense* (**Bari**), *Cordia dodecandra* (**Siricote**), *Dendropanax arboreus* (**Sac chaká**), *Haematoxylum campechianum* (**Palo de tinto**), *Lonchocarpus castilloi* (**Machich**), *Manilkara zapota* (**Chicozapote**), *Metopium brownei* (**Chechén**), *Pseudobombax ellipticum* (**Amapola**), *Simira salvadorensis* (**Chakte-kok**), and *Spondias mombin* (**Jobo**).

An example of a low-value timber which has become economically important is *Dendropanax arboreus*, a flavourless softwood, large volumes of which are in demand for toothpicks. The most valuable species to come onto the market is *Cordia dodecandra*, a hardwood in demand for its beautiful grain. However, its occurrence in the **ejido** forests is rare. A more common species is *Metopium brownei*, small quantities of which sell in Japan for US$300/m³. This is 50% more than the local price for *Swietenia macrophylla*. The increasing markets for small diameter hardwoods for flooring, toothpicks, and other processing industries are of particular significance. They mean that a much higher proportion of the tree can be sold, including a large proportion of the branches.

The inventory data are important during inspections by certification companies. The early visits tended to elicit favourable remarks in general terms, but noted the lack of data to make real assessments of the sustainability of production. Inspectors now have some of the most detailed inventory data in tropical forest management to evaluate. If the project is certified in accordance with the principles and criteria of the Forest Stewardship Council, new market opportunities offering premium prices may emerge.

The utilisation of a greater number of species may affect the inventory analysis and costs directly in the future. At present the division of cutting areas on the basis of *Swietenia macrophylla* volume alone is at the stipulation of the **ejidos**. Their reasoning is that it is the most valuable species and the one for which there is most demand. However, *S. macrophylla* has certain site preferences, and a clumped distribution. Important implications of using *S. macrophylla* alone as the 'guide' species are as follows:

The choice of *Swietenia macrophylla* as the guide species by the **ejidos** reflects past market preferences for *S. macrophylla* as well as present demand. However, it is inconsistent with current trends in natural forest management which are clearly towards more holistic, rather than species-based, systems.

- Volumes of other species within an annual cutting area are variable.

- A higher intensity of sampling is needed than if many 'guide' species are used. This increases the costs of the inventory.

- Annual cutting areas may vary considerably in total area and in shape, which renders implementation awkward.

Logs outside the ejido-run sawmill in Nohbec. A wide variety of timber species are processed here.
Photograph:
Anna Lawrence

If markets for other timbers become sufficiently reliable, **ejidos** may be convinced of the advantages of defining annual cutting areas on the basis of the combined volume of a range of species. Since the combined distribution would be more uniform, sampling could be less intense and the inventory cheaper. *Swietenia macrophylla* is relatively scarce in the **ejidos** of the southern zone of SPFE, so they are more affected by markets for other timbers. It is very likely that this change will be adopted by them, so that a more reliable prediction can be made more cheaply.

Other future changes in the inventory may include sampling down to 5 cm dbh to allow the inclusion of material for charcoal production. The feasibility of this depends less on markets, which already exist, than on silvicultural recommendations. If research results indicate that it would be better to remove more basal area during felling, to encourage regeneration of particular species, then it is worth including smaller diameters in the inventory.

The model of inventory data costs can be used to show the effects of using **corrientes tropicales** compared with *Swietenia macrophylla*. At current market prices, the profit margin is lower but the employment generation is higher with such species. Different sectors of the **ejido** are therefore affected in different ways. Not surprisingly, those directly employed in the forest industry are most in favour of increasing the numbers of species used.

4.7 Current and Future Developments

Sustainability and Research

As discussed in Chapter 1 of this book, the concept of 'sustainability' has different meanings for different interest groups. The parties involved in the PPF are no exception, although since the project aims to address the priorities of the **ejidos**, their definition is central. For them, managing the forest so that it continues to bring in income for the 'whole of their lives' is of key importance. This vague but long-term concept is interpreted by the project in terms of generations, rather than a single human lifespan.

There are three aspects to maintenance of income from the forest:

- continued supply of timber
- continued demand for the product
- acceptable costs of forest management

Increasing product demand and the costs of inventory have been discussed above. This section focuses on the assessment of future timber supply from the forest.

The detailed programme of PSPs established in the **ejido** forests will provide much useful data in the assessment of biological sustainability. Technical staff will use these data to predict whether the existing regeneration and reserve components of the forest will replace the current harvest within the 25-year cycles at the existing minimum diameters. Analysis so far suggests that the existing parameters are acceptable, although it could be necessary to extend the cutting cycle beyond 28 years. This would mean dividing the same forest volume into 28 parts instead of 25, with an 11% reduction in the annual cut.

However, it is unlikely that optimal regeneration is being obtained under current management systems. This is particularly the case for *Swietenia macrophylla*, which responds to large-scale disturbance and fire. In order to examine all the options, more experimental work is required. An opportunity is provided here for useful doctoral research, although the results of that carried out in the project area so far have been contentious (see Box 4.3 summarising the work of Snook, 1993a). Another researcher found unexpectedly low diameter increments in *S. macrophylla*. She recommended that silvicultural activities in Quintana Roo should be based on these results and stated: 'At the current rate of extraction, mahogany could be almost eliminated from this tropical forest in less than 30 years' (Negreros, 1991). However, her results were based on a sample of only 19 trees.

Box 4.3 The Argument for Changing Current Logging Practices with Regard to *Swietenia macrophylla*

The forests of Quintana Roo are characterised by drastic natural disturbances – both hurricanes and fire. *Swietenia macrophylla* is well adapted to capitalise on these disturbances, as an adult surviving high winds because of its aerodynamic shape and buttresses, and fire because of its thick bark. With its wind-dispersed seeds it colonises open areas rapidly, to form even-aged stands. As a light-demander, it does not establish in under-storey shade. Small canopy gaps caused by single tree falls or fellings rarely produce sufficient sunlight for its establishment.

It is argued that selective logging impedes *S. macrophylla* regeneration in the following ways:

- It removes *S. macrophylla*, leaving other species to expand into the growing space.

- The canopy openings created are too small to allow *S. macrophylla* regeneration.

- Harvesting *S. macrophylla* removes seed sources (particularly as harvesting occurs a few months before seed dispersal, and *S. macrophylla* seed has short viability).

Evidence from other parts of Latin America, particularly Belize, supports this argument. The researcher's observations indicate that *S. macrophylla* regeneration in the Quintana Roo forests has already been adversely affected by past and current selective logging. According to her, 'To continue current practices is to risk mining out existing mahoganies and foregoing future mahogany harvests'. Priority should therefore be given to the development and implementation of silvicultural practices that actively encourage *S. macrophylla* regeneration.

Source: Snook (1993a)

The research findings have caused alarm within the PPF, particularly in anticipation of the adverse political effect that they might have. Staff are confident that the more drastic predictions of the research will not be borne out in practice. They are convinced that a major reduction in the annual predicted cut would make forest management economically undesirable to the **ejidos**. The result would probably be a rapid conversion of the forest to other land uses. Nevertheless, it is agreed that more data are needed over a wider area, and detailed research is being encouraged in the subject.

So far, existing data can only be used to predict timber supply over the next 25 years with reasonable certainty. In the 50 years following this, the supply can probably be sustained by adjusting harvest levels according to the results of growth modelling. To make predictions beyond this time, more knowledge is needed on the recruitment of valuable species, an aspect to which the project is giving attention. A doctoral study has recently begun to compare regeneration in disturbed and undisturbed areas, whilst other outside funding has supported regeneration and growth studies. The PPF has also established its own growth plots, with 398 *Swietenia macrophylla* trees.

Integration of Ejidos in Technical Aspects and the Adoption of Technology

Currently, data collection but not data analysis is carried out by **ejido** members. The SPFE inventory method and analysis are now well developed and flexible decision-making tools, which have evolved in response to the priorities and needs of the **ejidos**. The possibility, or even the desirability, of **ejidatarios** ultimately conducting the whole process themselves is a subject of some debate. A number of those involved argue that successful resource management does not require that the managers undertake all data analysis themselves. What is important is that they establish a relationship with specialist advisers on whom they can rely for appropriate data.

This said, several sons of **ejidatarios** are now studying forestry at university, and will return to be employed by the **ejido**. This will reduce the pressure on the foresters employed by the SC and help to increase the institutional sustainability of the forest management. In addition, the recent relocation of the PPF technical offices closer to the field (one each in the northern and the southern zones) should result in technical staff travelling less and having more time to train **ejidatarios** in data analysis.

It is important to recognise that sustainable natural forest management in Quintana Roo (and indeed elsewhere in the tropics) is still at an experimental stage. A vast amount of data collection is needed merely to assess the quality and usefulness of current data. Unsubsidised rural communities cannot be expected to finance this work. Who provides the funding is a largely political question, but it is likely that foreign aid will continue to be an important factor in the foreseeable future.

Evaluation of Alternatives to Timber Resources

In order to maintain or increase income from the forest, **ejidos** are anxious to diversify the products harvested. One way of doing this is to include more timber species, and by doing so open up larger gaps and encourage more regeneration. Other options include the harvesting of non-timber products.

One NTFP, chicle gum, has been produced from the forests of Quintana Roo for longer than most timbers. Chicle extraction is more accessible to **campesinos** than timber because it requires almost no capital to start, only the cost of a few basic tools. Although demand for the gum has fallen during the last decade, the market has recently recovered. Chicle is currently the second most important export of Quintana Roo State after timber, accounting for 30% of foreign trade. It is still being harvested well below the potential yield of the forest, although no statistics on this are available. It is by far the most common species in the forest. Due to the historical importance of chicle, **ejidatarios** will not fell the trees for timber, although markets exist for the timber and some believe that a proportion of trees could be used without affecting the chicle supply.

Like chicle, other local NTFPs (both actual and potential) are produced from trees and therefore included in the forest inventory. Beyond this, no separate evaluation is made of their products, which are still not an important component of the **ejido** cash economy. Examples include the fruit of *Cordia dodecandra* (**Siricote**) which has a small market, various palms used for thatch, and meliflorous trees (honey is another important product of Quintana Roo and bee hives are located in forest clearings).

Another potential use for the forest is in eco-tourism. **Ejidos** have already defined their own conservation areas without outside pressure. For example in Nohbec **ejido**, an area which was not exploited by MIQRO has been set aside simply because 'it is primary forest' and contains particularly fine *Swietenia macrophylla*. In other **ejidos**, a population of *Pinus caribaea*, the only one in Mexico, has been protected. Good hunting areas have been designated 'no-felling zones'. **Ejidos'** evaluation of such areas is largely based on local knowledge and consensus, although visits from biologists have highlighted the value of some areas such as the *P. caribaea* stand. In Nohbec a doctoral student is carrying out a study of the fauna in the Permanent Forest Area of the **ejido**, where the assembly has agreed to ban hunting (at least to outsiders). They plan to attract tourists interested in wildlife, but no facilities are available as yet. One of the southernmost **ejidos**, Tres Garantías, is beginning to develop tourist facilities but is rather remote from existing tourist routes. The **ejido** has made some early attempts to attract paying hunters, but has encountered problems with permission to exploit the wildlife.

Value of the Inventory Model for Other Forest Management Projects

The model developed by the technical team in SPFE is in demand with other projects, both within south-east Mexico and amongst visitors from other Latin American countries. Furthermore, technology transfer has progressed within the **ejidos**, so that technical staff now envisage having up to four months per year available for work outside the **ejidos**. Inventory staff within the SC and the AMA have recently formed a consultancy group as a business framework in which to carry out such external work. This will directly reduce the cost to the SC of the technical staff, and the subsidy from external sources to the AMA.

The first work for which the group has been contracted is the National Inventory, a periodic survey of Mexican vegetation. During planning, they were able to use their experience to recommend smaller and more appropriate-sized sample plots, and to locate the sampling in forest areas rather than the randomly selected and often deforested areas chosen from satellite images. The involvement of the group should help improve the value of this massive data-collecting exercise, and provide well-paid employment for the specialist **ejido** inventory brigades. With this development, inventory itself has become a commodity of value to the **ejidos**.

4.8 Conclusion

Conditions which have favoured the development of the PPF include secure well-defined tenure, valuable products and expanding markets, political support, and long-term but low-profile foreign assistance. It is important that the **ejidos** have had the confidence to assert their rights to forest management, and to take the relevant decisions. Furthermore, the project has worked directly with existing social structures which have a well-defined control over the resource, and has been able to by-pass intermediate bureaucracies (Janka and Lobato, 1994). Despite having their own motives for forest management and conservation, the technical staff have always worked through the priorities of the **ejidos**. They supply information, not decisions, to the **ejido** councils. By aiming for economically attractive forest management, resource conservation is achieved through the choice of the **ejidos**.

The inventory process represents the overturning of a superficial legal requirement in favour of a real practical tool. Although not all international experts agree about the technical excellence of the system in use, many are convinced of its advantages. Certainly PPF staff have demonstrated flexibility and insight in developing a model adapted to the needs of participatory data-collection.

Inventory data-collection is now an efficient operation, although work continues on refining it to reduce the time and expense

> The **ejidos** do not derive their cohesiveness from traditional groupings; most are less than fifty years old. This indicates that communal resource management can be created where the incentives are strong and the rights clearly defined.

required. PPF staff are aware that sustainability depends not only on the equal division of existing resources but also on the replacement of those resources over a longer time-scale. The focus of resource evaluation problems has now shifted from inventory to modelling growth and yield, and regeneration studies. The latter are largely in the field of experimental silviculture and will continue to need outside technical and financial support. The interest in and ability to experiment, both with growth and regeneration studies, are a particular feature of the project. Research is never viewed in purely academic terms; it is focused on problems that have direct implications for the economy of local communities.

The continued success of the PPF has more than local importance. The participatory inventory model which has been developed could be applied by communities in a wide range of tropical vegetation, with a relatively small external technical input. The demand for demonstration and repetition of the PPF model is one of the most promising results of the plan. The main criteria on the application of the PPF model elsewhere are likely to be the security and confidence of the communities living in and around the forest, and the political will to support them in managing the forest themselves.

References

Alder, D. (1992) 'Forest Inventory Techniques – Plan Piloto Forestal, Quintana Roo. Notes on a visit to Chetumal, 26 Oct. 1992'. (Mimeo).

Arguelles, A., Gutiérrez, S., Ramírez, E. and Sánchez Román, F. (1992) 'Un modelo de inventario forestal adecuado para apoyar las operaciones de extracción, de silvicultura e industriales de las empreseas forestales ejidales de Quintana Roo'. PPF.

Carreón, M. M. (1991) 'Desarrollo de una metodología para el establecimiento de sitios permanentes de muestreo en los ejidos forestales de la zona maya de Quintana Roo'. Professional thesis.

Edwards, R. C. (1986) 'The Human Impact on the Forest in Quintana Roo, Mexico', *Journal of Forest History*, July: 120–7.

Janka, H. and Lobato, R. (1994) 'Alternativas para enfrentar la destrucción de las selvas tropicales: algunos aspectos de la experiencia del Plan Piloto Forestal de Quintana Roo'. Paper presented at the workshop 'Government Policy in Relation to Forest Resources', 1–3 June, Washington, DC.

Negreros, C. P. (1991) 'Ecology and Management of Mahogany (*Swietenia macrophylla* King) Regeneration in Quintana Roo, Mexico'. PhD thesis, Forestry Department, Iowa State University, Ames, Iowa.

Ramírez, E. and Sánchez, R. F. (1991) 'Informe del análisis de la extracción de preciosas en el ejido Nohbec de 1964 a 1991 y su relación con el inventario forestal de 1986'. PPF internal report.

Richards, E. M. (1992) *The Forest Ejidos of South-east Mexico: A Case Study of Participatory Natural Forest Management*. ODI Rural Development Forestry Network Paper 13c. ODI, London.

Scrase, H. (1992) 'The Roles of International Development Agencies in Tropical Forestry – with Emphasis on Communal Forest Management in Latin America, Using a Case Study from Mexico'. MSc thesis, Oxford University.

Snook, L. K. (1993a) 'Stand Dynamics of Mahogany (*Swietenia macrophylla* King) and Associated Species after Fire and Hurricane in the Tropical Forests of the Yucatán Peninsula, Mexico'. PhD thesis, Yale School of Forestry and Environmental Studies.

Snook L. K. (1993b) 'Forest Management in Mexico: Social, Technical and Institutional Aspects'. Draft report to World Bank.

SPFE (1988) 'La participación campesina en el Plan Piloto Forestal de Quintana Roo, Mexico'. (Mimeo).

Synnott, T. J. (1993) 'Quintana Roo Forest Management Project'. ODA project memorandum, October. ODA, London.

Acronyms and terms specific to this chapter

AMA	**Acuerdo México Alemania** (Mexico-Germany Agreement)
GTZ	**Gesellschaft für Technische Zusammenarbeit** ([German] Agency for Technical Co-operation)
MIQRO	**Maderas Industriales de Quintana Roo** (Industrial Timbers of Quintana Roo)
PIQRO	**Pisos y Cubrimientos de Quintana Roo** (Floors and Parquet of Quintana Roo)
PPF	**Plan Piloto Forestal** (Pilot Forestry Plan, but more usually referred to as the Quintana Roo Forestry Project)
SARH	Secretariat for Agriculture and Water Resources
SC	**Sociedad Civil** (Civil Society), in this chapter usually referring specifically to the SPFE
SPFE	**Sociedad de Productores Forestales Ejidales de Quintana Roo** (Society of Ejido Forestry Producers of Quintana Roo)

campesino	small-scale farmer or member of largely agricultural community
chicle	latex of *Manilkara zapota*, used in the preparation of chewing gum
corrientes tropicales	all timber species other than the traditionally valuable *Swietenia macrophylla* and *Cedrela odorata*

ejido	group of campesinos sharing hereditary and non-transferable ownership of land
ejidatario	ejido member, usually male head of family
jefe de brigada	brigade leader

5 Collaborative Forest Resource Assessment Surveys for the Management of Community Forest Reserves in Ghana

Jane Gronow and Eric Safo
With contributions from Patrick Owusu Asante, Orteng Darko, and Daniel Assan

This chapter briefly describes some of the forest resource assessment work being conducted by the Planning Branch of the Ghana Forestry Department with assistance from the Overseas Development Administration (ODA) of the British Government. It focuses on one activity, that of collaborative forest resource assessment surveys in informing community management decisions. Such pilot surveys are being conducted by local people with the assistance of the Planning Branch in the forest areas of Adwenaase and Namtee (see Figure 5.1). It is hoped that the approach adopted will provide a model for similar initiatives elsewhere in the country. Although at an early stage of development, the surveys already provide a number of interesting lessons.

Since the Planning Branch has a national remit, it is appropriate to provide a brief overview of forestry in Ghana. The country covers an area of 23.9 million hectares spanning two major ecological zones. The south-western third of the country is high forest (HFZ), while guinea savanna dominates the north and east. The high forest forms the easternmost extremity of the Upper Guinea forest block and contains a number of rare forest types. Seven distinct vegetation types are recognised within the HFZ, ranging from wet evergreen to dry semi-deciduous forests. The most important for commercial timber exploitation are the moist evergreen and moist semi-deciduous forests. The most valuable areas in terms of biodiversity lie in undisturbed patches scattered across the HFZ, but particularly in the wet evergreen forests (IIED, 1993).

Within the HFZ, 1.76 million hectares (21% of the area) have permanent legal protection. Most of this (1.63 million hectares) comprise forest reserves. The remaining area is for game protection and is managed by the Department of Game and Wildlife.

Figure 5.1 Adwenaase and Namtee Community Forest Reserves, Ghana

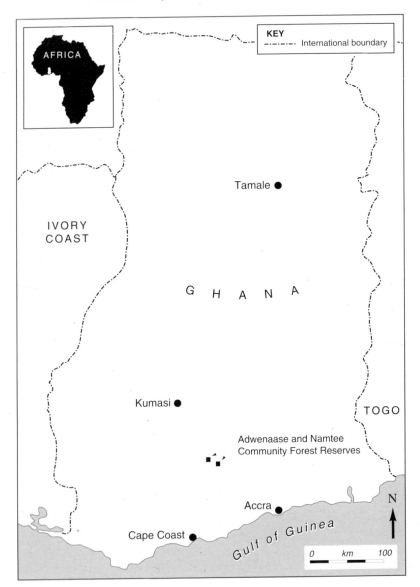

5.1 Forest Legislation and the Role of the Government of Ghana in Forest Management

The Forestry Department (FD) is an implementing agency of the Ministry of Lands and Forests (MLF), and is responsible for ensuring that the strategies outlined in the government's forest policy, which has been recently revised, are put into practice. The FD is at present a civil service department, but in recognition of the constraints inherent in this institutional framework, the MLF and FD are currently preparing detailed proposals for radical institutional reform, to be placed before cabinet in late 1995. It is envisaged that the FD will become an autonomous, partially subsidised public agency to be known as the Ghana Forest Service (GFS). This will enable the new GFS to operate with increased efficiency and responsiveness. The MLF will continue to set forest policy. A number of other institutions play a critical role in the forestry sector, including the Forestry Commission, the Timber Export Development Board, the Forest Products Inspection Bureau, and the various associations which represent the interests of the timber industry.

In spite of the considerable pressure being exerted on the forest resource by the timber industry (which has a surplus milling capacity), the Government is committed to ensuring that its timber comes from sustainably managed resources by the year 2000, and that all segments of Ghanaian society benefit from the conservation and development of the nation's forest resources. An indication of the resolve of the MLF is the new legislation on the allocation of concession areas to ensure that only well equipped timber companies committed to re-stocking their concession area and to operating in a socially responsible manner have access to the resource.

Forest Legislation

All forest legislation is currently under review with the object of producing a single, consolidated Forest Act that will address the realities and objectives of the day effectively. The new Act will give greater legislative backing to the FD in its efforts to establish new systems for forest protection and management in forest reserves, while guaranteeing sufficient incentives to landowners and farmers to maintain trees on their farms and fallows off-reserve.

A significant change in the legislation will concern rights over timber trees on farms. Up to the present rights in all trees are vested in the President and generous rights to harvest timber trees are granted to timber firms by the FD under a system of timber concessions. The farmer gains nothing in the process. This has been a significant disincentive to the maintenance of trees on farms. In future all planted and nursed trees will be wholly owned by the cultivator, while landowners and farmers will also be consulted during the allocation and operation of concessions and will receive a share of the benefits commensurate with their position as stewards of the resource.

Since current rules and regulations governing forest management are linked with utilisation, some of the most important are briefly discussed in Section 5.2 on forest utilisation.

Forest Ownership

Legislation vesting in the President authority over the management of all timber and trees, and all land within forest reserves, has been superimposed on customary (traditional) land tenure. The government recognises the rights of lineage communities – stools and clans – to ownership of their traditional lands. Decisions over the allocation of such land among community members are vested in each community's chief (the term 'stool' is derived from the seat on which the chief sits). An example of how this works in practice is provided later in this chapter, with regard to Adwenaase forest. Much of Ghana's area comprises stool land, including most of the forest reserves. Whilst these are managed and controlled by the Forest Department in trust for the stools (with three exceptions), they are not owned outright by the State.

5.2 Past and Present Forest Utilisation in Ghana

Most of Ghana's forest reserves were established by the colonial authorities in the early part of this century, to meet local needs for forest products, to create a suitable local climate for agriculture (particularly cocoa), and to safeguard water supplies. While they were mainly established for environmental reasons, their use for productive purposes was never excluded. Throughout most of the colonial period, timber extraction was largely confined to areas outside the reserves. As the timber off-reserve was liquidated and agriculture took its place, attention turned in the 1950s to exploitation of the forest reserves. The timber industry developed rapidly after the Second World War. Ghana's forests were viewed by many at the time as a key resource to support the country's industrialisation. After a brief period of decline in the early 1980s, the timber industry is once again a major export business. In 1993, timber ranked third, after gold and cocoa, in the country's export earnings.

Outside the permanent forest estate there is very little remaining intact forest and much of this is confined to sacred groves and other culturally protected areas. A large part of the HFZ is now either cultivated (particularly for cocoa or food crops) or degraded secondary forest. Logging, fire, farming, and to a lesser extent mining and the conversion of natural forests to plantations have all contributed to this situation, but logging has been the most important single influence.

Early exploitation in the reserves was limited to eight species. Some of these are now near economic extinction (they include some of the mahoganies, *Khaya anthotheca/grandifoliola* and *Khaya ivorensis*, and species belonging to the genus *Entandrophragma* such as *E. cylindricum* and *E. utile*, **sapele**). However, given the far wider range of species, and lower size classes, that are now used by the timber industry, some potential for the economic exploitation of the reserves remains.

Recent demand for previously unexploited timber species has precipitated the logging of the remaining patches of forest off-reserve and isolated trees on farms. Indeed, the proportion of the total timber harvest that came from off-reserves was recently estimated (based on figures for 1993) to be over 80% (Planning Branch, 1995b). Much of this logging is conducted in a highly destructive manner by illegal chainsaw operators, and is causing considerable concern at all levels. In September 1994 the FD was instructed to take responsibility for sustaining the remaining off-reserve tree and forest resource, most of which is on farms, fallows and in sacred groves. The FD and MLF acted rapidly, working with a range of stakeholders to draw up new felling procedures and legislation to control illegal activities. The government envisages that farmers and communities will take the lead in monitoring and maintaining the off-reserve resource.

Traditional forest management has concentrated on the scientific regulation of timber harvesting and it is these systems which are best developed in Ghana. Within forest reserves, timber production is based on the principles of sustained yield management using low-intensity selection harvesting and natural regeneration as silvicultural tools. Management procedures require a 100% stock survey of all Class 1 trees (those in demand for export, defined as the species exported over the period 1973–88) above 50 cm dbh before exploitation can begin (Planning Branch, 1995a; see also Chapter 2, Box 2.3). From the stock survey, the FD produces a map showing species location and diameter class, calculates the maximum allowable cut by species and allocates the yield evenly across the compartment. Various checks at the time of felling and transportation of logs in theory ensure strict adherence to the yield allocation, for which the concessionaire pays the FD a standard fee.

By comparison with timber, non-timber forest product (NTFP) harvesting in forest reserves is poorly regulated. Control is limited to the issue of permits (on payment of a fee). Disregard of this legal requirement is widespread and well-known. As a consequence, local NTFP users tend to view the FD with distrust and are unwilling to admit to on-reserve harvesting. Some of the most important and widely collected NTFPs in Ghana are described in Box 5.1.

5.3 The Development of the Forest Inventory and Management Project, and the Collaborative Forest Management Unit

Ghana's forestry sector was reviewed in 1986 by a multi-donor mission under the Global Tropical Forest Action Programme. This exercise recommended support for the Forestry Department under the Forest Resource Management Project (FRMP). Scheduled to run from 1989 to 1995, this project is co-financed by the Government of Ghana, the World Bank (under an IDA credit agreement),

DANIDA, and ODA. The ODA component of the FRMP comprises technical support to the FD's Planning Branch under the Forest Inventory and Management Project (FIMP). Building on the work done on the static and dynamic national inventories, the aim of the FIMP is to refine management systems for the HFZ, including plantations, NTFP management and collaborative management with local communities (Flint and Hardcastle, 1992; Kemp, Flint and Vanclay, 1993).

Box 5.1 Important NTFPs Harvested from Ghana's HFZ

Canes

Canes are found in most forest types of the HFZ, but particularly the wet evergreen zone, from which all traded cane is harvested. Cane stems are used to weave a wide variety of articles used in daily life in villages – houses, roofs, furniture, storage containers, ladders, fish traps, etc. Of these articles, baskets have the greatest economic importance, since they are in considerable urban as well as rural demand. The collection, processing and trade of cane and cane products provides an income to many thousands of people in southern Ghana. Men are particularly involved in the harvesting and weaving, whilst women dominate the trade.

Wrapping leaves

Leaves from several species in the family Marantaceae are widely used by traders and food sellers as packaging material, in preference to alternatives such as plastic or paper. The plants are commonly found in the HFZ in disturbed and swampy sites. They are harvested by well organised groups of gatherers who usually sell them to others to market, in a complex trade network dominated by women.

Chewsticks

Chewsticks (for cleaning the teeth) are a very important NTFP in Ghana and provide the main means of dental care for over 90% of people in the southern part of the country. The most important species for trade are *Garcinia epunctata*, *G. afzelii*, and *G. kola*. *Celtis* spp. is also widely used.

Plant medicines

There is a strong and steady market in plant medicines in Ghana, reflecting the reliance of both rural and urban people on this form of health care. The trade in plant medicines appears to be more informal than that for other NTFPs, and one that is often used as a source of income in times of difficulty.

Bush meat

Wild game, or bush meat as it is commonly called, is one of the most popular foods in both rural and urban Ghana (and the rest of West Africa). Many of the animals killed by hunters never reach the market, being consumed locally. Those that do fetch a high price, in a trade that is tightly controlled by wholesalers selling on to (mainly women) traders. The species most commonly traded as fresh meat are Black and Maxwell duikers, grasscutters and bushbuck, all of which are usually caught in farm or fallow land rather than dense forest.

Source: Falconer (1992)

The Planning Branch is responsible for forest resource assessment to provide information for national-level planning, and its activities are dictated by national priorities. However, these increasingly include an element of local involvement, with the possibility of local communities participating in forest management now being nationally recognised and supported under the new Forest Policy.

Based in Kumasi, the Planning Branch has a geographically central location for the High Forest Zone (see Figure 5.1). Institutionally, it occupies a slightly anomalous but potentially powerful position within the Department as a centre for planning, monitoring and co-ordination directly under the Chief Conservator of Forests.

Management systems for the conservation and sustainable exploitation of Ghana's permanent forest estate are well advanced. Resource assessment has been, and will continue to be, a fundamental element of forest planning and control in Ghana at all levels, be it to set the annual allowable timber cut for the timber industry or to regulate the harvesting of snails from a community managed forest.

The information currently available on the status and standing volume of Ghana's forest reserves is considerable, and far more detailed than for most West African countries. The FD has conducted several different types of resource surveys which have been designed to address particular problems and to meet specific information needs. These include national forest inventories, biodiversity surveys, forest regeneration surveys, a growth monitoring inventory, an NTFP inventory, and community resource assessments. It is on the latter activity, which directly concerns the needs of local people, that this chapter focuses. The other forest resource assessment activities of the Planning Branch supported by the FIMP are outlined in Box 5.2. More information on the NTFP survey is given in Chapter 9 (Box 9.4).

Box 5.2   Forest Resource Assessment under the Planning Branch/FIMP, Ghana (excluding the NTFP Inventory and Community Forest Resource assessments)

The Static Inventory: Temporary Sample Plot (TSP) Programme
The objective of this inventory was to provide data on the volume of timber in forest reserves for strategic planning purposes. A systematic 0.25% national temporary sample plot (TSP) inventory was initiated in 1985 and completed in 1993 when 1.4 million hectares of high forest had been sampled. By 1989 40% of the reserves in the HFZ had been surveyed, providing sufficient data to inform national-level decision-making. The programme was then adapted to provide information for reserve-level management planning. In the latter stages of the inventory the enumeration of selected NTFPs was added to the procedures.

The Dynamic Inventory: Permanent Sample Plot (PSP) Programme
The objective of the PSP programme is to monitor the dynamics of the forest stand so as to estimate future growth. The Forestry Department's PSP programme began in 1969 and was revised in 1988 to include all tree species (earlier only 14 species were enumerated). There are now 600 one hectare sample plots throughout the HFZ which are re-enumerated every five years. These plots are to monitor changes in the forest, and thus they will be subject to normal management practices. The first cycle of measurement of the new style PSPs has been completed, and a representative sample of plots have been re-enumerated after 2 years. Analysis of the data collected is in progress.

(continued/...)

117

> **Box 5.2** *(continued)*
>
> **Botanical Diversity Survey**
> A two-year survey of the distribution and status of vascular plants in the HFZ was undertaken between 1990 and 1992. The aim of this survey was to give the Forestry Department a clearer picture of plant distribution across the HFZ and to identify areas of rich biodiversity and which were in need of more stringent protection in forest. Data collected have been combined into a Genetic Heat Index (GHI) which can be used to assess the biodiversity of different forest sites. Data from this survey and the static inventory have been used to build a computer system which displays information on all forest tree species (known as FROGGIE) (Hawthorne, 1995).
>
> **Regeneration Surveys**
> Surveys were conducted to assess the impact of logging and fire on forest regeneration. The results are presented in Hawthorne (1993 and 1994).
>
> **Timber Inventory outside Forest Reserves**
> The Forestry Department has recently been given the task of overseeing timber harvesting outside forest reserves. It must design a strategy to encourage farmers to retain and nurture more trees on their land and control illegal felling. As a first step in addressing the long-term management issues, it has instituted a rapid assessment of this resource. The survey design is to assess 200 plots across four vegetation zone strata (50 to each stratum). The teams conducting this work have been trained to hold discussions with farmers and community leaders before embarking on surveys on farms. The inventory has generated keen interest from many farmers.

The collaborative forest resource assessment surveys have involved the assistance of many different units at the Planning Branch, but are co-ordinated by the Collaborative Forest Management Unit. They represent an attempt at supporting community-led assessment of small patches of remnant forest off-reserve, taking account of both timber and non-timber forest products. Both the forests of Adwenaase and Namtee described in this chapter lie outside forest reserves.

The Collaborative Forest Management Unit of the Planning Branch

The CFMU was set up to investigate the potential and limits of a collaborative approach to forest management across Ghana's High Forest Zone (HFZ). The word 'collaborative' was chosen deliberately as an alternative to terms such as 'social', 'participatory', 'community' or 'rural development' forestry, since all these terms have certain specific meanings (either in Ghana or elsewhere). The Unit wanted to emphasise that its approach of involving local people in forestry activities is new and tailored to the Ghanaian HFZ situation. To this end, it is adopting a 'learning process' approach of phased activities, as follows (CFMU, 1993):

- Phase 1 – exploration, investigating the many ways in which collaborative forest management could take place across the HFZ.

- Phase 2 – strategy development, working to develop ways in which collaborative forest management can be instituted and supported at the level of the District Forest Office.

- Phase 3 – institutionalisation of a collaborative approach to forestry across the HFZ, if its utility has been demonstrated in the first two phases.

Phase 1 was scheduled for 1993–5, with Phase 2 starting during this period, in early 1995. The funding and implementation of Phase 3 will be decided following this (Planning Branch, 1995c).

Collaborative Management of Adwenaase and Namtee Community Forest Reserves

The developments that have taken place at these sites represent a new approach to forest management in Ghana. The work has attracted widespread publicity; the Minister for Lands and Forestry has visited Adwenaase Forest twice. The initiatives have also received substantial inputs, with FIMP/CFMU staff contributions far in excess of levels that could be replicated elsewhere. However, this has been necessary for the generation of ideas in the overall learning process adopted. There is potential for the work to advance significantly current forest policy in respect of local control of off-reserve forest management, as well as providing insights into how this may be achieved in practice.

The evolution of forest and village surveys has been a major element in the development of community-based management systems. The survey techniques that have been adopted are simple and they will almost certainly be modified as experience grows, and as different forests present different information needs. Nevertheless, they are of interest because the work is innovative in attempting to marry existing FD inventory procedures as used in stock surveys and PSPs with local information needs. It also demonstrates the ability of rural Ghanaians to conduct their own forest assessments.

The people and forests of Adwenaase and Namtee
The formerly dense high forest of Adwenaase covers 219 hectares, and belongs to the people of Assin Akropong under the Akoti stool. Adwenaase forest is the site of an abandoned settlement. It was set aside by the elders of the town as a memorial to the ancestors who settled their people there after migrating from Ashanti-controlled territory to the north in around 1823. The town was later moved to its current location. The forest was considered

sacred, and was protected by the whole community. The **Abusua Panin** (Head of the Royal Family) sadly noted that even though their ancestors were illiterate, they were able to preserve the forest, whilst the present generation has not done so. Small incursions and illegal activities in the forest have escalated during the last decade or so (over the period of the chieftaincy dispute – see Box 5.3), to the extent that most good quality timber trees have now been logged by unscrupulous local individuals, and sizeable patches of land are under cultivation. Six migrant villages have grown up in the area over the last thirty years or so, and parts of them lie within the forest. The migrants were mainly invited to farm the stool land for cocoa (on a share-cropping basis), although some are farming without permission. The forest currently consists of a mosaic of thick forest, recent secondary growth and land that has been farmed and left to fallow, swamps, cocoa farms and chop farms (on which food crops are grown). The current population of the area is a mixture of ethnic groups. Most of the citizens of Assin Akropong are **Assins**, although there are also a few **Fantis** and **Ewes**. The settlers comprise **Ewes**, **Fantis** and Northerners.

Box 5.3 Ownership of Adwenaase Forest

As noted above, Adwenaase forest is not a gazetted or government controlled forest reserve. It lies on unallocated stool land – that is, land owned by the local community and held in trust for them by their chief. Adwenaase forest was not rigorously exploited in the past because of its sacred status. The chief is assisted in his activities by a traditional council. The last chief of Assin Akropong died 14 years ago, and a dispute over his successor has divided the traditional council to the present day. It is partly for this reason that control over Adwenaase forest has weakened, and its condition has degenerated. In the absence of a chief, two men have gained particular prominence in local decision-making – the regent (who is the **Gyasehene**), and the **Abusa Panin** or Head of the Royal Family of Assin Akropong. Traditionally responsible for royal affairs only, the latter is now taking an active interest in general community matters. Both men have now joined forces to protect the forest.

The timber trees growing on stool land are vested in the state and often given out under permit or concession to timber companies. When they are felled, the stool is entitled to a royalty payment from the timber men.

It is established practice for stool land to be given out by the chief to interested parties for exploitation or development, e.g. oil palm plantation, on payment of a fee or rent to the stool. The stool can in this way generate revenue from the land while itself playing a passive role. Invariably in such cases the returns to the stool are low.

In 1992, a number of Assin Akropong citizens became so incensed about the way a few individuals were profiting from Adwenaase Forest that they approached the Forestry Department to intervene and halt the illegal logging operations. The District Forest Officer (DFO) was able to stop the illegal felling. He then invited the CFMU to help the community develop systems for maintaining the forest.

5.4 The Need for Forest Resource Assessment

A number of meetings were held in early 1994, from which a consensus emerged that the only way to prevent individuals from further destroying the forest was for the community – here defined as the people of Akropong and nearby villages – to take control. As a result, a group of inventory specialists (mensurationists and botanists) from the Planning Branch was invited to visit Adwenaase Forest in May 1994 and advise the community on how they could proceed. This decision contrasted sharply with the way in which stool land has been managed in the past (see Box 5.3), and was not at first accepted by everyone living in the area. Indeed, CFMU staff have spent much time visiting people to explain what is being suggested, finding out about current forest utilisation, and counteracting false rumours. The latter included a persistent belief that 'some white ladies were coming to buy up the forest' (several CFMU staff are expatriate women).

The situation at nearby Namtee forest (comprising 190 ha) is very similar, with the added complication that the forest is 17 km away from the two towns that own it, Wurakese and Akinkausu. These are both also part of the Akoti stool. Like Adwenaase, Namtee forest was set aside by the elders of the two towns as a memorial to the ancestors who first settled there before moving the towns to their current locations. In recent years it has also been devastated by illegal logging and unauthorised farming. Having seen the initiative taken by the people of Assin Akropong, the owners of Namtee forest asked the FD for assistance in June 1994.

Reconnaissance of Adwenaase and Namtee Community Forest Reserves

The two forests are classified as moist semi-deciduous forest (Hall and Swaine, 1981). The Planning Branch team observed that both areas had been thoroughly logged, and that few timber species of exploitable size remained. However, they found both immature specimens and good natural regeneration of a variety of economically important species. These included *Nesogordonia papaverifera* (**Danta**), *Triplochiton scleroxylon* (**Wawa**), *Khaya anthotheca* (mahogany) and *Milicia excelsa* (**Odum**). The forests appeared rich in a number of NTFPs, with many patches of swampy ground in which plants such as canes and Marantaceae wrapping leaves were plentiful. A wildlife specialist (who visited the forest at night, joining a group of hunters) found evidence of a variety of animal life – mainly species that were expected (such as duikers, grasscutters, brush-tailed porcupines, rats and giant snails), but also one rarer mammal, the Pels Flying Squirrel. Discussions with hunters indicated that animal numbers were sufficient to support hunting parties from all the settlements surrounding the forests.

Reporting back to the communities, the Planning Branch team recommended that the bulk of the forested area should be allowed a convalescence period of 40 years before any further logging is allowed. However, they felt that the exploitation of a variety of NTFPs might be possible, and suggested that their distribution and abundance should be further investigated. Following their visit, programmes of forest assessment and boundary demarcation were initiated in July 1994. The first attempt at a resource assessment survey was made at Adwenaase forest (in advance of demarcation). At Namtee the townspeople concentrated on demarcating and surveying their forest boundary in advance of professional support on resource assessment.

5.5   The Forest Assessment Process

Boundary Demarcation

Members of the Assin Akropong community demonstrating one of the corners of the Adwenaase forest boundary. This is marked with a stake, and delineated to the right by a river.
Photograph: Jane Carter

A large part of the boundary of Adwenaase forest is delineated by three rivers, with another substantial part adjoining farmland. The land boundary has been subject to serious dispute, over which the traditional council negotiated with those concerned. Eventually, after heated discussions, an agreement was reached. However, the dispute over the siting of the boundary meant that the resource assessment began without a base map being available. This severely affected survey operations and data compilation and analysis.

Since the forest at Namtee is bounded on all sides by rivers, it was relatively easy for the elders to demarcate. A TO (Technical Officer of the Forestry Department) then worked with volunteers to survey the boundary and to produce a boundary map for them.

Survey Design for Adwenaase Community Forest Reserve

The Planning Branch specialists designed a survey that would provide an overview of current land-use patterns, and information on the distribution of important species throughout the forest. This entailed cutting transect lines through Adwenaase forest at 100 m intervals, using as a baseline the old logging road that traverses the forest. A record was then made of land use, important useful plants, and any signs of animals along these transect lines. The data were recorded on simple forms and then transferred directly onto one long roll of tracing paper, to create a map, which would then provide the information base from which the community could start taking decisions regarding different parts of the forest.

A need for more detailed surveys or inventories of, for example, particular areas or species, might then be identified and addressed. The key point was that the whole process of data collection and utilisation was in local hands.

> This means of assessing the forest was suggested since, once trained, local people could proceed with it unassisted. The use of maps was indeed found to increase the accessibility of data – to both the local and the professional forest managers.

Volunteers for the Work at Adwenaase Forest

The task of boundary cutting and forest surveying was undertaken by volunteers from both Assin Akropong and the migrant villages, with technical assistance from CFMU and local Forestry Department staff (particularly TOs). There was no difficulty in recruiting volunteers. Too many people wanted to join in. This fact must be set against the currently high rate of unemployment in rural Ghana, and the hope of acquiring new skills and possible jobs that the initiative undoubtedly engendered.

As it is customary in Ghana to provide food and transport when organising labour for communal activities, this type of assistance, at the very least, was expected by the volunteers. Expectations were heightened after various senior government figures visited the area and promised their backing. The CFMU did not want to undermine the sustainability of the initiative by providing excessive assistance, but it was agreed that the DFO should make an initial gesture of support. This consisted of one pair of boots, a haversack and a cutlass for each volunteer, and a small allowance to cover the cost of transport and snack food.

Most of the volunteers were men, but a number of women came too – mainly to bring water and refreshments for the men. This swelled the numbers to well over 40, and in fact proved to be far too many for the available staff to supervise effectively. When the DFO pointed out that equipment and allowances could not be extended to everyone who participated, a certain amount of disappointment and resentment was generated, but a clear lesson was learnt that an agreement in writing should have been made at the outset, and careful time-sheets kept of who participated each day.

The work proceeded well, with great enthusiasm, but slowly. The volunteers could only participate nine hours per week, and initially most of this time was taken in training. The quality of work achieved by the volunteers was generally encouraging. A number of volunteers had once worked in clerical positions and quickly became adept at the survey and record-keeping work.

Transect Cutting and Booking

Once transect cutting was well under way, the TO explained how the record-keeping (booking) would be conducted. Eight individuals (all men) who showed the greatest aptitude were selected and divided into two teams of four. All members of the team took responsibility for spotting useful plants or animal signs, with Booker 3 writing them down. They proved to be extremely good at noting a wide range of useful plants – partly because several of them had particular expertise in traditional medicine and knew many plants with medicinal properties. Two of the bookers were also experienced hunters and so saw and identified animal signs that an inexperienced observer would not have noticed.

The substance of the records was left entirely to the bookers. They decided on the land-use categories, and which plants and animal signs were important. This was deliberate, so that the map which was eventually prepared would reflect local perceptions of forest use.

Leaving the bookers to decide the details of the records proved to be problematic, as discussed further below.

Modifications to the survey design were made as the work progressed and it became clear what was or was not feasible.

- A provisional plan to cut transects at 200 m intervals was changed to the 100 m intervals actually adopted, both because accurate booking demanded this and because it was clear that enough labour was available for the work.

- The use of the road running through the forest as a baseline proved unworkable and generated a brief confusion in transect cutting because it was not straight. A more accurate baseline was cut at the point at which the road began to curve, the transects then being cut at right angles from the baseline to the forest boundary.

Volunteers cutting transect lines into Adwenaase forest
Photograph: Jane Carter

A booking team at work in Adwenaase forest. Members of the team note land use and important plants and animal signs along a transect.
Photograph: Jane Carter

Mapping – Data Compilation and Analysis

Once the survey was finished there was a significant lag before a base map became available due to the ongoing boundary dispute. Responsibility for transferring the booking data onto the roll of tracing paper, and thus creating a map, was conferred on one proficient individual in the community. He began with the land-use data collection forms. Mechanically transferring the detail onto the tracing paper from the booking sheets proved to be easy once the compiler was sure that a certain sheet corresponded to a particular location on the map. This was often difficult to ascertain, however, as distances on the ground had been measured by pacing, thus the transect lengths on the map and on the sheets would often not correspond. It took four attempts and considerable ground truthing to produce a satisfactory map.

A second major problem arose when attempts were made to analyse the data on the booking sheets; all species were recorded using local names, without clarifying their scientific identity or agreeing on a common spelling, which made analysis exceedingly difficult. In addition, no distinction was made on the sheets between the different uses of NTFPs, making the huge mass of data difficult to use.

It was clear that a major design overhaul was needed after the Adwenaase experience. Particular lessons learnt were as follows:

Some confusion was caused by varied opinions over the local names of species and their use, particularly as enumerators used a number of different local languages.

- It is best to prepare a base map of the forest, and cut the boundaries, baseline and transect lines, before the survey work begins. This should be done even if it means delaying the survey work.

- The layout of the booking sheets should be aligned as much as possible with the layout of the map and the actual transects on the ground.

- Distances should be measured, not paced.

- Volunteers should prepare a definitive lists of species names before starting the survey. This list should be verified by a botanist, and scientific names assigned to each local name. All species should then be given a code number.

5.6 Current and Future Developments

The Revised Survey Design – Namtee Community Forest Reserve

Based on experience gained during the work at Adwenaase, the survey was substantially re-designed before beginning at Namtee. In the new survey, data were collected on four aspects of forest management. A separate team of volunteers was responsible for collecting, compiling and analysing the data on its subject area. The four survey areas were:

- land use
- forested land – ecology and condition
- exploitable timber
- non-timber forest products

Before the data collection began the four teams joined together to survey and cut the base line and transect lines. The baseline was set at 25 degrees and the transects at right angles to it. The transects were set 100 m apart. A volunteer then measured down the lines pegging every 25 m, 50 m, 75 m and 100 m. Thus on the ground a grid of 100 m x 100 m squares (i.e. one hectare) was established. Once the lines were cut, dye-line base maps of the forest showing the boundary and location of the baseline and transect lines and the one hectare squares were prepared and copies given to each team. The booking sheets prepared for each team were also set out so that each team collated its data with reference to a specific one hectare square. This greatly eased the plotting of data onto maps. Instruction sheets were prepared for each team and reviewed during the training period.

Training

During the training period the volunteers were asked to work with a Planning Branch botanist to compile reference lists of land-use types, tree species, non-tree useful species and animal signs known to them. A definitive list of species and spellings was produced and a code number assigned to each one by the volunteers to reduce the risk of ambiguous spellings. To ensure that unknown species were not ignored or guessed at, the volunteers were given a botanical press and shown how to collect specimens for identification at the Planning Branch herbarium.

Land-use Survey

This team comprised a booker, a tape-man and two spotters. Moving down a transect line they recorded changes in land use, such as cocoa, marsh land, and forest. The team also visited each food-crop or cocoa farm they found and noted its size, age, ownership and any recommended prescription.

Each afternoon the data were transferred directly onto a base (tracing paper) map. In this way a picture of the land-use patterns over the forest area was built up very quickly. Once the map was complete the team members were able to quickly prepare summaries of their data based on the number of hectare squares under a particular land use. Examples include the percentage of land under forest, and the potential area (in hectares) available for planting. This analysis will probably become part of a management plan for the forest (Part I, known as Situation Analysis). It will also feed directly into the decision-making process, for example, in determining the location of tree-planting sites.

The land-use map produced by the land-use survey team, and an example of a booking sheet, are shown in Figure 5.2.

Forested Land – Ecology and Condition Scoring

This team comprised a booker, tree code caller, and four spotters. Following behind the land-use team, they moved down the transects noting the forest condition score and recording all trees over 10 cm dbh across the entire width of the transect – that is, a 100 m swathe. The condition score is a monitoring and management tool used by the FD in stock survey, which worked very well when transferred to local resource assessment. Counting all trees proved to be exhausting and time-consuming. The process needs to be reviewed, and possibly replaced by a more sophisticated sampling or indicator species strategy. Where possible, seed trees were also noted.

Each afternoon the data were transferred by the volunteers directly onto two maps, of condition scores, and tree counts. At the end of the survey the volunteers were able to synthesise their findings quickly to produce a section of a management plan.

Exploitable Timber Survey

The FD already has a sophisticated system of stock surveys for determining the current allowable timber yield for a particular compartment. The stock survey design was modified to fit in with the system of transect lines and one hectare squares. The team comprised a booker, a tree code caller and four spotters, all with diameter tapes. All timber trees over 30 cm dbh were measured. Logs left lying on the ground were also recorded.

The data collected were plotted onto a base line map, which was later compiled into a section of the management plan. During this process, the volunteers learned about official minimum felling limits.

Non-timber Forest Products

The NTFP team probably had the largest task, given the number of different species present in the forest. The team comprised a booker, a plant and animal code caller and four spotters. The spotters recorded only the presence of a particular NTFP; no attempt was made to quantify it or describe its condition. In the afternoon the team plotted its findings onto four separate maps covering:

- medicines
- animal signs
- wrapping leaves, canes, and sponges (climbers which can be pounded to form a sponge-like material used for cleaning)
- firewood, pestles, and chewing sticks

Like the other teams, this one had no difficulty in compiling their data to produce a section of the management plan. The data collated by this team complemented a map of current NTFP collection sites prepared by the village survey team, whose activities are described in the sub-section below.

From the combined experience of survey work at Adwenaase and Namtee, the following practical lessons may be drawn.

- In the case of small forests (Adwenaase is only 219 ha and Namtee 190 ha), it is probably best not to sample but to conduct a 100% enumeration. This is especially true for exploitable timber.

- It is worthwhile planning carefully what data are needed and collecting everything in one survey. Re-surveying is very time-consuming.

- The careful identification and storage of booking sheets for future reference is essential. Due provision of files and storage space should be made for this purpose.

- There is much to be gained from mixing FD procedures with local information needs and ideas. However, the survey design must be kept as rigorous and professional as possible. The 'rough and ready' approach can lead to complications.

- It is advantageous to compile, summarise and analyse data as the survey proceeds. This increases the speed of operations, allows for the early identification of mistakes, and generates discussion on possible management options.

- Ensuring that the data are reliable and accurate is dependent on good initial design, extensive training, careful selection of volunteers, regular supervision and occasional check surveys.

Figure 5.2   Namtee Community Forest Reserve Land-use Map produced from combining the information recorded on booking sheets

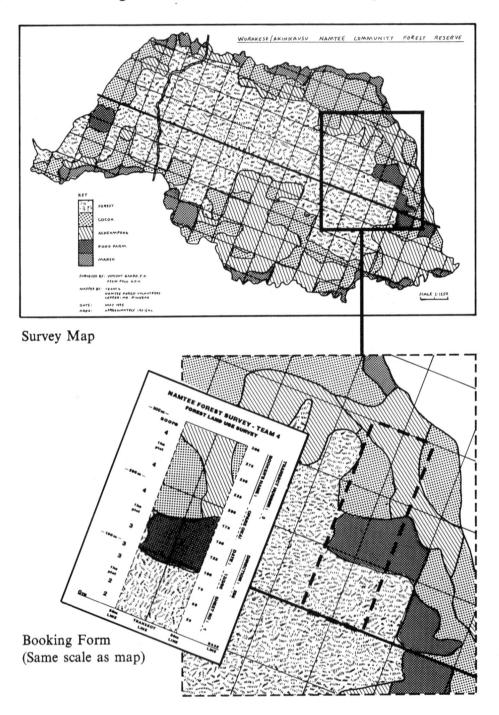

Survey Map

Booking Form
(Same scale as map)

Village and Market Surveys

To complement the work being undertaken by the volunteers in the forest, a second group of volunteers carried out a series of village surveys. The aim of the surveys was two-fold. It provided an opportunity for people in all the villages concerned to learn about what was happening in the forest – to ask questions and express fears. It also gave the survey volunteers an opportunity of learning about the relationship the villagers currently have with the resource, and what they hope to have in the future. The volunteers also tried to encourage people to consider how they could help to protect and manage the forest. The latter point is particularly important, in that the migrant villagers have no right to be where they are. If they are to stay, they need to demonstrate to the forest owners that they can fulfil a useful function by so doing.

A training session for the village survey volunteers
Photograph: Jane Carter

The survey volunteers received training and assistance from CFMU staff in conducting their work. They used a structured questionnaire, with a limited number of carefully chosen and worded questions. Whilst they were aware of many of the disadvantages of this approach, CFMU staff found that a clear advantage of using a questionnaire in working with literate local people was its *transparency*. The questionnaire could be used as a briefing sheet for chiefs when seeking permission to conduct the survey in a village. Furthermore, interviewees were put at their ease by written questions. Unstructured enquiries, by contrast,

The use of structured questionnaires for interviewing rural people is often criticised as being likely to generate suspicion. Open-ended, informal questioning is considered to be less threatening. However, this clearly depends on circumstances.

generated suspicions of a hidden agenda. The surveys played an important role in establishing a dialogue between the migrants and the future decision-makers.

Implementation of the village survey. A volunteer conducting an interview with a family in one of the migrant vIllages around Adwenaase forest
Photograph: Jane Carter

A further set of volunteers collected data on local markets for forest products, particularly NTFPs. Finally, the elders and local elected representatives also prepared reports on the legal and historical aspects of forest administration and on the local socio-economic context, of which the forest is only a part.

The next phase in the collaborative management of Adwenaase and Namtee forests will be the discussions over management options. These will begin shortly; indeed, there has already been considerable informal discussion on the subject.

5.7   Conclusion

An important point demonstrated by the case study, and which should be self-evident, is that the professional forester must be aware that it is his or her professional responsibility to ensure that the data collected at considerable opportunity cost by volunteers are indeed usable. The professional must ensure that the parameters are appropriate, the design is sound, training is provided and the technical support is the best available. He or she should also ensure that the empirical data-set complements and enhances rather than replaces traditional knowledge and beliefs about the resource.

The output of a very long learning process for the volunteers and Planning Branch staff has been a new forest survey methodology which seems capable of producing a resource data-set which can form the first part of a local forest management plan and can inform the development of prescriptions for the second part of a plan.

References

CFMU (1993) A *Strategy for the Development of Collaborative Forest Management in the High Forest of Ghana*. Collaborative Forest Management Unit, Planning Branch, Forestry Department, Ghana.

Falconer, J. (1992) *Non-Timber Forest Products in Southern Ghana: A Summary Report*. ODA Forestry Series Number 2, ODA, London.

Flint, M. E. S. and **Hardcastle, P. D**. (1992) 'Evaluation of the Forest Inventory Project, Ghana'. Draft Evaluation Report, ODA, London.

Hall, J. B. and **Swaine, M. D.** (1981) *Distribution and Ecology of Vascular Plants in a Tropical Rainforest*. W. Junk, The Hague.

Hawthorne, W. (1993) *Forest Regeneration after Logging. Findings of a Study in the Bia South Game Production Reserve, Ghana*. ODA Forestry Series No. 3, Natural Resources Institute , Chatham, UK.

Hawthorne, W. (1994) *Fire Damage and Forest Regeneration in Ghana*. ODA Forestry Series No. 4, Natural Resources Institute, Chatham, UK.

Hawthorne, W. (1995) FROGGIE (Forest Reserve of Ghana: Graphical Information Exhibitor). Programme, database and manual.

IIED (1993) *Study of Incentives for the Sustainable Management of the Tropical High Forest of Ghana*, Part I: *Situation Analysis* (Draft Final Report). IIED, London.

Kemp, R. H., Flint, M. and **Vanclay, J. K.**, (1993) 'Forest Inventory and Management Project: Review and Project Preparation Report'. The Government of Ghana, Ministry of Lands and Forests, Ghana. (Under assignment from the ODA).

Planning Branch (1995a) Manual of procedures High Forest Management Section D – Stock Survey and Yield Allocation. Forestry Department Planning Branch, Ghana, March 1995.

Planning Branch (1995b) 'Ghana: Steps Towards Sustainable Forestry and Wise Use of Timber Resources'. Paper prepared for the XVIII Session of the ITTC and XVI Session of the ITTO Permanent Committees Accra, Ghana 10–18 May.

Planning Branch (1995c) 'Made in Ghana: Collaborative Forest Management'. Paper prepared for the XVIII Session of the ITTC and XVI Session of the ITTO Permanent Committees Accra, Ghana 10–18 May.

Acronyms and terms specific to this chapter

CFMU	Collaborative Forest Management Unit
DANIDA	Royal Danish Ministry of Foreign Affairs
DFO	District Forest Officer
FD	Forestry Department
FIMP	Forest Inventory and Management Project
FRMP	Forest Resource Management Project
GFS	Ghana Forest Service

HFZ	High Forest Zone
IDA	International Development Association
MLF	Ministry of Lands and Forests
TO	Technical Officer (of the Forest Department; roughly equivalent to Range Forest Officer in other Forest Departments. They are technical level staff, not university graduates).

Abusa Panin	Head of the Royal Family (in this case, of Assin Akropong)
chop	food – hence chop farm, farm on which food crops are grown
stool land	Land held by the local community and administered by the chief

6 Resource Assessment for Forest Management by User Groups: Two Case Studies from Nepal

The Nepal-Australia Community Forestry Project
Andrew Ingles, Bill Jackson and Hukum Bahadur Singh

The Nepal-UK Community Forestry Project
Om Prakash Dev and Peter Branney

This chapter considers forest resource assessment in the context of a community forestry programme strongly supported by the national government. In this respect Nepal's forestry legislation is amongst the most far-reaching in the world, allowing for the handing over of forests previously under State control to local forest user groups (FUGs), who then have responsibility for forest management. The discussion focuses on information needs for planning community forestry in the middle hills of Nepal – both with regard to the forest users themselves and the Department of Forests (DoF) which has responsibility for implementing the hand-over. The last section also considers forest assessment for monitoring purposes – an aspect that is currently being developed. Community forests in the middle hills are managed for a wide variety of subsistence needs. Any commercial exploitation is largely subsidiary and rarely involves timber extraction. The appropriate assessment methods in this situation are largely descriptive, and do not extend to detailed inventories of statistical validity.

Two donor-supported projects, both of which operate through the DoF, are used to illustrate different aspects of forest resource assessment for community forestry. They are the Nepal-Australia Community Forestry Project (NACFP), and the Nepal-UK Community Forestry Project (NUKCFP). Both projects have an operational history of over 15 years, although their activities have changed considerably over that time (particularly the NUKCFP, which grew out of a broad rural development project). The geographical coverage of the two projects is shown in Figure 6.1. The NACFP covers two districts of Central Nepal (Kabhre

Palanchok and Sindhu Palchok), whilst the NUKCFP now operates in both East and West Nepal. Its activities in the East, in the Koshi Hills area, are the most developed and extend over four districts (Dhankuta, Sankhuwasabha, Terhathum and Bhojpur). Whilst the chapter focuses on different aspects of the two projects' activities, it should be stressed that both are implementing Nepal's national Community Forestry Operational Guidelines, and that the activities focused on are part of the national process of handing over control of forests to FUGs.

Figure 6.1   The Nepal-Australia Forestry Community Forestry Project and the Nepal-UK Community Forestry Project (Koshi Hills)

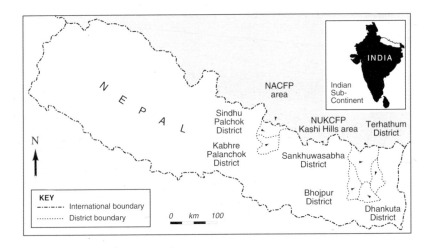

6.1   Forest Legislation and the Role of the Government of Nepal in Forest Management

Initiatives encouraging the involvement of local people in forest management began in the late 1970s, and have been actively supported by His Majesty's Government of Nepal (HMG-N) through successive legislation. The most recent Forest Act was passed by parliament in 1993, and was enacted following the approval of its associated rules and regulations in early 1995. Under this act, two major categories of forest are distinguished – private and national. National forest is further divided into:

• Community Forest, handed over to Forest User Groups (FUGs).

• Leasehold Forest, given out on a fixed term lease.

- Religious Forest, managed by temples and/or religious communities.

- Government-managed Forest, under the control of the Forest Department.

- Protected Forest (notably reserves and important catchment areas, with restricted access).

Community forestry is given prominence in national forestry planning, and it is intended that considerable areas of forest will eventually be handed over to FUGs (Kanel, 1993). To date, about 125,000 ha of forest have been handed over as community forest, most of this falling in the middle hills. Although this represents only some 5–6% of Nepal's total forest cover, the hand-over of considerably more is envisaged. One report suggests that up to 60% of the total forest area may be handed over (Nelson and Karmacharya, 1989). In some hill districts, community forests are expected to form the vast majority of the entire forest area. Of the forest areas already handed over to a particular FUG, some are less than one hectare, whilst others are over 500 ha.

As part of an overall programme of government reorganisation, the DoF recently underwent major restructuring. At the higher levels of administration, forestry is similar to the organisation of other government departments. There is a District Forest Office, headed by a District Forest Officer (DFO) who in some cases has one or two Assistant Forest Officers (AFO), in 74 of Nepal's 75 districts. As far as the implementation of community forestry is concerned, the most significant feature of the restructuring was the redrawing of forest Beats to become larger Range Posts, with an associated reduction in field staff in the middle hills of about 30%. One Range Post is staffed by a Ranger and usually four Forest Guards. In area, it may cover from four to over fifteen VDCs (Village Development Committees). A VDC is usually described as the smallest administrative unit in Nepal (although in fact it is split into nine wards), and has an average population of 1,500–3,000 people. (However, this figure varies according to District.) Clearly the current workload of Rangers is very high.

6.2 Past and Present Forest Utilisation in the Middle Hills of Nepal

The middle hills form a band of terrain running roughly East-West between Nepal's flat lowland plain to the South, and the high Himalayan mountains to the North. They form a system of deeply dissected ridges and valleys, the lower reaches of which can be less than 500 m above sea level whilst the ridges can rise to over 2,000 m. Northwards, the hills rise to the Himalayas, the 3,000 m contour often being taken as the divide between the hills and the lower slopes of the mountains. At least 15 forest types occur within the middle hills, reflecting the diverse topography and microclimatic and soil conditions. There is a clear overall vegetational change from West to East, with a number of common tree species in the West being absent in the East, and vice versa (Jackson, 1987).

Between 1,000 and 2,000 m, the middle hills are heavily populated, to the extent that virtually all cultivable land is already under agriculture. Considerable tracts of forest were lost to agriculture in the past, but in the latter part of the present century the forest area of the hills has remained roughly constant. Its condition has not, however.[1] The agricultural system practised in the middle hills makes heavy demands on nearby forests as a source of timber, fuel, charcoal, livestock fodder, food, and various other non-timber forest products (NTFPs). Until the advent of artificial fertiliser, the replenishment of agricultural fertility depended heavily on the forest, either in the form of leaf compost or the manure and bedding of livestock largely maintained on forest products. This is still a significant feature of forest use in many areas. Whilst forestry in the middle hills of Nepal is still largely driven by subsistence needs, the country's expanding road network is giving rise to increasing market opportunities – particularly in areas not far from towns.

6.3 The People of the Middle Hills of Nepal

The population of the middle hills is characterised by ethnic diversity, on which the Hindu caste system has been superimposed to create a social hierarchy. Brahmins and Chhetris form the top of this hierarchy, whilst at the bottom are the artisan castes such as blacksmiths, tailor/musicians and leather-workers. Amongst these groups, land-holding size, wealth and educational possibilities tend to be strongly correlated with caste status. Slotted in the middle of the caste hierarchy are the many groups of indigenous hill people such as Sherpas, Rais and Limbus. Their economic opportunities vary considerably, but some have prospered from seeking work away from their farms. Seasonal and more long-term out-migration of labour (mainly male) is a common livelihood strategy in the middle hills amongst all ethnic groups.

Villages in the middle hills may comprise a single caste or ethnic group, or they may be mixed. Where the population is mixed, patron-client relationships are common, and often strong. It is also common for villages to be politically factionalised. Since 1991 (when Nepal's single-party system came to an end), this has been increasingly expressed along party political lines. Overall, women tend to be marginalised in decision-making (although the extent of this varies according to ethnic group).

In many parts of the middle hills, strong customary forest uses are associated with different castes or ethnic groups (for example, the blacksmith caste traditionally make charcoal to fuel their

People in the middle hills of Nepal are often extremely knowledgable about forest use and have many insights into forest management. At the same time, few village inhabitants have a secondary school education, and many (especially women) are illiterate and have only very basic numeracy. Both these facts had to be taken into account in developing an appropriate method for systematic community forest assessment and management.

forges). Locally defined usufruct rights to forest areas according to settlement or inheritance are also common. In some areas, these have been elaborated into systems of indigenous forest management under which the forest users came to agreement (without outside intervention) to manage the forest in a certain manner (Fisher, 1989; Tamang, 1990).

In the implementation of Nepal's community forestry programme, an awareness of and sensitivity towards all the factors mentioned above are essential. A particular theme recurring throughout this chapter is the importance of involving all legitimate users in forest management discussions, not just the most vocal and influential.

6.4 The Need for Forest Resource Assessment

Forest Resource Assessment for Different Levels of Planning

Within the overall context of forest resource assessment for planning community forestry, there are clearly different needs at different levels. Appropriate assessment techniques must be adopted for each of these levels. They may be broadly outlined as follows.

At the *global* and *regional* level, there is a need for information to monitor the effect of community forestry on the world's global biodiversity heritage and on the effectiveness of community forestry in promoting community development. Forest resource assessment at this level mainly entails aerial photographic interpretation and mapping which is conducted as part of Nepal's national forest planning. In future, some of the information collected as part of Range Post planning and from the measurement of permanent sample plots (in particular concerning species diversity in forests) may also feed into such monitoring (see Section 6.6).

Nationally, community forestry information is needed for policy formation and the monitoring of implementation. At present forest resource assessment at this level is mainly drawn from aerial photography, although in future additional information should be provided by Range Post plans aggregated to form forest address and information lists.

At *district* and *Range Post* level, the need is for information to assist the effective and efficient allocation of government resources, and to facilitate the empowerment of the legitimate forest users. Obviously this must be linked with national-level priorities and budget allocation. Range Post planning, and the forest resource assessment techniques used for it, are discussed in detail in the NACFP case study.

Forest-level information is required by both Department of Forest staff and forest users in order for forest hand-over to take place. Such

139

information should also lead to improved forest management through technical advice, and should feed into the planning of Range Post and district-level activities. Forest resource assessment methods used at this level are discussed in the NUKCFP case study, in the drawing up of Operational Plans (OPs).

Local, *forest user group* information should assist FUGs in the management of their forest. This is also discussed to a certain extent in the NUKCFP case study.

This chapter focuses initially on the latter three levels. Recent developments in forest monitoring for district/national level purposes are discussed in Section 6.6. Before detailing any of the methods used, a number of broad observations may be made.

Identification of forest information needs. Forest resource assessment needs have been identified through the combined experience of forestry policy-makers, planners and practitioners in Nepal. At the level of discrete forests, forest users are considered to be the main users of forest assessment information. Nevertheless, the need for the information was not, in general, identified by them.

Methods of forest resource assessment. For both Range Post and forest-level planning, the way in which information is collected is designed to be as participatory as possible. However, at the Range Post level, in particular, it is not collaborative, in that villagers are not treated as partners in the information collection process.

Development of assessment needs and methods over time. Different needs have been identified more recently than others. Some are institutionalised, some are not. Some of the methods are still under development.

Social information and technical information. Both types of information are necessary for effective community forestry planning. Although this chapter is concerned with the ways in which forest users have been involved in the more technical aspects of forest resource assessment, the importance of gathering complementary social data cannot be over-emphasised.

The role of traditional forest inventories in community forestry

At present, there is little or no role for traditional forest inventories as a tool for the management of community forests in Nepal. This is recognised in the regulations for the Forest Act (1993), which do not require any inventory of FUG-managed forests. Instead, they state that the 'boundary, condition and capacity' of the forest should be included in the plan. Forest inventories are inappropriate in this context for the reasons listed below (Branney, 1994c).

- A single (static) inventory is inadequate to determine sustainable harvesting rates; for this, a system of repeated (dynamic) inventories is needed. Logistically, it would be difficult to organise.

- Forest product yields can only be calculated from inventory data if yield tables (or yield curves derived from them) are available. Such tables do not exist for the forest types and conditions found in the hills of Nepal. Indian yield tables for certain tree species do exist, but they are only for timber.

- Traditional inventories are concerned with measuring wood production. Most FUGs wish to manage forests for a far greater variety of products than wood alone. Inventory techniques for even the most common NTFPs used in Nepal have not been developed.

- Inventory work is extremely time-consuming, and can be conducted only by trained staff (of Ranger level, at least). Additional training would in fact be necessary to equip Rangers for the task. The workload of District Forest Office staff is such that an accurate inventory of all community forests would be impossible. Furthermore, it is more important for field staff to allocate time to the investigation of social issues and forestry extension.

- An inventory would produce a set of data that local people would find extremely difficult to interpret. The feasibility and reality of user involvement in forest resource assessment is discussed further in the case studies.

Box 6.1 The Three Phases of Handing over Forests to Forest User Groups (FUGs) in Nepal

The national community forestry guidelines set out three phases in handing over forests to local people: investigation, negotiation, and implementation. Key features of these phases are as follows.

Investigation

This phase requires the identification of all forest users, and the collection of pertinent information about the forest(s) that they use. Although simple in theory, in practice the identification of all legitimate forest users is often difficult and requires considerable time. If investigation is not conducted properly, the result can be the empowerment of the wrong people, or only some of the legitimate users.

Negotiation

This should entail working with all the forest users to devise a plan for managing the forest which is acceptable to them all. It is particularly important that deliberate efforts are made to include women and other commonly marginalised groups (such as members of low castes) in this process. The negotiation phase is formalised in the development of an *Operational Plan* (OP). This is an HMG-N requirement for handing over the control of a forest to a FUG.

Implementation

Legal authority for implementation of the plan is provided by the DFO, when he signs the plan submitted by the FUG. Whilst the OP is ultimately implemented by all members of the FUG, responsibility for ensuring implementation is vested in a forest committee, whom they elect.

Forest resource assessment in the context of working with FUGs
The process of forming FUGs and handing over control of forests to them is broadly described as comprising three phases, as outlined in Box 6.1. The case study of the Nepal-Australia Community Forestry Project considers an early aspect of the investigative stage, notably the collection of information for Range Post planning. This takes place before embarking on investigation for individual forests, a process which is not described here. Once investigations of individual forests are complete, an integral part of the negotiation and implementation phases is the preparation of an operational plan for managing the forest in question. The Nepal-UK Community Forestry Project case study focuses on the forest assessment undertaken to prepare this plan.

6.5 The Forest Assessment Process

Forest Assessment for Range Post Planning: The Nepal-Australia Community Forestry Project

This case study focuses on the system of Range Post planning (RPP) – a bottom-up planning method which utilises the 'rapid diagnostic tools' of participatory mapping and informal surveys, as well as a method of forest assessment using rapid appraisal (NACFP/CPFD, 1994). The NACFP project has been highly influential in developing this planning approach, which is gaining increasing acceptance amongst foresters in Nepal.

The overall aim of RPP is to link the capacity and interests of local people with the capacity and interests of the nation for forestry development. It is argued that if such links are not made, the implementation of community forestry in specific areas will be *ad hoc* and potentially wasteful of national resources, and may fail to empower the genuine forest users. Therefore, field workers must have an overall picture of rural conditions in their entire work area. This should include a general understanding of the status of forests and forest use, the people who live in the area, their needs, interests, and problems. Such information allows field workers to set priorities for Department of Forest programmes based on the relative interests of villagers and the condition of forests.

The objectives of RPP are to:

An additional advantage of RPP, in a workforce that is subject to fairly frequent transfers, is to maintain continuity in field-level information.

- Generate periodically and prioritise a list and schedule of tasks to be undertaken within the plan period (usually one year), in consultation with senior staff.

- Maintain information about the present status of forests, forest use and forestry activities (in a Management Information System).

• Review the progress made in implementing community forestry.

In practice, this is undertaken by field workers: referring to existing information and/or collecting and storing new information about their entire work area; setting work priorities; and allocating resources to meet these priorities.

RPP has now been adopted by the Community and Private Forestry Division of the Forest Department, which is promoting it in all districts of Nepal. However, only a few districts are as yet implementing it. There are various reasons for this, including the need to train Rangers, AFOs and DFOs before work can begin (Poudyal and Edwards, 1994). Even in the NACFP area, the use of RPP data in the actual planning of Range Post and District Forest Office activities has only recently begun.

As originally developed, RPP drew heavily on information collected through participatory maps (see Chapter 1, Section 1.4). Indeed, some Rangers have come to view participatory maps as the main tool for RPP. However, RPP should use a variety of diagnostic tools, as indicated in Box 6.2. Their use still needs to be institutionalised. Some of these methods have been described in a video produced by the project, entitled *A Tool Kit for Community Forestry* (NACFP/CPFD, 1994).

Conventional maps of a detail sufficient for community forest management planning are not readily available in Nepal (see Box 6.6). Participatory mapping provides important baseline planning information, and is now a regular feature of Rangers' work. Its importance lies both in the limited availability of alternative maps and in the fact that it involves forest users in planning. Following the mapping exercises, all forests should be assessed using a means of rapid appraisal that is not as yet fully institutionalised. Rangers have, however, received training in the method, which has been introduced recently in certain parts of the project area. Rapid appraisal entails:

• The preparation of forest profiles by asking questions, drawing sketch maps, and estimating forest characteristics by eye (ocular assessment).

• Measuring a small number of temporary plots to calibrate ocular estimates.

As part of community forest monitoring, the site occupancy, abundance of valuable species, regeneration and number of seed trees is also recorded within the plots. This is discussed separately in Section 6.6. The simple plot measurements should not be confused with formal forest inventories of the type argued against in Section 6.4.

Box 6.2 Tools/Methods Used in Range Post Planning and Forest Investigation, Nepal	
Information category	**Appropriate tools/methods**
Forest names and locations	Semi-structured interviews and/or transect walks with key informants Participatory mapping Participatory analysis of aerial photographs, if available Secondary sources (e.g. DoF records)
Forest types, sizes and biophysical condition	Forest profile by rapid appraisal Semi-structured interviews and/or transect walks with key informants Participatory mapping Participatory analysis of aerial photographs, if available Secondary sources (e.g. DoF records) Workshops and group meetings
Forest use	Semi-structured interviews and/or transect walks with key informants Participatory mapping Participatory analysis of aerial photographs, if available Interest groups Direct observation Time charts (seasonal diagrams) Workshops and group meetings
Local forest management systems and silvicultural knowledge	Semi-structured interviews and/or transect walks with key informants Participatory mapping Participatory analysis of aerial photographs, if available Interest groups Wealth ranking Direct observation Secondary sources (e.g. VDC records, National census information) Workshops and group meetings
Community interest for participation in community forestry programmes	Semi-structured interviews and/or transect walks with key informants Interest groups Workshops and group meetings
Current status of community forestry activities	Secondary sources (e.g. DoF records) Semi-structured interviews and/or transect walks with key informants Interest groups Workshops and group meetings

Participatory Mapping

As used in RPP, participatory mapping is a more extractive tool than when it is employed in the context of investigation and negotiation for preparing an OP. Nevertheless, it is essential that the outsider (in this case the Ranger) is careful to facilitate, rather than direct, the process (Jackson, Nurse and Singh, 1994).

Familiarity with the area to be mapped may be gained from transect and group walks, and direct observation by the Ranger. This can be particularly useful in establishing place names before mapping is attempted.

In practice, there is a strong temptation for Rangers to make do with one map produced by a limited number of users. This can result in inaccurate information, biased (even if unintentionally) according to the perceptions of a small group. It is extremely difficult to check on whether a Ranger has consulted many users or just a few. Indeed, without an in-depth site visit, it may be impossible (Chapter 1, Box 1.6).

Early NACFP attempts to use GPS have been disappointing, probably due to interference caused by the mountainous terrain.

The first step is to develop a basic understanding of the area to be mapped (in this case, the VDC), and to establish rapport with the local people. It is pointless trying to undertake a mapping exercise without this rapport.

Once the Ranger is confident of his relations with the local people, s/he invites a group of key informants to participate in the mapping exercise. Key informants should preferably be regular forest users, with a good general knowledge of the area. As with many other participatory exercises, the active involvement of all participants decreases with increasing numbers. Limiting group numbers to 10–12 or less is therefore desirable. If possible, participants should include men and women of a spread of age groups. Given sensitive facilitation, mixed groups of men and women can work together to produce a map that is often more detailed than one produced by a single gender group. However, women of some ethnic groups may be very hesitant to participate in a mixed group. If this is so, separate gender groups may produce more useful results which can later be aggregated.

The site chosen for the group meeting to conduct the mapping exercise should ideally be level, with a relatively unobstructed view of the area of interest. It should also not be exposed to wind; indeed, fine weather is essential for the exercise. The way in which the map is drawn is described, using the example of one particular exercise conducted in the settlement of Jyalachiti, in Box 6.3.

The order in which information is elicited is also important. It is best to focus initially on non-threatening information, such as settlement and road location, before moving on to issues such as forest use.

A single mapping exercise is inadequate for Range Level Planning (or indeed other uses). Since mapping exercises can be conducted only with quite small groups, they have a high potential for bias. It is important to repeat the exercise with different groups, in different locations. The Ranger then uses these different maps to cross-check information, identify any discrepancies and follow-up on them with further questioning. His final map should be a 'best fit' amalgamation of all the information gathered.

Participatory mapping is not a very good tool for establishing the scale of areas, nor for determining boundaries. As discussed in the introductory chapter, there are ways of increasing the accuracy of such maps, by comparisons with conventional maps (if available), aerial photographs, or through the use of Global Positioning Systems (GPS). Although the combined use of such techniques with participatory mapping is only at a rudimentary stage in Nepal, it is likely to be developed further in the future.

> ## Box 6.3 A Participatory Mapping Exercise in Practice – Jyalachiti, Khabre Palanchok
>
> The group of key informants gathered after their morning meal at an underground water tank, close to a ridge top. The concrete surface of the tank provided an excellent flat area for drawing the map, whilst the view of the entire surrounding area was excellent. The participants numbered ten, including three women, and were of varying age. In reflection of the ethnic composition of the nearby settlement, they were all of the same ethnic group. All were well known to the Ranger, as forestry activities began in certain parts of the VDC some time ago; one of the participants was a nursery worker, and another the village leader. The mapping exercise was new to the participants, however – as was the exercise of Range Post Planning for this particular VDC.
>
> Explaining the reasons for the mapping exercise, the Ranger suggested that they should begin with the area immediately around them, and marked a point on the ground accordingly. He then asked for a volunteer to mark in the road running not far away. The village leader took up this challenge, and gradually the nearby roads and rivers were marked, using brown earth for the roads, and dry grasses for the rivers. The participants indicated the location of settlements in relation to these. The names of each and their ward number (VDCs are divided into 9 wards) were written on pieces of paper by the Ranger, and put in place with a stone. River names and directions of flow were also marked. People other than the village leader began adding to the map, with the Ranger's encouragement. The VDC boundary was marked, using red earth, and then settlements at all points within it. There was some disagreement on the exact positioning of some features, but the Ranger kept quiet and consensus was reached. Up to this point, the women had sat back and watched. However, they began to add comments themselves, and to gather materials for marking the map. By the time the communally used forests came to be marked in, they were adding to the map themselves, using pine needles to mark the predominantly pine forests, and the leaves of other dominant species (*Schima wallichii* – **Chilaune** and *Alnus nepalensis* – **Uttis**) to mark such forests as appropriate. The Ranger then asked who used which forests (according to settlement), and thus determined the user group of each, according to the number of households estimated by the participants in each settlement. This identified a number of settlements that had no access to communally used forests, but relied on private resources. Finally, these private forests were marked in too. At the end of the exercise, the participants all expressed pride and pleasure in the map that they had produced, whilst the Ranger copied it carefully into his notebook.
>
> Source: Prem Sapkota, Ranger (pers. comm.)

Forest Assessment by Rapid Appraisal

Forest profile preparation. Forest profiles are a 'quick and dirty' assessment, providing a broad overview of the forest, but not sufficient information for planning its management. The profile is prepared primarily by the Ranger, although s/he may consult with users – particularly over the main species present. It comprises an estimation by eye of the forest area, type, the main species present, and its overall condition. The estimation of condition should include soil cover, crown cover, the extent of natural regeneration, and the presence of seed trees. A simple classification of condition for forests in the Project area has been prepared to assist the Ranger in his estimation. It was from this system that the NUKCFP developed the system of condition classes that they currently use (described later in this Section). The forest profile information is all recorded by the Ranger on an appropriate form, to which a sketch map indicating matters such as the location of different forest types within the forest area should be attached.

Preparation of the participatory map of Jyalachiti's forest resources. Key informants work together to create the map.
Photograph: Jane Carter

The completed participatory map of Jyalachiti's forest resources.
Photograh: Jane Carter

The fact that a forest profile can be prepared quickly is an important advantage, given the heavy workload of Rangers. However, it is a method which has limitations, particularly if the entire forest cannot be viewed from a single point and there is therefore the possibility that certain features will be missed.

Calibration of ocular forest assessment. This entails the measurement of rectangular temporary sample plots to check the visual estimate described above (i.e. forest type, main species, and condition). The long and thin plots, measuring 20 m x 5 m (0.01 ha), are laid along the contour. They should be selected to be as representative as possible of the general forest condition. A minimum of two to three plots in each forest type present should be measured; clearly the more variable the forest, the more plots should be measured. Within each plot, the measurements recorded are:

Rectangular plots are used because they are far easier to establish on steep slopes than circular plots. In addition, the calculation of plot area is simpler for rectangles than circles.

- for all trees over 2 m high, species and dbh
- for all other shrubs, seedlings and saplings, total abundance by species

Calibration of an ocular assessment of Jyalachiti forest. The Ranger and villagers are shown here measuring out a sample plot. Photograph: Jane Carter

The process of calibration allows the Ranger to verify her/his rapid assessment, which s/he then adjusts if it proves to have been inaccurate. If properly conducted, it should reveal any discrepancies that might have arisen from all parts of the forest not being visible on initial observation. Project staff have found that Rangers quickly achieve the ability to make good ocular assessments of forests after practice with calibration. However, the number of plots measured and the choice of their location are very

Calibration as described here is of use and value only when conducted by competent, motivated Rangers. The way in which it is carried out is not something that senior staff can easily check and enforce.

subjective. Rangers who are not highly motivated could be easily tempted to measure as few plots as possible, choosing areas with the lowest stocking density (and thus few measurements).

At the same time as calibrating their ocular assessments of the forest, Rangers may go on to make more detailed records of forest site occupancy for district/national monitoring purposes. This is discussed in more detail in Section 6.6. First, forest assessment for planning the management of individual forests by FUGs is described, using the NUKCFP as a case study.

Forest Assessment for FUG Working Plans: The Nepal-UK Community Forestry Project

This case study focuses on how FUGs in the NUKCFP area in Eastern Nepal determine their plans for forest management, and the forest assessment techniques that are used for this. The same principles for drawing up Operational Plans (OPs) apply in other parts of Nepal, although the NUKCFP is one of several projects that has particularly developed and refined the process.

The concept of the Operational Plan is not one that originated amongst users; it was introduced by HMG-N. This said, the information collected for it is gathered by Rangers in as participatory a manner as possible. The forest assessment is carried out with the users, using terms and concepts with which they are familiar.

The Context of Operational Plan Preparation

Since 1988, Nepal's forest law has required an OP to be drawn up before forest can be handed over to a FUG. This was reiterated in the 1993 Forest Act, with the 1995 rules and regulations drawing a distinction between two aspects of formal user group formation and discussions, the Constitution and the Operational Plan.

- The *Constitution* covers administrative and institutional aspects of the FUG. These include its registration, the naming of the users, the selection of the forest committee, and the rules and regulations to be followed.

- The *Operational Plan* (also referred to as the Working Plan) concerns the management of the forest, and should be developed after the Constitution has been agreed.

Once the Constitution and the OP have been completed in full, they are sent to the Department of Forests for approval. Following approval, responsibility for the management of the forest in question is formally handed over, with a hand-over certificate, to the FUG.

The two parts of formal user group formation reflect the importance attached to both the social and the technical aspects of forest management. In facilitating the formation of early FUGs, sometimes more attention was given to the former – following the rationale that FUGs will not function effectively unless all (or the majority of) users are fully involved in the process. Many of the early FUGs also concentrated more on forest protection than management, preferring to adopt a cautious approach initially. As experience has grown in the whole process of handing over forests to FUGs, more attention is being given to the technical aspects of forest management. This applies not only to FUGs currently preparing OPs, but also to older FUGs which have already received their hand-over certificate but are now reconsidering their forestry operations in greater detail.

The OP is a tool for the user group to use in planning the activities that it wishes to conduct in the forest. If users are not involved in every stage of its preparation, they will not have a sense of ownership of the plan, they may not understand some of its provisions, and they will be unlikely to implement it. Thus in many ways, the **process** of preparing the OP is more important than the final written document – an aspect recognised at national level, and strongly emphasised by Project staff.

There are certain differences of approach to OP preparation amongst different projects. That adopted by the NUKCFP has been described in detail elsewhere (Branney and Dev, 1994), but the five stages are summarised in Box 6.4.

Drawing up the Operational Plan

This section focuses on what happens during stage two of the five stages of OP preparation outlined in Box 6.4. As indicated above, OP preparation can only begin after the FUG Constitution has been agreed. In the NUKCFP area, the elected committee then becomes the main body through which early discussions are channelled. A representative, interested and active FUG committee is essential for effective OP preparation. Usually numbering five to fifteen persons, its exact composition varies between FUGs. Typically it includes at least one woman, a member of all the main caste/ethnic groups forming the users, and at least one representative from each of the settlements using the forest.

Most OPs are drawn up in late winter/early spring. At this time, users have more time to discuss forest management as there is little agricultural work to be done, and forests are a focus of their attention with the pre-monsoon fuelwood harvest. In addition, the weather tends to be good – favouring long forest visits.

The type of information that an OP should contain is shown in Box 6.5. The information outlined is the minimum requirement; users may make additions if they wish. The information source is indicated in the right-hand column. Of all the information collated, that of particular interest as far as this case study is concerned is the forest description – overall, and by blocks.

General description of the forest

The way in which most of this information is collected needs no further explanation than that given in the Box. The matter of forest area is of note, as various methods can be used. This is indicated in Box 6.5. The need for an accurate assessment of the forest area is of course mainly a bureaucratic requirement of the DoF. The

The extent to which Operational Plan preparation is determined by the FUG committee varies between different projects and districts of Nepal, and partly depends on the individuals concerned. The role of DoF staff in this respect ensures that all legitimate forest users are involved – whether through representation by their committee, or more directly.

forest users are well aware of the location of the forest and its boundaries, and as far as they are concerned, the need for a boundary map arises only in cases of boundary dispute.

Box 6.4 Summary of the Process of Operational/Working Plan Preparation

1. Discussions with the FUG committee
Discussions are held between the Ranger (and possibly other DoF staff, including Forest Guards) and the committee about the benefits of preparing an OP for the forest, the work that it entails, and to determine their willingness to proceed.

2. Visits to the forest to prepare the plan
By visiting all parts of the forest and discussing management options with the committee, the aim is to collect all the information needed for inclusion in the OP. The outcome of this work will be a full draft OP.

3. Small group discussions to explain the plan
This stage is intended to allow all users to become familiar with the draft OP that has been prepared by the committee (with the assistance of the Ranger), and to comment on it before a final version is presented at a users assembly.

4. Users assembly to discuss and approve the plan
This assembly should be attended by all members of the committee, and at least one member of every user household, plus the Ranger. Other persons may also be invited by the users. Only when a final version of the OP has been agreed at this assembly should the Ranger proceed to stage 5.

5. Approval of the OP by the DFO
The Ranger submits the FUG Constitution, OP, and a copy of a boundary map (often traced from the cadastral survey map – see Box 6.6) to the DFO for approval. If satisfied with the plan, the DFO signs it and returns it to the FUG chairperson for his/her signature on behalf of all the users. The FUG also receives a Hand-over Certificate, giving them legal authority to start forest management in accordance with the provisions of the plan.

Source: Branney and Dev (1994)

It is not a legal requirement to include a sketch map in the Operational Plan submitted to the DFO. What is required is an accurate assessment of the forest area (see Box 6.6). DFOs in Nepal vary in the importance they attach to sketch maps produced by users. Both the NUKCFP and the NACFP stress the need for sketch maps as part of the participatory process of Operational Plan preparation.

Sketch map
The sketch map is drawn by the committee in a participatory mapping exercise facilitated by the Ranger. The process is similar to that described in Box 6.3, in the use of participatory mapping for Range Post Planning. In the context of OP preparation, the purpose of the map is to provide a tool for forest management decisions. The map should therefore indicate in detail any significant features within the forest, such as forest types (particularly whether planted or natural), water sources (wells and springs), streams, roads, paths, cliffs, rocks, etc.

Box 6.5 Contents of an Operational Plan

Information	Information source
A. General description of forest	
• forest name	• decided by users
• altitude (approximate)	• estimated/measured from map/altimeter reading
• aspect (overall)	• visually/from map
• slope (average condition)	• visually, in users' terms (steep, moderate, flat, etc.)
• area	• measured from map/users' estimates/cadastral surveys/forest boundary survey
• number of blocks	• decided by users
• historical background, including any existing management systems	• PRA, relating historical events to the history of the forest, key informants
• date for plan to become effective	• agreed at the users' assembly
B. Sketch map	• participatory mapping
C. For each block:	
• name	• local name given by users
• number	• given by users (often easier for reference than names, especially when forest operations are conducted in rotation)
• boundaries	• described on all sides using features identified by users
• area	• described in users' own terms; source various, but if estimated, figure should be agreed by FUG
• forest description by	
• forest type	
• main species	• described mainly in users' own terms, using project guidelines
• forest age	
• canopy density	
• natural regeneration	
• forest condition	
• soil description	• described by users in their own terms (local systems of soil classification are quite detailed)
• erosion features	• users' description of any evidence of soil erosion (e.g. landslides, gullies) and recent changes (for better or worse)
• slope	• described in users' terms
• aspect	• e.g. North, South West, etc.
• management objectives	• drawn up by users assisted by Department of Forests staff, using project guidelines
• forestry operations	• drawn up by users assisted by Department of Forests staff, using project guidelines
• income generation activities	• as considered feasible (e.g. NTFP collection, agroforestry, etc.)
• timetable for operations	• timing of activities by month and year, at least for the first two years (note flexibility of OP allows for subsequent changes as decided by users)
• type and yield of forest products; method of distribution	• estimates of yield may be obtained from project *Thumb Rules*; distribution is decided by the users

(continued/...)

Box 6.5 *(continued)*

D. List of useful plants in the forest	• compiled by users (using local names) from the species recorded in each block
E. Protection system for the forest and wildlife	• users decide
F. Rules for forest product distribution and sale	• users decide
G. Seedling production (if any)	• users decide on nursery arrangements
H. Arrangements for plantation establishment and maintenance (if any)	• users decide (if appropriate)
I. Arrangements for income distribution from forest products	• users decide

---

The committee may at this stage feel able to demarcate the forest into blocks, or they may wish to visit the forest first. Various criteria may be used to make the decision over block demarcation, although the most important feature of a given block is that it should be easy to distinguish from others. Criteria that have been used by FUGs to divide forests into blocks include the following:

- Forest type – each type might be a different block.

- Forest condition – parts of the forest in different condition could form separate blocks.

- Natural boundaries – such as streams, ridges and paths.

- User needs – the forest may be divided into blocks so that users in different settlements are each allocated the block nearest their homes.

- Area – a uniform forest might be divided into blocks of similar area.

Box 6.6   Assessing the Forest Area: Common Methods in Nepal

Measured from maps

Nepal is covered by maps of a scale 1:50,000, but these are only enlargements of 1:125,000 maps, produced under a Land Resources Mapping Project (LRMP) and based on data collected in the late 1970s. They only showed forests greater than 25 ha. The 1:50,000 maps contain some additional information provided by DFOs, but this is of a very limited nature. In some districts of Nepal, more detailed land-use or topographical maps are available as the result of specific project activities. This is true in the Koshi Hills, where accurate maps of scale 1:25,000 are available (they were produced with British assistance in 1987). These have been found to be useful in providing rough area figures for larger forests. In some cases, DoF maps of the forest in question are available, as the result of past surveys.

Cadastral survey

Almost all districts of Nepal have been surveyed in the last 20 years, and the cadastral map is a legal document. Reference should be made to it when preparing the OP, although determining the forest area from it may not necessarily be simple, if encroachments have occurred. In this case, the committee will need to decide how they wish to treat encroachments.

Users' estimate

This is usually made in the local unit of area measurement (**ropani**), the metric equivalent of which is also noted by the Ranger. If the area of forest is small, user estimates can be reasonably accurate although care must be taken that the figure estimated by the committee members is agreed by the entire users group before being formalised in the OP.

Forest boundary survey

This option, although an obvious one, is not often conducted in practice. This is because it is time-consuming, and ideally requires two Rangers (Forest Guards do not have the necessary training). The users do not usually have the skills or experience to participate to any significant extent themselves. The circumstances under which a survey may be necessary are when

- there is dispute or uncertainty over the forest boundaries, or
- a large forest area is being divided between different FUGs, or
- only part of a forest is being handed over to a FUG.

Description of each forest block

In order to describe the forest blocks, the committee and the Ranger must visit each in turn and write the description whilst in the forest. The information required is indicated in Box 6.5. For describing the forest by type and condition, the project has produced a set of guidelines (in Nepali as well as English), to which the committee and Ranger can refer. The guidelines have been tailored to forestry in the Koshi Hills, but draw in part on similar work by the NACFP in Central Nepal (Branney, 1994b).

Sketch maps as a tool for forest management decisions. Here members of a Forest Users Group committee use a sketch map to begin discussing forest management.
Photograph: Jane Carter

Forest type. The project guidelines set out the eight basic forest types found in the eastern hills project area (see Box 6.7). For ease of identification, the guidelines list both the dominant tree species and common associate species, with comments on typical presentation. Using these guidelines, users rarely have difficulty in determining the forest type.

Box 6.7 The Eight Main Forest Types in the Eastern Hills of Nepal

1. *Shorea robusta* **(Sal)** forest
2. Subtropical deciduous forest (main species *Adina cordifolia, Acacia catechu, Lagerstroemia parviflora*)
3. *Pinus roxburghii* (Pine) forest
4. *Castanopsis hystrix* and *Schima wallichii* **(Katus – Chilaune)** forest
5. Oak – Rhododendron (main species *Quercus semecarpifolia, Q. lanata* and *Rhododendron arboreum*)
6. *Alnus nepalensis* **(Uttis)** forest
7. Subtropical scrub (dominated by *Lantana camara*)
8. Temperate scrub (dominated by *Eupatorium adenophorum*)

Main species. On visiting the block, the committee notes all the important plant species found within it and hence draws up a list (using their Nepali names). The definition of 'important' in this context is left to them. Apart from valued tree species, they might include plants yielding NTFPs such as fodder (particularly plants considered to provide exceptionally high quality fodder), food, dyes and medicines (some of which have commercial value).

Forest age. This is usually given in broad descriptive terms such as mature; pole stage (immature); shrub land (from coppice regrowth); or mixed (meaning that there is no true forest canopy).

Canopy density. This is categorised simply as follows:

- Dense (crown cover > 70%) or
- Open (crown cover < 70%) or
- Very open (no canopy, isolated trees only).

Although crude, this system has the advantage that there is no need for any measurements, and the estimate can be made by the committee members themselves.

Regeneration. Again, this is estimated by the committee using a simple categorisation as follows:

- Abundant (seedlings present and plentiful in most places)
- Scattered/Few (seedlings only found in some places, and quite rare)
- None (no seedlings present).

Forest condition. The project guidelines note that forest condition depends on *age* and *canopy density* and *amount of regeneration*. Having determined the forest age, canopy density and amount of regeneration, the broad forest condition can be deduced by the Ranger and committee members using the appropriate management chart (for the forest type) in the guidelines. The chart not only indicates forest condition; it also provides suggestions of appropriate management options that may be considered.

Management objectives

Three broad management objectives for forests managed by FUGs are generally accepted. They are that the forest should be managed to:

- provide users with their basic needs for forest products
- improve the condition of degraded forest
- provide forest products in a sustainable way

These broad objectives are of little help in making decisions over the management of individual forest blocks. The management objectives for each block must, of course, be tailored to the forest type and condition in a realistic manner.

Forestry operations

The selection of forestry operations should be:

- suitable for the forest type and condition (this can be checked in the Project guidelines),
- consistent with the management objectives for the block,

- feasible as far as the users are concerned.

Sixteen possible forestry operations are listed and fully described in the Project guidelines, which can be used for reference. Commonly practised operations include selective felling, thinning, coppicing with standards, pruning, fodder lopping, leaf litter collection, grazing control, agroforestry, and enrichment planting. Some of these operations have been carried out in Kirtipur forest, which is given in Box 6.8 as an example of the FUG decision-making process over forest management.

Returning to the information included when drafting an OP, three further aspects should always be considered: income generation activities, the timetable of operations, and the type and yield of forest products (including the method of distribution). The latter is of greatest relevance to the current discussion.

Type and yield of forest products

The expected yield of different forest products is not always easy for the committee to predict at the outset of management operations. It is not uncommon for early estimates to be based more on user requirements than a realistic assessment of forest productivity.

For this reason, the project has produced some *'Thumb rules' for Assessing the Sustainability of Harvesting by Forest User Groups*, which can be used with the forest management guidelines to gain a rough estimate of the annual yield (in tonnes/ha) of timber and/or fuelwood that can be harvested without degrading the forest (Branney, 1994c).

This has to be converted into units with which users are familiar (usually in the case of fuelwood, in headloads which are calculated at an average 30 kg). The project accepts that these 'thumb rules' are very rough, but they are nevertheless a useful guide. They are based on forest management demonstrations, published research, and practical field experience, and are currently applicable only to the three main forest types handed over to FUGs in the eastern hills – *Shorea robusta* forest, *Castanopsis hystrix – Schima wallichii* forest, and *Pinus roxburghii* forest.

Once all these aspects of forest management have been thought through and written down in draft form, the process on OP preparation can move to stage three – discussions of the draft plan with small groups. This is not described further here. Instead, in the final sections of this chapter, we focus on the training needs for participatory forest assessment in Nepal, and on projected future forest assessment developments (notably in monitoring). Although drawing in particular on the experience of the NACFP and the NUKCFP, the discussion is more broadly applicable to community forestry in the middle hills.

Box 6.8 Forest Management by a FUG in Practice: Mangdhana Forest, Kirtipur

The Kirtipur FUG was formed five years ago and numbers 45 user households, almost all of whom are Limbus. Cohesion amongst the users is strong, and management decisions have been followed strictly. Most users have access to trees on their own land, as well as being members of a second, larger FUG for a different and larger forest. They thus do not rely on Mangdhana forest for all their forest product needs.

Magdhana Forest lies at approximately 1,700 m elevation on a steep, mainly north-facing slope. It covers some 5 ha (as estimated by the users) and was originally divided into five management blocks. The broad forest type in all blocks is **Katus – Chilaune**. At the time of forest hand-over, the dominant species was *Castanopsis hystrix* **(Patle Katus)**, whilst a few scattered trees of *Schima wallichii* **(Chilaune)** and *Juglans regia* **(Okhar)** were also present. The forest was broadly described as dense shrub (comprising heavy coppice regrowth), with scattered regeneration, giving it an average condition score. Soil erosion was not considered to be a problem.

Possible management options for such a forest include singling, and coppicing with standards. However, the FUG felt that a forest dominated by *Castanopsis hystrix* was not what they wanted (although the species can be used for timber, fuelwood and fodder and under appropriate management produces edible nuts, the quality of these products is not considered to be high). The FUG wished in the long term to convert it to a mixed forest managed to produce good quality timber, fuelwood, fodder and possibly other products. They divided the forest into five blocks of roughly equal area, largely on the assumption that a five-year management rotation would be the most convenient. A further criterion for block demarcation was forest density (which varied between blocks), and planting potential (block 1, for example, has a number of small, damp gullies which were thought to be suitable for bamboo planting). Block demarcation was thus conducted in terms of practical utilisation.

Activities in early years concentrated on removing old, deformed and heavily coppiced *Castanopsis hystrix* trees for fuelwood, and raising seedlings to infill gaps with desirable species – mainly *Alnus nepalensis* **(Uttis)** for timber and fuelwood, but also *Juglans regia*, *Prunus cerasoides* **(Painyo)**, *Rhododendron arboreum* **(Guras)** and *Choerospondias axillaris* **(Lapsi)** and others. Some of this enrichment planting has been successful. However, many plants were killed by an exceptionally hard frost, whilst in general growth would have been better if the forest had first been more rigorously thinned. The FUG received little silvicultural advice early on (it began activities when relatively little attention was paid to this matter). It has effectively learned from its own mistakes, from visiting other forests (one committee member participated in a project-organised study tour), and from more recent professional comment. It now plans to draw up a new, more rigorous OP dividing each current block into two, giving ten blocks managed on a ten-year rotation to allow far greater regeneration between harvests. It is also conducting a programme of far more intensive thinning, leaving only trees of good form and allowing for further enrichment planting.

Training

It is widely recognised in Nepal that the conceptually radical approach to community forestry that has been adopted will only succeed if the Department of Forests staff entrusted with its implementation are highly motivated and appropriately trained. There is therefore provision for such training at the national level. In addition, projects have provided considerable support for training, both locally and overseas. At the local level, appropriate courses and manuals have been developed as needs arise – one need being for participatory forest assessment techniques. Much training support has focused on Rangers as the key field staff, but a growing need for Forest Guard training is also being recognised and addressed. This need has arisen from the increasing workload of Rangers, thrusting Forest Guards into a far greater support role.

Training for DoF staff

The NACFP has developed a comprehensive manual for Community Forestry Field Workers, divided on a subject basis into modules with different sessions (theoretical and practical) (Jackson, Malla, Singh, Ingles and Baldwin, 1995). This includes a module on Participatory Tools for Community Forestry, including several sessions on participatory mapping, a module on Range Post Planning, and a module on Investigation and Negotiation for Community Forestry, which includes several sessions on rapid appraisal techniques for forest assessment. Both expatriate and local Project staff have made a substantial contribution to the manual, which is written in English since this was preferred by Nepali trainers. The handout materials, accompanying videos and overhead projection sheets are in Nepali. Direct expatriate involvement in training is now minimal; courses are organised and run by local Project and DoF staff. All Rangers in the NACFP area have received a two-day training course in participatory mapping, including field practice, and a three-day course in Range Post Planning. These courses were first given in 1992 and have been repeated in later years for new Rangers and as follow-up for some previously trained Rangers. In early 1995, Rangers participated in a five-day course in forest profiling, the calibration of ocular assessments, and simple inventory techniques for monitoring forest condition. These techniques are therefore new to them, particularly given that in their original (national-level) Ranger training, instruction was largely theoretical with few practical sessions. Forest Guards within the NACFP area also undergo community forestry training. However, forest resource assessment is not given extensive coverage as it is mainly a Ranger task.

In emphasising the role of DoF staff as community forestry facilitators, the NUKCFP developed a three-week re-orientation or 'start-up' course for all Rangers working in the project area (Dev, 1993). Such courses are still held for newly posted Rangers. Participatory forest management training is provided in a two-week course which includes PRA techniques (notably participatory mapping) and forest condition assessment. Another five-day course is also held in conducting boundary surveys, since this is a task with which Rangers commonly have difficulty. Forest Guards in the NUKCFP area also now undergo a three week 'start up' course, and a two week course in operational plan preparation. Although developed with the assistance of Project staff, all these courses are currently run by DoF staff. Their main objective is to provide training in accordance with field-identified needs.

The NACFP and NUKCFP also support overseas training, mainly with the objectives of long-term capacity building and staff motivation. They are thus more for senior level staff, and few have directly addressed participatory forest resource assessment. However, the NUKCFP did support one largely Indian-based course on PRA techniques for a selected group of Rangers. Provided by an Indian NGO, this entailed a visit to West Bengal as well as field activities in Nepal facilitated by the NGO.

Training for villagers

At village level, both the NACFP and NUKCFP have held study tours for selected forest users to learn from the experiences of others. These have often included aspects of forest assessment for the planning management operations. Study tours have proved a useful way for innovative individuals to gain new ideas (as indicated in Box 6.8). However, participants need to be selected with care to ensure that they are willing and motivated to pass on lessons to other users.

6.6 Current and Future Developments

There are perhaps two key areas of community forest assessment that are likely to develop further in the future. These are:

- forest assessment for long-term monitoring at district and national level
- forest assessment by users for their own monitoring purposes

Monitoring at District and National Level

As the community forestry programme expands over time, it is likely that both HMG-N and donors will require quantitative information on any changes in forests managed by FUGs. Ideally, a monitoring system should determine whether or not forests are being managed on a sustainable basis. Given the complexity of product harvesting from many FUG-managed forests, this will be difficult to determine precisely, although indicators such as forest condition and species diversity will provide valuable information. It is also possible that monitoring information will be required to meet certain international commitments made by HMG-N. An obvious example is provided by the Biodiversity Convention, to which Nepal is a signatory (see Chapter 1, Box 1.4). Systematic information on the biodiversity of Nepal's forests is not being collected at present, but in due course this is likely to be required (Ingles, 1994; Jackson and Ingles, 1994).

Forest monitoring has been addressed by the NACFP and NUKCFP in slightly different ways. In both cases, it is only at a preliminary stage.

Monitoring of Forest Condition in the NACFP Area: Simple Forest/Shrubland Inventories (SFIs/SSIs)

It is planned that the condition of forests handed over to FUGs will be monitored over time using temporary plots of the same shape and size currently used by Rangers in their calibration of ocular forest assessments. A method of simple forest inventories (SFIs) and simple shrubland inventories (SSIs) has been developed for this purpose. After extensive field testing, Rangers were trained in the technique in early 1995. Field implementation began after this.

A summary of the information collected in the SFIs/SSIs is given in Box 6.9. They include a form for field measurements, and separate calculation and summary forms which the Ranger completes once s/he returns to the office. In Box 6.10, the practical implementation of SFIs/SSIs in two forests is described. In both cases, they represented one of the first attempts of the Ranger concerned to conduct forest condition monitoring in his field area. From the description, it can be seen that forest users had only a limited degree of involvement in the process, as might be expected given the limited direct use to them of the information being collected. The one aspect in which users can take an active part is in species identification, use and relative value for a given purpose. On this subject it is common for users, particularly those who use the forest regularly, to have a deeper knowledge than Rangers.

One potential problem with the system as described is that the choice of plot location is left entirely to the Ranger. There is a clear temptation to choose easy to measure, poorly stocked areas (particularly in dense shrub). There is also the temptation to measure as few plots as possible, with the result that the numbers measured are insufficient to represent the variation in the forest. High Ranger motivation is thus essential for the task. In addition to this, the whole exercise can be very time-consuming if conducted thoroughly. This is especially true as it does not end with the measurements in the field. After these, the Ranger has to complete the form by conducting calculations such as the basal area. At present, Rangers are clearly hesitant over this work, and will require further training to increase their confidence and ability. Although they are likely to become more efficient with practice, it remains to be seen how the work can be fitted into their already heavy schedules.

Like the calibration method described earlier, information collected in SFI/SSIs is only of use and value when conducted by competent, motivated Rangers. The way in which it is collected cannot be easily checked or enforced by senior staff.

In both NACFP and NUKCFP areas, species are recorded using local names. Names for some species vary between different parts of Nepal, and particularly between ethnic groups speaking different languages. For the main tree species, there is not usually any problem with identification. For national monitoring purposes, consultation with botanists to determine the botanical identity of uncertain species will probably be necessary. In a few cases, even the distinction of separate species may be debatable and will need to be clarified. (See Chapter 9, Box 9.2).

Assuming Rangers do become more skilled and efficient in conducting SFIs and SSIs, the method will provide valuable monitoring information. Most importantly, a forest monitoring system will have been institutionalised at Range Post level which feeds into district and national forest monitoring.

Box 6.9 Summary of Forest Condition Monitoring Records used in Nepal

	SFI (Simple Forest Inventory)	SSI (Simple Shrubland Inventory)
Plot form	• plot identification information[2] • trees > 2 m high: species, dbh, basal area (BA) • valued tree species < 2 m high: number of each species • other tree species < 2 m high: number of each species	• plot identification information • trees > 2 m high: species, dbh, seed trees or not • regenerating plants and shrubs: number of each species • crown separation (gaps and sizes in cm)
Calculation form	• plot identification information • site occupancy by tree species (BA) • total site occupancy by trees • forest structure (size-class distribution) • stocking • total tree species regeneration	• plot identification information • site occupancy by regeneration, shrubs, seed trees and non-seed trees • site occupancy by trees only (based on BA) • site occupancy by shrubs only (based on crown separation ratio)
Summary form	• forest identification information • species summary (dominant five tree species by BA, regeneration; species diversity) • site occupancy summary • comments	• forest identification information • shrubland summary (dominant ten plant species, dominant four tree species by BA; species diversity) • site occupancy summary • comments

---

Box 6.10 Simple Forest/Shrubland Inventories in Jyalachiti and Thumki Forests, Kabhre Palanchok

Jyalachiti forest comprises two main forest types, only one of which was sampled on the day. The dominant species are *Alnus nepalensis* **(Uttis)** and *Machilus odoratissima* **(Seti kath)**, and the forest is in good condition. Thumki forest also comprises two main forest types, *Pinus roxburghii* **(Salla)** and *Schima wallichii – Castanopsis spp* **(Chilaune – Katus)**. However, the latter is degraded to shrubland.

In both cases, the Ranger was accompanied for the plot measurement by a Forest Guard as assistant, and a small group of local users to whom the purpose of the exercise had been very briefly explained. At Jyalachiti, they included three women; at Thumki, they were all male. The decision on where to locate the plots was made by the Ranger. For reasons of time, convenience and sheer courtesy to the users, it was clearly easier for him to choose readily accessible areas, not far from the path. Demarcation of the plots was conducted using a 20 m length of rope as the central axis. A shorter length of rope was tied across it in such a way that it could be moved up and down the longer rope, and measure 2.5 m away from the central rope in either direction. The ropes were held in place by some of the users. Both forests were on a slope, and care was taken to align the plots lengthwise along the contour. The Ranger then began by measuring the dbh of all trees over 2 m (all measurements being taken from the side of the tree up-slope), with the users supplying the species name. This was recorded on the appropriate form by the Forest Guard. Next all smaller plants were noted, with the users supplying the species names and commenting on the usefulness of each. Some people were particularly knowledgeable on this – a notable example being a young woman (it is often younger women who have chief responsibility for fodder and fuelwood collection). With this information collected for the forests, the Ranger moved on to start measurement in another plot. He would conduct the necessary calculations from the measurements back at his office later in the day. The one measurement that caused him some difficulty was that of crown separation in shrubland – an aspect on which he felt he needed more training.

Overall, the local users seemed happy to give up their time for the measurement of one or two plots, but after this they clearly wished to leave. Had the forests been highly diverse, necessitating the sampling of many plots, there might have been a distinct hesitance to continue. No-one asked any questions of the Ranger when he explained the measurements; the bureaucratic need seemed to be politely accepted.

Source: Prem Sapkota and Ram Chandra Subedi, Rangers (pers. comm.)

Monitoring of Forest Condition in the NUKCFP Area: Baseline Forest Resource Assessment

Rather than adding community forest monitoring to regular Ranger responsibilities, in the NUKCFP area baseline forest resource assessment has been initiated as a separate programme staffed by designated, appropriately trained officers. However, within the NUKCFP there is currently some debate over the appropriateness of this approach, partly because of the amount of staff time that it entails. The aim of the programme, which began in 1994, is to provide baseline data covering a range of forest types and conditions, from both community and non-community forest areas. This is intended to indicate and quantify any changes in forest condition over time. In addition, by combining such information with other data about quantities of forest products harvested from community forests, it should be possible to assess the sustainability of existing forest management practices and off-take rates. Key features of the baseline forest resource assessment are as follows (Branney, 1994a).

The simple forest inventory in Thumki forest. The Ranger is shown here measuring tree diameter, while villagers hold ropes to demarcate the plot.
Photograph: Jane Carter

- **A stratified sample**. Data collection from all forests is not intended. Measurements are conducted in a stratified sample of forests, selected as broadly representative of the forests being handed over to FUGs. It includes all the main forest types being handed over to users, in varying starting conditions (very good/good/average/poor). All four districts of the Koshi Hills are covered.

- **Forest groups**. Part of the rationale for including non-community forests is to determine whether handing over one area of forest to a FUG puts greater pressure on nearby forest areas, leading to their degradation. To test this hypothesis, groups of community and non-community forests lying less than two hours walk apart have been identified for sampling. The groups cover a range of forest types and condition combinations, and differing access (near a road, or remote).

- **Forest blocks**. Each forest to be sampled is divided into blocks, as is usual for OP preparation. Approximately six blocks are chosen for sampling from each forest group. Each must be typical of the forest type and condition that it represents, and relatively accessible for measurements.

- **Permanent plots**. Permanent plots are located within the blocks on a random basis. This is achieved by taking traverses from a clearly identifiable reference point into the forest, using randomly chosen bearings (from a random numbers table). The plot centre is established at a standard, pre-selected distance. The rectangular 10 x 5 m plot is then laid out using ropes. This standard plot size may be varied according to circumstances (although if it is, due note should be made in the records, and calculations adjusted accordingly). If regeneration is extremely abundant, it is only necessary to record it in half the plot (10 m x 2.5 m). If the plot falls on open ground devoid of trees, it may be necessary to increase the plot size.

- **Recording criteria**. **Trees** are classed as all woody plants > 3 m tall; for all, the local name and the dbh are recorded. **Shrubs** are classed as all woody plants 0.5–3 m; they are recorded by local name and number. Heights are not recorded (calculations of volume are not part of the purpose of data collection). Tree and shrub species < 0.5 m are classed as **regeneration**, and recorded by local name and number. Other information recorded includes percentage canopy cover, shrub crown diameter and crown separation, litter layer characteristics, evidence of recent physical damage, and evidence of recent forest management or harvesting. For the block overall, a record is also made of the number of species falling into different growth forms (tree, shrub, climber, herb, etc.).[3]

- **Overall records**. Scrupulous records must be maintained, from the location of the sampled forests to the position of the PSPs, and the data recorded within them. Appropriate forms have been compiled for this purpose. They include calculation forms similar to those developed by the NACFP for the SFI and SSI, on which figures for stocking, BA, etc. are calculated.

- **Sampling frequency**. Repeat sampling on a five-year basis is planned.

Baseline forest resource assessment as conducted by the NUKCFP is not intended as a participatory exercise, although it is hoped that the information it generates will support the community forestry programme. The involvement of local people in the inventory itself is very limited, although where there are existing FUGs, the reasons

There are clear and deliberate similarities between the SFI/SSIs of the NACFP and the NUKCFP's baseline forest resource assessment. Indeed, NUKCFP staff drew on the former in developing their current system, which was designed to be compatible with it and thus permit cross-regional comparisons.

for conducting measurements are explained. If they already have OPs or systems of blocking the forest, these are used as the basis for selecting blocks for assessment. Field experience has shown that the assessment can become an extension exercise, with interested FUG members accompanying the enumerators and discussing their work in detail.

Perhaps one of the most significant differences between the two projects is the choice of temporary versus permanent sample plots, which in some ways reflects the deeper choice between attempting to integrate monitoring into regular field staff activities, and keeping it as a separate activity. In standard forest inventories, temporary sample plots (TSPs) and permanent sample plots (PSPs) have clearly different roles, and different measurements are taken in each (as outlined in Chapter 1, Section 1.4). In the context of plot measurements for monitoring community forests in Nepal, these differences are not so clearly defined. The appropriateness of using temporary versus permanent plots may be debated. Forest monitoring using temporary plots may be seen as quick, simple, and of probably acceptable accuracy. Permanent plots should provide more accurate data, but this assumes that they can be precisely identified and remeasured after an interval of five years or so. Whether or not this is possible is uncertain. The DoF is unlikely to have the necessary resources, meaning that plot remeasurement will probably depend on donor interest. Even assuming resource availability, re-identifying plots may be difficult as a result of user activities. This might be overcome by involving FUGs to a greater extent in the establishment of PSPs. However, it is possible that FUGs would then manage the PSPs rather differently and more carefully than other parts of the forest.

Box 6.11 Trials Established by a FUG near Kusma, Parbat District

This FUG has laid out its own trial plots in its community forest. The plots consist of three thinning treatments of a young **Sal** (*Shorea robusta*) forest. Each tree has been numbered and the diameter of each has been recorded by the user group. The initial impetus for this initiative came from a Ranger (and it is probably significant that the FUG is very close to the DFO's office), but all the records and measurements have been carried out by the FUG committee, no payments were involved, and the standard of execution is exemplary. It remains to be seen how the FUG will assess the condition of the differently treated blocks in a few years time, and decide on which treatment gives the best results.

Source: P. Branney (1995, pers. comm.)

Monitoring by FUGs

Forest assessment by FUGs for their own monitoring purposes has yet to be developed. However, as the experience and number of

FUGs grows, it seems likely that they will become more involved in such aspects of forest management. This is illustrated by the example of one FUG in Parbat District (Western Nepal), as detailed in Box 6.11.

6.7 Conclusion

The forest resource assessment methods described in this chapter have been developed over time and experience in response to the needs of Nepal's community forestry programme. Considerable attention has been directed to finding the most appropriate means to gather forest information for different end users: whether forest users, local DoF staff, or national level planners. There is scope for refinement of some of the methods, and many unanswered questions remain with regard to the most appropriate means of monitoring the condition of community forests. These will be interesting issues for future development. With field experience growing steadily, the pace of change is rapid.

Notes

1. Comparing satellite images of the middle hills taken in 1964 and 1979, Carson *et al.* (1986) concluded that there was an increase in damaged forest, but not a loss of forest cover. They estimated 55% of the forest to be in poor condition.

2. Plot identification information includes forest name, location, altitude, the name of the recorder, plot number, etc.

3. To minimise plot re-location problems, reference points (clearly identifiable features such as the junction of two streams, large rocks, temples, houses, etc.) around the edge of the forest and inside or close to each forest block are selected. These are described in the field notebook, and their location marked on a sketch map. A photograph is also taken of a person standing at the reference point holding a survey rod. The bearing to each plot from the reference point is recorded, as are any significant features that are crossed by the traverse line into the forest. The fact that the plot centre is established at a pre-selected, standard distance from the reference point should also facilitate future re-location.

References

Branney, P. (1994a) *Handbook for Baseline Forest Assessment.* Project Report G/NUKCFP/03 Nepal-UK Community Forestry Project, Co-ordinator's Office, Kathmandu.

Branney, P. (1994b) *Guidelines for Managing Community Forests in the Koshi Hills* (2nd edn). Community Forestry Guidelines Series,

Project Report E/NUKCFP/05 Nepal-UK Community Forestry Project, Coordinator's Office, Kathmandu.

Branney, P. (1994c) *'Thumb Rules' for Assessing the Sustainability of Harvesting by Forest User Groups*. Nepal-UK Community Forestry Project and LTS International Ltd, Edinburgh, UK. NUKCFP Internal Document.

Branney, P. and **Dev, O. P.** (1994) *Guidelines for Preparing Working Plans for Community Forests in Nepal* (rev. 2nd edn) Nepal-UK Community Forestry Project, Coordinator's Office, Kathmandu and LTS International Ltd, Edinburgh, UK.

Carson, B., Neild, R., Amataya, D. B. and **Hildreth, G.** (1986) 'Land Resource Mapping Project Agriculture Forestry Report – Present landuse and the potential for improvement'. Report by Kenting Earth Sciences Ltd for the HMG-N/Government of Canada Land Resource Mapping Project, Kathmandu.

Dev, O. P. (1993) *A Manual for Community Forest Management Workshop*. Koshi Hills Community Forestry Project, Dhankuta.

Fisher, R. J. (1989) *Indigenous systems of Common Property Forest Management in Nepal*. Working Paper 18, Envirnment and Policy Institute, East-West Centre, Honolulu.

Ingles, A. W. (1994) 'Conserving the Biological Diversity of Nepal's Forests: Some Opportunities Provided by Community Forestry'. Nepal-Australia Community Forestry Project Discussion Paper presented to the IUCN Workshop on Biological Diversity Conservation Outside Protected Areas, Madrid. 11–14 April.

Jackson, J. K. (1987) *Manual of Afforestation in Nepal*. Nepal-UK Forestry Research Project, Forest Survey and Research Office, Department of Forest, Kathmandu.

Jackson, W. J. and **Ingles, A. W.** (1994) 'Developing Rural Communities and Conserving the Biodiversity of Nepal's Forests through Community Forestry'. Nepal-Australia Community Forestry Project Discussion Paper presented at a Seminar on Community Development and Conservation of Forest Biodiversity through Community Forestry, Bangkok, 26–28 October.

Jackson, B., Nurse, M. and **Singh, H. B.** (1994) *Participatory Mapping for Community Forestry*. Rural Development Forestry Network Paper 17e From the Field. ODI, London.

Jackson, W. J., Malla, Y. B., Singh, H. B., Ingles, A. W. and **Baldwin, P. J.** (1995) *Community Forestry for Rural Development in Nepal: A Manual for Training Field Workers* 2nd edn (in preparation). Nepal-Australia Community Forestry Project, Kathmandu.

Kanel, K. (1993) 'Community Forestry and the 1993 Forestry Legislation: Implications for Policy and Implementation', *Banko Janakari* 4 (1): 2–5.

NACFP/CPFD (1994) *A Brief Guide to Range Post Planning*. Nepal Australia Community Forestry Project and Community and Private Forestry Division Technical Note 6/94, Kathmandu.

Nelson, D. and Karmacharya, S. (1989) *Potential Community Forestry Land in Nepal*. Department of Forests, Ministry of Forests and Soil Conservation, His Majesty's Government of Nepal, FAO/UNDP. Report No. NEP/85.017. Kathmandu.

Poudyal, A. S. and Edwards, S. L. (1994) 'Evaluation of Range Level Planning in Bajhang District Bajhang District Forest Office, Chainpur, Bhajang, Far Western Development Region, Nepal'. unpublished report submitted to Community and Private Forestry Division, Kathmandu (mimeo).

Tamang, D. (1990) *Indigenous Forest Management in Nepal: A Review*. Research Report Series 12. His Majesty's Government of Nepal, Ministry of Agriculture. Winrock International, Kathmandu.

Acronyms specific to this chapter

AFO	Assistant Forest Officer
DFO	District Forest Officer
DoF	Department of Forests
FUG	Forest User Group
HMG-N	His Majesty's Government of Nepal
NACFP	Nepal-Australia Community Forestry Project
NUKCFP	Nepal-United Kingdom Community Forestry Project
OP	Operational Plan
RPP	Range Post Planning
SFI	Simple Forest Inventory (term used by the NACFP)
SSI	Simple Shrubland Inventory (term used by the NACFP)
VDC	Village Development Committee (village-level administrative unit in Nepal)

Mapping and NTFP Inventory: Participatory Assessment Methods for Forest-dwelling Communities in East Kalimantan, Indonesia

7

Mary C. Stockdale and Bianca Ambrose
With contributions from Godwin Limberg, Frank Momberg,
Samuel ST. Padan, Dolvina Damus, Martua T. Sirait,
Ketut Deddy, Mathilde Snel

This chapter considers the use of forest assessment methods by the forest-dwelling peoples of East Kalimantan, in a different context from that of the other case studies described so far. Kalimantan forms the largest part of the island of Borneo, and is Indonesian territory (see Figure 7.1). Much of it is still covered by dense tropical evergreen rainforest, although this is being cleared at a rapid rate. The indigenous people of Kalimantan have been dependent on the forests for their livelihood for centuries. Their right to live in the forest and harvest its products for subsistence needs is recognised in traditional law, but as this chapter explains, this is often over-ruled by modern Indonesian law. In response to the loss of what they consider to be their forests to logging and development activities, the people of East Kalimantan are beginning to seek stronger official recognition of their rights to forest lands and resources. Various non-governmental organisations are working with them to this end. In the process, a variety of participatory forest resource assessment methods have been developed, although all are still at the pilot stage. They include territory mapping (mapping the location of territory boundaries with local people, and using a Global Positioning System to verify locations), resource mapping (mapping the location of important resources), and NTFP (non-timber forest product) inventory (the qualitative and quantitative assessment of important plants providing NTFPs – particularly rattans).

The chapter focuses mainly on work being conducted with the people living inside the Kayan Mentarang Nature Reserve. It is hoped that the status of this reserve will be changed to that of a National Park, which would allow a greater range of activities within its boundaries than is currently legally permissible. Amongst the various NGOs that have been involved in supporting the people of Kayan Mentarang, WWF (World Wide Fund for Nature)-Indonesia is the most notable.

Figure 7.1 East Kalimantan Province and the Kayan Mentarang Nature Reserve, Indonesia

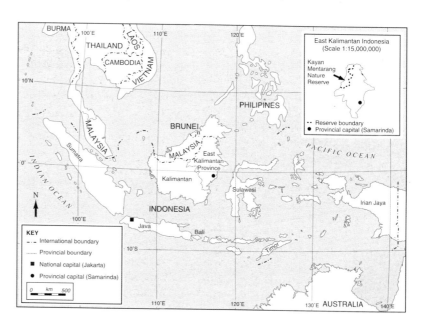

7.1 Forest Legislation and the Role of the Indonesian Government in Forest Management

Legislation over land and forests is somewhat complex. However, an awareness of the main principles is central to this chapter.

Traditional land and resource tenure in Indonesia is one of many aspects of community life covered by traditional law, or **adat**, and has formed the basis of indigenous forest management systems for centuries. Land tenure and resource tenure are not necessarily synonymous, so that one parcel of land is often encumbered with a variety of resource rights held by different individuals or groups. A variety of tenurial arrangements exist within villages or amongst related or neighbouring tribal groups, and they will often change dynamically in response to changes in local circumstances. However, within modern Indonesian legislation the status of traditional tenure systems is often ambiguous, and subject to wide interpretation. There are two main ways in which traditional tenure systems are affected by Indonesian law, namely, through the Basic Agrarian Law (BAL) and the Basic Forestry Law (BFL).

Introduction of the BAL in 1960 granted statutory rights to all Indonesian citizens and recognised **adat** as the 'basis for national land law' (Barber, Johnson and Hafild, 1994). The BAL recognises local **adat** systems in those places where registration of **adat** rights occurred, although only as long as they do not contradict national and State interests (Zerner, 1990). However, many communities have remained unaware of the need to obtain certificates of land title through the BAL registration process, with the result that unregistered **adat** rights have become the common property of the nation (Moniaga, 1993).

The BAL may lay down the foundations for land-use legislation, but the BFL holds supremacy over practices on national forest land. The BFL was introduced in 1966, when the 'New Order' regime overhauled and reorganised existing forestry institutions. This law empowered the national government to control, manage, and administer all designated forest lands, thereby giving the State primary legal jurisdiction over 'public' forest lands (Zerner, 1990). The government of Indonesia therefore owns all property rights to the natural forest, unless rights are temporarily assigned (for example, as logging concessions) or permanently transferred (for example, to transmigrants or other private parties).

Designation of forest areas establishes spatial and legal certainty over areas of State-controlled forest, where forest lands are classified as:

- production forests – which may be either normal production forests, limited production forests or conversion forests
- protection forests – used in sensitive areas such as important watersheds
- nature reserve or conservation forests
- recreation forests
- unclassified forests

The Consensus Forest Land-use Planning process provides a 'master plan' for the forest sector, through a province by province survey of forest areas. Forest classification categories are determined and recorded on 1:500,000 official Department of Forestry maps. Forest classification is based on criteria such as the slope, the rainfall patterns and the soil type and erosion potential, and not on criteria such as the location of local communities or their traditional uses for these forest lands.

Constitutionally, the BAL and BFL cannot be interpreted to mean that, unless registered, indigenous communities have no claim to local forest resources. However, because oral rather than written history defines **adat** boundaries and practices for households, families, clans, villages and tribes, traditional claims are easy to disregard. In effect, traditional tenure and **adat** rights are respected only until officially sanctioned development arrives, at which point the Ministry of Forestry has tended to operate as if it were the sole owner of the forest regardless of **adat** rights to ownership. It has proved difficult for local people to reclaim their land from Forest

Production Concession areas, regardless of whether their **adat** rights had been registered or not.

Although the development of small-scale logging operations for local markets by local communities is theoretically possible, in practice there are a variety of effective barriers. These take the form of a centralised system for licensing logging operations, and costly and complicated Forest Production Concession procedures. Thus the focus of local communities tends to be on the development of commercial uses for NTFPs.

Traditional management regimes have been undermined by various forces in recent years. The State's Village Administration Act of 1979 standardised local administrative structures and dissolved traditional leadership institutions. Formal speeches and declarations concerning forest policy continue to be dominated by themes of control or sedentarisation of swidden agriculture, and many other laws and regulations are often used against traditional resource management systems. Furthermore, 'new laws and regulations governing timber plantations, rattan, sago, and nipah concessions are completely silent on **adat**' even though complex **adat** systems of rights to these resources already exist (Barber *et al.*, 1994). This has eroded control and access mechanisms to traditionally managed forest areas. In addition, improved access to the most remote areas and increased expectations of indigenous peoples (especially the youth) have resulted in increased commercial extraction of NTFPs, which may or may not be controlled by traditional laws. Migrants and transmigrants have also turned to extraction of any NTFPs that the market demands when they can neither subsist nor accumulate the surpluses they anticipated in the jobs that initially attracted them, or as government schemes fail. A good example is the reported looting of Bentian and Pasir rattan gardens by young rattan cutters from outside the local area.

Peluso (1992) summarises the situation of forest-dwelling people by stating that 'traditional rights and local controls over the products of the forest have become entangled in a morass of government regulations and access laws'. The overall result is that forest products management has changed from a common property to an open access situation beyond effective control.

7.2 Past and Present Forest Utilisation in East Kalimantan

The nature of exploitation of the forests of East Kalimantan, the largest province in Indonesian Borneo, has changed substantially in recent decades. Trade between the Dayak inhabitants of interior Borneo and the outer world in forest products such as rattans, edible bird's nests, incense woods, tree resins and timber, has taken place for centuries (Peluso, 1992). Some of the plant species providing the NTFPs most valued by local people are listed in Box 7.1.

Box 7.1 Some of the Important Plant Species Yielding NTFPs Particularly Valued by the People of East Kalimantan

Rattan (**rotan**)	*Calamus* spp. are the most important rattan species, although other genera are used. Rattans are both cultivated and collected from natural stands. Their flexible but durable stems are used for a variety of subsistence purposes. In split form they are used for binding purposes or for weaving mats, baskets, and other items. In whole form they are used for constructing furniture and other household implements. They are also often a major source of cash income.
Bamboo (**bambu**)	Bamboos (*Bambusa* spp.) are also both cultivated and collected from natural stands. They serve various subsistence needs, their shoots, in particular, being an important food.
Honey trees (**kayu bilas**)	These comprise various emergent trees, most notably *Koompassia excelsa*. They are generally not planted, but are rather found and then managed. They are favoured as sites for honey bee hives, honey being an important product for both subsistence and cash purposes.
Eaglewood incense tree (**gaharu**)	If infected with a particular strain of fungus, this tree species, *Aquilaria malaccensis*, produces an aromatic wood which fetches an extremely high price. The tree is as yet uncultivated and is only found in natural stands.
Fruit trees	A wide variety of trees producing edible fruits occur in the forests of Kalimantan, and may be deliberately planted by local people. They include the durian (*Durio zibethinus*), rambutan (*Nephelium lappaceum*), langsat (*Lansium domesticum*), **cempedak** (*Artocarpus integra*), sugar palm (*Arenga pinnata*) and jackfruit (*Artocarpus heterophyllus*), amongst others.
Damar resin tree	**Damar** is the name given to the resin produced from trees in the genus *Agathis* and *Dipterocarpus*. The resin has a variety of local uses, including as an inflammable material for torches or as caulking material. It is also a valuable commodity for sale or exchange. **Damar**-producing trees are usually found and managed rather than cultivated.
Illipe nut tree (**tengkaweng**)	These trees belong to the genus *Shorea*. Their nuts are pressed for their buttery-like oil, for domestic consumption or sale. The most valued species are planted by local people.
Candlenut tree (**keminting**)	The nuts of this species, *Aleurites moluccana*, are used in many Javanese dishes. There is no traditional market for the nut in Kalimantan, but as the population of Javanese has grown over the last twenty years, a market has developed. The tree is generally found as a wild successional species

Until as recently as 1966, NTFPs were a more significant export from East Kalimantan than timber products. Since the late 1960s, however, the situation has reversed, with timber products now playing a pre-eminent role in exports. Commercial logging activities, although fuelling spectacular economic development for Indonesia, have been responsible for a massive increase in deforestation and forest degradation in East Kalimantan. They have also directly impinged upon local communities' use of forest resources and their opportunities for continuing traditional livelihoods.

7.3 The People of East Kalimantan

The population of Kalimantan is very heterogeneous. It includes **Punan** hunter gatherers and tribal swidden agriculturalists loosely termed Dayaks (e.g. **Kenyah, Kayan, Lundaye**) who tend to occupy the interior of Borneo, and more recent arrivals living in the coastal areas amongst whom are Malay groups (e.g. **Kutai, Banjir**), the **Bugis** from Sulawesi and the Chinese. Rapid changes to the population composition are occurring due to the government policy of transmigration, involving the relocation of people from the more populated islands such as Java and Bali to both the coastal and interior areas.

Community organisation amongst the interior forest-dwelling peoples varies somewhat with ethnic grouping. Villagers mostly make decisions about resource use as a community. They meet to plan the location of swidden fields, the schedule and workforce for swidden cultivation and regulations for the harvest and distribution of timber and NTFPs. Older men in the community, particularly those from the **paren** class, tend to take a dominant role in the decision-making. The **paren** represent a hereditary upper class of elites or aristocrats; access to this class is only gained by birth. Women of all classes generally take a less prominent role in decision-making, although this depends upon the use and value of the resource concerned.

Decisions on land allocation, based on **adat** principles, vary slightly amongst different communities. A typical case amongst most Dayak communities is that of the **Luangan** tribal swidden agriculturalists of Central and East Kalimantan (as documented by Weinstock and Vergara, 1990). Lands now or once cultivated as swidden plots may be under one of three main tenure categories. They may be owned permanently by the households which first cleared them from primary forest, or they can be borrowed from these permanent owners by other households, or they can be borrowed from, and later given back to, the village commons. Apart from this, some areas of village commons may have religious or cultural significance. These are managed by the community as protected forest reserves for specific purposes.

The use and ownership of different economic NTFPs may also be governed by a series of **adat** rights. Ownership is recognised of individual economic plants which have been planted for cash income, including rattan, rubber, coffee, coconut and fruit trees in gardens. Such rights can be sold for a specific duration or for perpetuity, and can be with or without ownership of the land on which they occur. Young planted rattan gardens are normally sold with the land, whereas mature rattan gardens are more likely to be sold on the basis of share harvesting without the land. Semi-domesticated or wild forest flora, such as rattan (mostly *Calamus* spp.), **damar** resin trees (*Agathis* spp. and *Dipterocarpus* spp.), **tengkaweng** (*Shorea* spp.) and **keminting** (*Aleurites moluccana*) are not subject to individual ownership but to community-level control over the resources within village territories. Where the commercial value of these NTFPs remains low, and competition for them is small, community control and an ethos of sharing remain effective. However, highly prized items, such as durian (*Durio zibethinus*) and honey trees (mostly *Koompassia excelsa*) often pass into private ownership, or are harvested on the basis of shares between a group of individuals.

A rattan garden owner in front of a clump of cultivated *Calamus caesius*. In some parts of East Kalimantan, Dayak farmers cultivate rattans as part of their swidden agriculture cycle.
Photograph: Mary Stockdale

7.4 The Kayan Mentarang Nature Reserve

The Kayan Mentarang Nature Reserve of East Kalimantan was created in 1980 in recognition of its high biological diversity and endemism. It encompasses forest ecosystems ranging, in the classification of Whitmore (1984), from lowland to montane tropical evergreen rain forest, and includes unique ecosystems such as heath forest or *Tristiana* forest. For the most part, these forests are dominated by trees from the family Dipterocarpaceae. A dry season occurs from July to August, with a main wet season from September to February. The mean annual rainfall is approximately 4,000 mm. Endangered animal species found in the reserve area include the clouded leopard, the sun bear and the Mueller's gibbon. Covering an area of 1.4 million ha, it is the largest protected and relatively undisturbed area in Borneo, and one of the largest in Southeast Asia. Figure 7.2 shows the location of the Nature Reserve, and of the villages within it which are mentioned in this report.

Figure 7.2   The Kayan Mentarang Nature Reserve Showing the Five Villages in which the 1992–4 WWF (Indonesia) Mapping Exercise Took Place

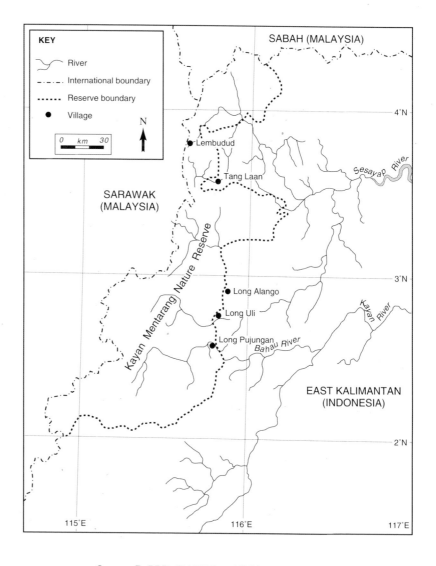

Source: RePPProT (1987) and field surveys by WWF (Indonesia) staff

The designation of Nature Reserve means that any form of resource use by local people is strictly prohibited. However, approximately 10,000 traditional peoples inhabit the reserve area, including Punans and Kenyah, Kayan and Lundaye Dayaks. Approximately half these people practise swidden cultivation, while the remainder farm mainly irrigated rice. Almost all rely upon forest products for subsistence and cash. Their form of life is traditional and largely sustainable. In fact, it could be argued that their use of resources in the past has had a major influence upon the 'natural' biodiversity seen today. In recognition of the fact that conservation in the Kayan Mentarang Nature Reserve can only be achieved with the support and participation of local people, an official team led by the Department of Forestry concluded, after an investigation in April, 1994, that the status of the reserve should be changed to National Park. This designation permits zonation of the park into areas in which sustainable traditional uses are permitted.

7.5 The Need for Forest Resource Assessment

Three forest resource assessment activities are described in this chapter. The first two were initiated at the request of the Directorate General of Forest Protection and Nature Conservation (DGFPNC), who encouraged the World Wide Fund for Nature (WWF)-Indonesia to determine appropriate zonation and management of the Kayan Mentarang Nature Reserve, with the participation of local people. This was addressed through:

- A pilot initiative to map the traditional territory and land-use system of one village.

- A subsequent exercise to draw similar maps for six further villages which developed participatory techniques more fully.

The third activity described is a pilot workshop to develop participatory techniques for inventory. This was conducted in a timber concession area outside the Kayan Mentarang Nature Reserve, and was initiated by local non-governmental organisations (NGOs) rather than at the request of the DGFPNC. Although this initiative was not a WWF (Indonesia) activity, the methods used were drawn from the participatory approach adopted by the WWF (Indonesia) mapping exercise.

Developing the methodologies for this work has been part of a learning process which is still in progress. All three activities well illustrate this point. A fundamental aspect of their development has been to involve local people in the collection of information, although the extent that they will play an active part in the final decision-making is uncertain. The collection of information for different purposes has, of course, required different techniques. Key purposes have included the following:

Although in two of the three activities described in this case study the need for forest resource assessment was identified by a government agency, as activities began it became clear that the need was also clearly perceived by the local people. Indeed, in some circumstances, they had already acted upon it.

- To secure tenure to land and rights to resources.

- To seek compensation for expected damage to land and resources.

- To manage resources on a sustainable basis.

Securing Tenure to Land and Rights to Resources

This purpose is of primary importance if rights to land and resources are still uncertain. In cases where there is no conflict between villages over the position of boundaries, the technique of mapping traditional territories is an appropriate tool for negotiating land tenure. In cases where boundaries are under dispute or where communities have settled more recently, experience has shown that mapping the location of resources used by the community reduces the likelihood of conflict, as it provides an 'objective' basis for seeking land tenure rights in negotiations with government. In one village visited by the WWF mapping team, a map of the community's territorial boundaries had already been drawn up by community members, without outside influence or assistance (see Box 7.3). This was done in response to the cutting of the boundary line of the Kayan Mentarang Nature Reserve within traditional lands. Such an initiative indicates recognition by local people of the need for mapping to secure tenure.

Seeking Compensation for Expected Damage to Land and Resources

The community concerned in the third activity described in this chapter was located inside a logging concession and had lost much of its traditional forest when it was clear-felled for an industrial tree plantation and transmigration project. On their own initiative, local people conducted an inventory of the resources that were about to be destroyed and estimated losses from areas that had already been affected (see Box 7.5). This again indicates a locally perceived need for the inventory of resources under certain circumstances.

Managing Resources on a Sustainable Basis

The extent to which communities are organised to manage resources varies. Some have traditional rules regulating the harvest and distribution of forest products, whereas others do not. No traditional management systems involve techniques such as mapping or inventory, which is not surprising in traditionally illiterate societies. However, the technique of participatory mapping of resources, introduced by WWF, has proved useful for discussing management practices. In some cases it has reinforced existing traditions, whilst in other cases it has provided the impetus for creating new ones. If there is enough harvesting pressure on a resource, a map of its location is clearly insufficient for sustainable management. It is important to have, in addition, some knowledge of the quantity and quality of the resource population, the natural population dynamics, and how the population responds to management. WWF-Indonesia has therefore initiated the development of participatory inventory methods for certain NTFPs. However, the extent to which local people perceive these methods as necessary for the management of their resources, and therefore adopt them, has yet to be determined.

The initiatives of local people in conducting their own mapping and inventory appears to reflect their most immediate priorities. Until secure rights to land and resources can be achieved in East Kalimantan, it is likely that securing tenure over resources and seeking compensation for their loss will continue to take priority over managing forest resources on a sustainable basis.

7.6 The Forest Assessment Process

A Pilot Initiative to Map the Traditional Territory and Land-use System of Long Uli Village

This mapping initiative began in 1992, when the Ford Foundation Social Forestry Project linked together WWF (Indonesia), the Ministry of Forestry and the East-West Centre (USA) in a pilot project to map the traditional territory of Long Uli village in Pujungan sub-district. This is described in greater detail in Sirait *et al.* (1994). The Long Uli lands overlap both the Kayan Mentarang Nature Reserve and a timber concession bordering the reserve. It was felt that mapping customary land uses and overlaying this map with government land-use maps of the area would facilitate more informed and co-ordinated management of these forests.

The mapping of the traditional territory of Long Uli was conducted first by sketch map, using information from interviews with key informants, cross-checked with other informants. Oral histories of the community and traditions relating to resource use were also documented. The traditional territory was found to consist of three distinct land-use categories. As shown in Figure 7.3, these are:

- Swidden cultivation areas.

- Traditional forest use areas, where villagers can harvest forest products including timber.

- Restricted forest use areas, where villagers cannot harvest timber and the harvesting of NTFPs is limited.

Figure 7.3   Land-use Classifications for the Region around Long Uli Village.
According to: a. Long Uli Village Traditional Law
b. The Ministry of Forestry Basic Forestry Law

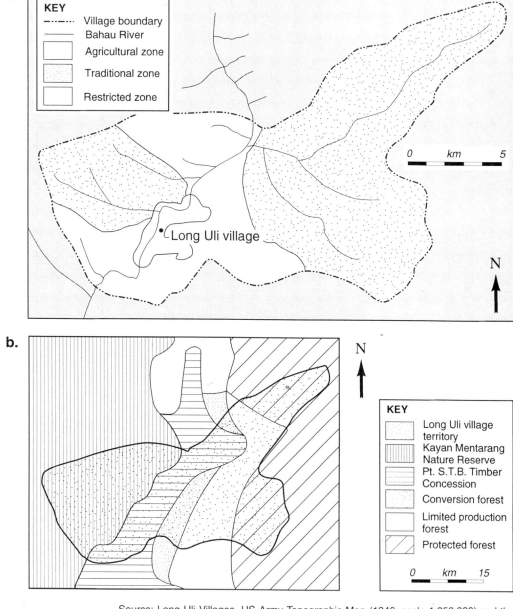

Source: Long Uli Villages, US Army Topographic Map (1946, scale 1:250,000) and the
Ministry of Forestry Consensus Forest Land-use (TGHK) Map (scale 1:500,000)

The exact latitude and longitude of points along the boundaries of the total area and the different land-use areas were then determined using a Global Positioning System (GPS). The particular system used can determine the spatial location of a point within 5–15 m accuracy. GPS recordings were also taken along the main river running through the traditional territory, as this river is common to all maps of the area and is easy to locate on the ground. The resulting data points were then digitised into a Geographic Information System (GIS), so that a map of the traditional territory could be created. Five maps used by the Indonesian Forest Department for forest planning and management activities were digitised and also entered into the GIS. The objective of the GIS analysis was to identify the position of the traditional territory of Long Uli and the amount of overlap with timber concessions, the nature reserve, and official forest land-use classifications. (The GPS equipment consisted of two Trimble Navigation receivers, one used as a base system and one as a mobile unit. The GIS used was ARC/INFO.)

A Dayak farmer taking a GPS reading of the site of his swidden field, Long Uli. The equipment used was older and less compact than that used in subsequent exercises. Photograph: Mary Stockdale

The involvement of local people in this first initiative was limited, and the map produced may have been over-simplified as a result.

The work was conducted by three outside technical staff, with local people acting as informants and guides. There was not enough time to involve or consult the community as a whole about the initiative. Time limitations, and the time-consuming nature of taking GPS readings, also meant that it was not possible to walk completely around the boundary of the traditional territory.

A constraint identified in this exercise was the limited ability of map-makers and social scientists to record the complex traditional resource management systems in the short time available. Since the information was obtained from key informants and not the community as a whole, some key groups (for example, women and young people) were excluded. As a result, information about their resource use was not obtained. Subsequent work which involved the participation of the community as a whole in villages neighbouring Long Uli revealed a greater complexity in resource management than that found in this exercise.

A further effect of using key informants rather than consulting the entire village was that the purpose of some of the technologies (notably the GPS) and the map-making exercise in general was not understood by everyone. Thus, although the mapping process provided a means of presenting the Long Uli traditional tenure and management system to the relevant government departments and to the outside world in general, it did not greatly empower people at the village level.

Technical problems identified and lessons learned are discussed for both this and the subsequent mapping exercise in Box 7.4.

Opportunities identified

This pilot initiative was very useful in demonstrating that sketch mapping, the recording of oral histories and traditions, and modern technologies such as GPS and GIS can be used to record customary land-use systems and compare villagers' perceptions of land ownership with those of the State. It was possible to use these maps to evaluate different means of co-ordinating indigenous resource-management systems with government-instituted systems of management. Given a favourable political climate, the maps could also be used as a basis for formal legal recognition and protection of customary forest-tenure arrangements.

Participatory Tools for Documenting Traditional Resource Use in Six Villages

Following the pilot mapping exercise, efforts to test and improve the relevant methodologies for mapping and zoning the Kayan Mentarang Nature Reserve were initiated. During one exercise, participatory rural appraisal (PRA) and participatory mapping methodologies were developed in order to fulfill three main objectives. These were to:

- Produce village resource- and land-use maps and discuss local resource management systems.

- Determine the views of local villagers on the recommended status change to National Park.

- Provide recommendations for the zonation of the conservation area and specify regulations for each zone.

This is discussed in greater depth in Momberg, Damus, Limberg, and ST. Padan (1994).

For the first stage of the PRA and participatory mapping exercise, two villages from each of three sub-districts (Pujungan, Krayan, Malinau) in the Kayan Mentarang Nature Reserve area were chosen. The results for four villages, Long Alango and Long Pujungan of Pujungan, and Tang Laan and Lembudud of Krayan, have been fully documented by Momberg *et al.* (1994) and ST. Padan, Momberg, Damus and Limberg (1994), respectively.

Details of the methods employed by the four-person WWF team may be summarised as follows:

- preliminary site visit
- PRA, especially sketch mapping and transect walks
- preparation of river and watershed base maps
- mapping workshop in a formal village assembly (**musyawarah**)
- immediate feedback to the village
- improving map accuracy using GPS

> The procedure adopted here may be usefully compared with that used in community forestry in Nepal (Chapter 6) and in the three National Parks in Uganda (Chapter 8).

Preliminary site visit

During this visit, the team introduces its approach to the village members, particularly the community leaders. The purpose of nature conservation is discussed, as is Nature Reserve and National Park legislation and zonation. The objectives of the PRA and participatory mapping project are also outlined and discussed. After this introduction, community leaders and members discuss amongst themselves whether they approve of the initiative. If approval is given, the team and the community leaders organise a formal assembly (**musyawarah**) of the entire community for the coming weekend or the second visit to the site.

PRA, especially sketch mapping and transect walks

During the preliminary visit (and subject to village approval), the team begins to collect information on resource management, settlement history, tenure systems and completed or current development activities. This is conducted using PRA techniques such as:

- secondary data collection
- resource sketch maps
- transect walks
- seasonal labour calendars
- analysis of formal and non-formal institutions and social organisations
- semi-structured interviews with collectors, middle-men and traders of NTFPs

- key informant interviews with local ecological experts, traditional leaders, government officials and change agents
- ranking of development problems and opportunities as a community exercise
- triangulation (cross-checking) of information

Preparation of river and watershed base maps

This is carried out in preparation for the formal village assembly. As no *a priori* decision was made regarding which scale of map to use, both 1:50,000 and 1:100,000 maps were made using a panthograph. The scale depended upon the reference maps used, which included river maps (by BAPPEDA, dated 1987, scale 1:100,000), topographical maps (by JANTOP/DITTOP, dated 1977, scale 1:50,000) and radar maps (by BAKOSURTANAL, dated 1986, scale 1:50,000). The maps were drawn on tracing paper with Rapido inkpens, enabling corrections or adjustments of rivers and other features. Interpretation of the radar maps using information from villagers provided the most accurate base map of rivers, watersheds and other geographical features.

Radar maps are notoriously difficult to interpret, but in this case they were used to good effect through supplementation with local knowledge.

Mapping workshop in a formal village assembly (musyawarah)

At the beginning of the workshop, the team repeats the introduction given at the preliminary visit, both in Indonesian and the local language. This time a map showing the location of the Kayan Mentarang Nature Reserve boundaries is also presented, with a written explanation of the difference between a Nature Reserve and a National Park. The village assembly is then divided into three or more groups, depending upon the number of participants, with one facilitator per group. Groups are based on gender and age. Usually they are separated into older men, younger men, and women, as resource maps and zoning recommendations tend to differ on this basis (see Box 7.2).

The mapping process is divided into three steps:

- Rechecking the accuracy of the base map.

- Drawing a village resource map, using marking pens of different colours to differentiate categories of resources or land use.

- Discussion and drawing of a zonation model, based on the village resource map.

The groups then reassemble, and each group presents its results. A consensus-oriented decision-making process (**musyawarah**) defines zoning recommendations and regulations for each zone of the conservation area.

Box 7.2 Differences between Gender, Age and Ethnic Groups Revealed in the Mapping Workshop

The same general trends between women's, older men's and younger men's perceptions were found in all villages where such group division was made. The women tended to map resources close to the village in greater detail than the men, but were less aware of the location of resources farther afield. The women emphasised that forests close to the villages should be protected as they provide important products for daily subsistence, such as vegetables, spices, medicinal plants, rattan, bamboo, grasses, leaves for wrapping food and firewood, which are all usually collected by women. Women also emphasised that forests around sources of drinking water should be protected. In Long Alango, the women asked that a dispute about land with another village be resolved. This involvement of women is not usual in Dayak village assemblies, and was encouraged by the separation of the village assembly into gender groups.

The men, both old and young, concentrated more on mapping the areas where game or commercial forest products could be found, and on the location of the boundaries of the protected forest territories (in Pujungan subdistrict) or the entire village territories. They were more concerned with restricting outsiders from access to these areas than were the women. The older men's groups tended to be dominated by members of the **paren** (upper) class, a situation that was less evident in the younger men's groups. The older men mapped the individually-owned agricultural lands and pastures in more detail than the younger men. They were also more concerned about resolving land disputes with neighbouring villages, maintaining traditional management regulations, and recommending conservation zones which limited access even to community members. The younger men mapped more areas of recreation or interest, such as waterfalls, abandoned villages and stone graves, and had the most detailed knowledge of the location of commercial NTFPs.

The young men were less aware of or concerned about the traditional regulations on resource management than the older men and sometimes did not agree with the restrictions on resource management proposed by the latter. The mapping workshop provided a forum for discussion of these differences, with the result that the views of the older men prevailed. However, this difference between the two groups may indicate that in future less attention will be paid to existing traditions and to conservation.

In Tang Laan village, where the WWF team expected possible marginalisation of the more recently settled Punan members of the village assembly, a mapping exercise with the Punan was conducted in advance of the meeting. This involved the moulding of three-dimensional topographical maps from sand. The exercise demonstrated that the Punan considered a much larger area to be important for resource use or cultural reasons (such as old settlements and graveyards) than the non-Punan members. Subsequent to this, a river base map was prepared which covered this larger area, and in the village assembly the Punan had the opportunity to give information and opinions on this area, about which the non-Punan members had little knowledge.

The last step is the election of a village committee, to work jointly with the Forestry Department on boundary identification and demarcation, implementation of park zonation and safeguarding of its regulations. Generally, three representatives are selected from each of the three groups by the people present at the village assembly. However, in Tang Laan 'location', which comprises five resettled villages, three representatives were chosen from each village. Village committees were elected for the first four villages (in Pujungan and Krayan subdistricts) in this mapping exercise, but not for the next two villages (in Malinau subdistrict). The step was discontinued because the elected village committees did not subsequently develop any activities, as government co-operation and support for their work had not been secured (and remains uncertain).

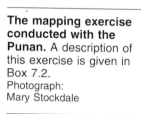

The mapping exercise conducted with the Punan. A description of this exercise is given in Box 7.2.
Photograph: Mary Stockdale

Immediate feedback to the village

After the village assembly, WWF staff duplicated the maps to leave one copy in the village. They also typed a short report on the results of the village assembly, including the recommendations for the location and management of the different zones. This report was then stenciled to provide several copies for the villagers.

Improving map accuracy using GPS

Following village work, the WWF team upgraded the accuracy of the participatory sketch maps using a procedure called

187

'rubbersheeting'. This procedure, which can be run on GIS software, involves shifting the points on digitised radar maps so that they correspond more closely to GPS locations recorded in the field. GPS recordings of villages and river confluences were obtained in Pujungan subdistrict in order to correct the positional inaccuracies of the radar base maps (Snel, 1993). In all three subdistricts, GPS recordings were obtained of the positions of boundaries of important areas which do not follow the natural topography, or important features such as graveyards and archeological sites. (The GPS model used was Magellan Nav 5000 PRO.)

An example of the maps that resulted from this exercise is provided in Figure 7.4.

Lessons for Future Workshops

The WWF team found that trying out different PRA tools in a village during the preliminary visit sometimes created confusion both for themselves and the community.

The team recommended:
- better integration of the various PRA methods
- clarification of the objectives for each PRA tool
- explanation of these objectives to the community

Of the PRA tools used, sketch mapping and transect walks proved to be the best preparatory tools for the participatory mapping workshop. This is because they assist the team and local people to view community problems and opportunities from a spatial perspective. Sketch maps show boundaries, infrastructure, topography, land-use systems and important social and cultural features. They were easily understood by all villagers, probably because they corresponded to the villagers' mental maps of their territories. Transect walks add more specific data on species composition, soil type, and resource management activities. Furthermore, data from informants can be cross-checked by observation.

For the participatory mapping workshop, the WWF team were of the opinion that three facilitators were the absolute minimum required, and that more facilitators would make the running of the workshop smoother. They also decided that the time spent in the village might have been too short; it was concluded that one week should be the absolute minimum. In cases where there are contentious issues, it may not be possible to resolve all problems in one mapping session. It is important that maps are seen as part of a *process* and that they are open to modification as this process continues.

Figure 7.4 Zoning Suggestions for Long Alango Village made by:
a. The Community
b. The Women's Group

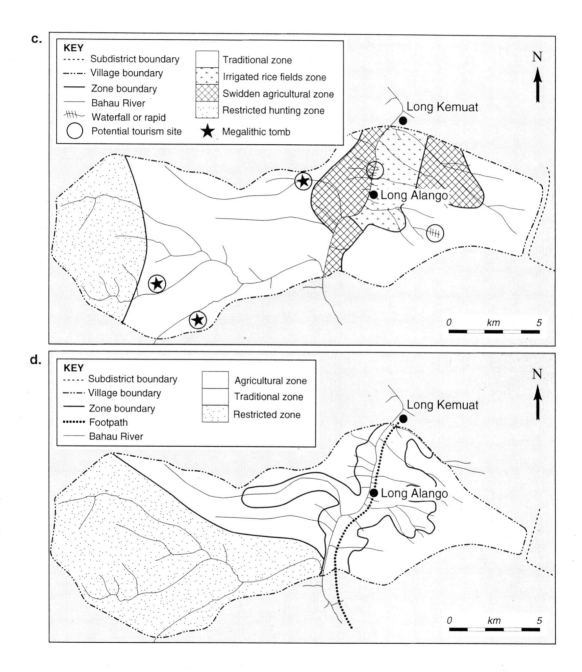

(continued/...)

Figure 7.4 *(continued)*
c. The Younger Men's Group
d. The Older Men's Group

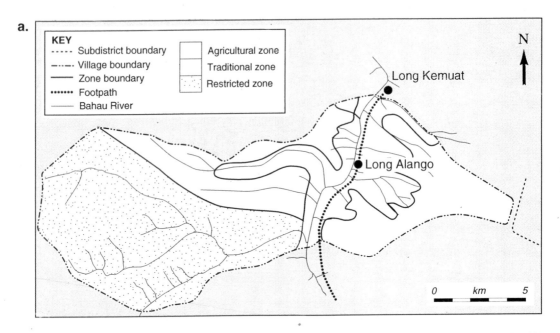

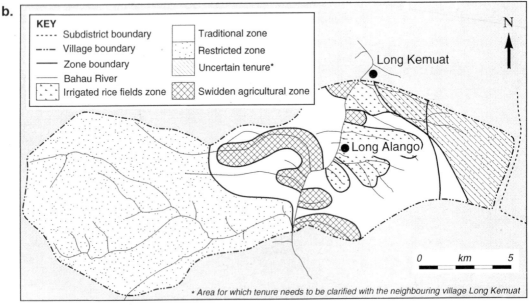

Source: The Participatory Rural Appraisal (PRA) in Long Alango Village, East Kalimantan; and River Locations, BAKOSURTANAL Radar Maps (1988, scale 1:50,000)

Training

Two local people have already received training in PRA and mapping techniques as part of this initiative, since two of the WWF team members are university-educated Dayaks originating from the Kayan Mentarang Nature Reserve area. (The two other members of the team are not of local origin.) In order to build the capacity of local communities to replicate the participatory approach, the WWF team is planning to hold workshops to train village facilitators.

Villagers have already demonstrated self-sufficiency in drawing informative sketch maps (see Box 7.3 for a description of a community mapping initiative). However, more accurate sketch maps can be produced through the use of the most accurate base maps available and upgrading the use of GPS data. The GPS/GIS initiative (also funded by WWF) has been run by two technical advisers who are not of local origin. However, they are training two local people to create base maps from radar maps, to take GPS recordings in the field, and to use these data to upgrade sketch maps by 'rubbersheeting'. It is difficult for villagers to obtain radar maps for use as base maps (as it requires Department of Forestry and military clearance). Furthermore, GPS equipment is expensive (currently, even the least expensive GPS unit costs approximately US $400.00). Therefore, support by WWF or possibly other local non-governmental organisations in supplying this equipment will be necessary.

A Dayak WWF trainee taking a GPS reading. The receiver used here is more compact than the one that was available for the Long Uli mapping exercise. Photograph: Mary Stockdale

Another aim of the GPS/GIS initiative is to feed spatial information about the Kayan Mentarang area into a GIS database (in this case, using a GIS software package called IDRISI). The maps created during the participatory mapping exercises can, after upgrading by 'rubbersheeting', be fed into a GIS database. Working with the GIS programmes requires a fairly high level of computer literacy, and therefore has to be run by a technical adviser. It is unlikely that the GIS database could be run by local people in the near future, or even by local WWF staff. However, local people can help in providing information for the database (such as by operating a GPS to obtain the exact location of an encroachment on their territory). As discussed in a later section, it is hoped that they will participate in, and benefit from, the various management applications of GIS. The involvement of WWF or a similar large organisation is necessary for the GIS component of the project, because of the capital cost of the equipment. The GIS software must also be run from a town or city of sufficient size for a reasonably reliable source of electricity to be assured.

Box 7.3   Community Mapping Initiative in Tang Laan Village, Krayan Subdistrict

One village presented the WWF mapping team, on their arrival, with a map of the community territory which they had already drawn. This had been in response to the field demarcation of Kayan Mentarang Nature Reserve boundaries by members of the government mapping division BIPHUT. A village team, consisting of local leaders, was given responsibility by the community for the mapping and demarcation of boundaries in the field. The map, drawn on a scale of 1:37,500 and incorporating 10 colours, depicted both the present village 'location' and abandoned village sites, as well as agricultural and forested lands used by the community. The community territory in this map covered a smaller area than in the map drawn later during the WWF workshop, because it was limited by the subdistrict boundary on one side. The WWF workshop map, which depicted resource use, ancestral land and old village sites, showed that in fact the community used resources in forests beyond the Krayan subdistrict boundary.

General Lessons Learned

Disagreement within villages

Ensuring that true consensus is achieved is never easy. WWF team members considered that older leaders sometimes dominated the village assemblies, to the extent that disagreements might not have been resolved to everyone's satisfaction. On the other hand, in one village, members of the assembly openly chastised an unpopular leader for not restricting access to protected forest by outsiders, as was required by customary law (**adat**). The division of the assembly into groups by age, gender and social standing attempted to give more marginalised groups a greater voice, and apparently succeeded to a certain extent (see Box 7.2).

Some disagreements within villages can be prevented by advance preparation. In the places where a number of villages had been resettled in one larger village 'location' approximately twenty years previously, the question whether it would be better to draw joint resource maps for all the villages or separate ones was discussed amongst village leaders. Invariably the villages agreed to hold a joint meeting, with the result that it was decided to manage resources in a more co-ordinated fashion than had occurred in the past. This probably reduced the potential for conflict within the 'location'.

The WWF team recognised that not all decisions can or should be made in one session. Different communities were seen as being as different stages in their ability to discuss and take over the co-management of natural resources. The final steps in the mapping workshop, including designating zones, developing regulations for zones or electing a village committee for zone management, were therefore not necessarily an outcome of the first mapping workshop in all villages. As noted previously, participatory mapping is considered by the WWF team to be part of a process, not an end in itself. Unresolved questions can always be examined in future meetings.

Disagreement between villages

It is possible for disputes between villages to be heightened by the mapping process, especially if one village unilaterally declares boundaries with which other villages do not agree. However, the participatory mapping process also provides a means of resolving disputes between villages. One way in which the WWF team defused boundary conflicts was by inviting representatives from neighbouring villages to the mapping workshops of a chosen village. The result was that the villages Long Alango and Long Kemuat in Pujungan subdistrict and Tang Laan and Long Layu in Krayan subdistrict chose to designate the areas under dispute as forest utilisation zones to be shared and managed by both communities.

Disagreement with local government

There was some concern on the part of both WWF and government representatives that villagers might see the maps as being more official than they actually were, and that disputes between government and villagers would result. As a result, one subdistrict head refused to give a stamp of approval to a community resource map and confiscated it from the villagers, saying that the determining of boundaries was not the job of WWF but of government. In contrast, another subdistrict head endorsed the project with enthusiasm, seeing it as a tool for resolving the existing dispute between local people and the government over the marking of the Kayan Mentarang Nature Reserve boundary within traditional land by the Forestry Department mapping division (BIPHUT).

Realising that focusing on territory boundaries in the participatory mapping exercise increases the risk of creating boundary disputes, the WWF mapping team eventually decided to put less emphasis on the exact location of boundaries and more on the location of important resources used by the community. This reduced the risk of disputes and supported legitimate claims for territory by identifying important resource areas which are actually used by the villagers.

From these experiences, the WWF team decided that to gain the support of the local government it was important to:

- Provide clear explanations of the maps and their legal standing to villagers as well as the relevant government officials at the subdistrict and district levels.

- Include subdistrict and BIPHUT government officials in the participatory mapping workshops.

- Hold subdistrict and district workshops in which villager representatives could present their resource maps and recommendations to the relevant governmental and non-governmental institutions.

- Seek official acceptance of the participatory mapping methodology by the Forest Protection and Nature Conservation division of the Forestry Department, in the form of a Letter of Agreement.

It is hoped that the participatory techniques used in the mapping workshops will enable villagers to speak directly to government and encourage government to listen to villagers. However, there is some concern that the presence of government representatives at the workshops could inhibit full participation by villagers.

By adopting this approach with subdistrict and district government, it is hoped that the aims of the initiative will be better understood. If so, it is possible that not only will there be more support for WWF activities, but government staff might themselves adopt a more participatory approach to discussions and decision-making with local people.

Possible conflict with conservation objectives

The WWF team is attempting to reach a compromise between the conservation objectives of the Reserve and the development goals of the community. As conservation was discussed in the initial talk given by the WWF team, other objectives besides those generated by the community may have influenced the mapping process. The communities generally agreed with the concepts of protecting endangered species and managing resources sustainably, although they may not see them as high priorities. Thus it was uncertain how truly enthusiastic the communities were about the restricted use zones or core zones that they proposed in the mapping workshop. However, in many senses, it was felt that the interests of the community and the Reserve coincided. For example, in the Pujungan subdistrict the communities proposed to include all their village land in the proposed Park territory, as this would provide better opportunities for them than having part of their village land in a logging concession.

Possible misuse of resource-use maps

The WWF mapping team is anxious that the maps are not misused. For example, if the exact location of edible birds' nest caves is indicated, outsiders with access to the maps may find them and steal from them, although this has not yet happened. For most resources this is not thought to be a problem, as everybody who lives in the area is aware of their general location. For this reason, the WWF team considered that in future participatory mapping exercises it would be important to discuss this potential misuse with villagers and emphasise that valuable resources need not have their exact location marked on the map.

Box 7.4 Technical Problems and Lessons Learned from the Use of GPS/GIS in the Kayan Mentarang Reserve

During the original mapping exercise, the main technical problem found was the limited accuracy of the government maps. The position of the main river on the three most accurate of these maps differed by as much as 2 km at some points. Some of the inaccuracy was probably due to insufficient ground checking when making the maps. Probably another cause was errors in digitising the maps into the GIS system. The maximum scale of the government maps used in the pilot initiative was 1:100,000. At this scale they had to be enlarged to 1:50,000. This caused the boundary lines, drawn by large pens on the original map, to be very crude.

In the second initiative, base maps of watersheds and river systems were created using 1:50,000 radar maps. Interpretation is necessary in areas of the radar maps which are obscured by shadows. As might be expected, the team found particular difficulty in interpreting radar maps of areas with which they were not highly familiar. They thus identified a need for obtaining information by 'travel truthing' (asking individuals familiar with the area to indicate where errors might exist on the maps) or 'ground checking' (visiting the areas themselves), and correcting the maps accordingly.

Unfortunately, the positional accuracy of the radar maps was found to be poor, with errors of 1–4 km when compared with highly accurate GPS readings made in the field. This may be because the radar map was overlaid with an inaccurate grid, or because of distortion from photogrammetric equipment such as the camera lens. This makes it particularly important to obtain GPS data in the field in order to upgrade or correct the radar maps using the 'rubbersheeting' procedure.

Obtaining accurate GPS readings is an expensive exercise. The most accurate method, which obtains locations within 5–15 m of the true position, uses the process of 'differentiation'. This is also the most time-consuming method, with one or at most two locations obtained per day.[1] Alternative methods are less time-consuming but also less accurate. They include the 'running average' and 'POS' methods, with accuracies of 75 m and 300 m, respectively. The choice of method depends on a number of considerations, such as the desired accuracy, the scale of the exercise (for example, the entire nature reserve or the protected forest of one village), the available time, and the number of locations to be obtained. An extremely high degree of accuracy may not be necessary for the purposes for which these mapping exercises are conducted.

Main sources: Snel (1993, 1994)

Opportunities Identified

Villagers seldom have the opportunity for any form of political participation. On the whole, the participatory mapping workshops were enthusiastically received by the communities, and many neighbouring communities have requested similar workshops, asking WWF to visit them and facilitate the mapping of their territories. The maps and information generated from PRA and participatory mapping, and the process of participatory mapping itself, were found to have three main uses. These are:

- Supporting the change of status from Nature Reserve to National Park.

- Revising the legal boundaries of community lands.

- Developing village resource management plans.

Supporting the change of status from Nature Reserve to National Park

This is the most immediate use of the maps. Village resource maps and zoning suggestions could be used in a dialogue between government, WWF and the communities on the creation of zones for the proposed Kayan Mentarang National Park.

Revising the legal boundaries of community lands

Generally when tenurial maps of customary land are prepared, as has been done in non-forested areas of some provinces by the Director General of Agriculture (in the Ministry of Home Affairs), there is no official process for consultation with the local people. However, clear and commonly agreed boundaries are essential for the protection of forests within the Nature Reserve/proposed National Park. Participatory mapping can be a tool for determining boundaries based on 'objective' information on resource use, and on discussions both within and between villages, as well as between villages and the government. If agreement can be reached between all these parties, the boundaries should then gain legal status.

Developing village resource management plans

The maps provide a communication tool for discussing resource management plans for forest zones within the proposed National Park. During the mapping project, the communities decided on different management zones and discussed regulations for the management of each. Villagers recommended that some areas be designated as 'buffer zones' without restrictions on use, and removed from National Park territory. These included swidden cultivation areas, wet rice fields, gardens, agroforests, and cattle grazing pastures. They recommended that other areas be provided legal protection as a National Park, but used by local people under a sustainable management system. These areas included:

- 'Traditional forest-use zones', where outsiders were to be forbidden entry and forest could not be cleared although hunting and harvesting of forest products would be allowed.

- 'Restricted forest-use zones', where, in addition to the above regulations, there would be restrictions on hunting and harvesting of forest products.

- 'Core zones', where even local people would be forbidden access.

In some cases, these discussions on resource management and its regulation resulted in the reinforcement of traditional laws, such as the prohibition of outsiders, that in more recent times have not been followed. The maps provided a forum for older members to teach younger members about traditional management practices. In other cases, new regulations were agreed upon, such as prohibitions on hunting or on felling timber in certain areas. The maps highlighted both problems, such as an area degraded by fire or areas under dispute with other villages, and opportunities, such as a suitable site for rehabilitation or a small hydroelectric project.

Future Developments in the PRA/Mapping Exercises

The WWF team has yet to finish all the maps and reports for the six communities visited. Once completed, the exercise will be evaluated internally within WWF. It is then hoped to consolidate the advances made through the following activities:

- Return visits to the six communities for their evaluation of the project.

- A district-level workshop with officials, during which village representatives will explain the participatory approach and present the results of the participatory mapping exercise to the officials.

- The seeking of legal recognition of participatory mapping as a tool for community involvement in land and resource use, in the form of a Letter of Agreement from the Forest Protection and Nature Conservation division of the Forestry Department.

- Training workshops for village representatives in participatory mapping techniques, as well as continuing the mapping process in other villages in the Kayan Mentarang Nature Reserve area.

- The use of GIS overlay and distance capabilities to help delineate zones in the proposed National Park and recommend the adjustment of legal boundaries. This would be conducted in a manner similar to that of the Long Uli village pilot initiative described earlier. This process will be highly dependent upon the quality of data input and the criteria used. It is therefore important for the WWF to concentrate on obtaining high quality data from the field and on maintaining a fully participatory decision-making approach in developing criteria.

The Development of Participatory Inventory Methods in Support of People Living in a Timber Concession Area

In 1992, field research to develop a method for the inventory of rattan was initiated by a non-local WWF research associate in the Kayan Mentarang Nature Reserve. This research resulted in the development of methods for sampling and measuring rattan, based upon criteria such as accuracy, precision, and efficiency in terms of time (Stockdale, 1994). However, these methods were not evaluated in terms of their potential for local people's participation. For this reason, following the development of the participatory methodologies for mapping described above, a workshop was held in December 1994 to develop participatory methods for the inventory of not only rattans, but all important NTFPs. The participants numbered three Dayaks and four non-Dayaks (Javanese or Europeans), representing local farmers, NGO foresters and NGO legal aid advisers. Because of constraints of time and money, the workshop was held in a region of East Kalimantan which was more accessible to major cities than the Kayan Mentarang Nature Reserve.

In the region selected for the workshop, forests near the villages are mainly individually-owned secondary forests in various stages of swidden cultivation. They are called 'rattan gardens', because during the rice planting stage of swidden cultivation, Dayak farmers plant commercial rattan species as well as honey, fruit and timber trees, which grow up with the recovering fallow. The ownership of these gardens by Dayak farmers has not been recognised by the government. Instead, many of the gardens have been classified as 'Limited Production Forest' by the Ministry of Forestry, because of their low volume of commercial timber species (below 20 m^3/ha). They have accordingly been scheduled for clear-cutting in order to prepare sites for industrial tree plantations and transmigration programmes. The Dayak communities, and local NGOs working with them, perceive a need for inventories of the resources in these rattan gardens to seek compensation for their loss. Evidence for this is an inventory conducted by one community on its own initiative (as described in Box 7.5).

Box 7.5   A Community Inventory Initiative in East Kalimantan

In response to an industrial plantation/transmigration project that was causing the clearance of their rattan gardens, villagers conducted an inventory of their resources to seek compensation for their losses. It is instructive to compare the methods used in this community inventory initiative with those developed in the workshop.

The way in which villagers calculated the compensation due to them for each resource was from the product of the following estimates:

- The total annual production of the resource.
- The number of years over which the resource would be expected to be produced (this was greatly underestimated, as it only considered the lifetime of an individual tree or clump).
- The current market value for one unit of the resource.

An inventory was conducted in order to calculate the total production per year of each resource. In the rattan gardens, the resources enumerated included five species of rattan, one species of bamboo, various species of honey trees and sixteen species of fruit tree or plant. The data recorded for each resource were:

- *Rattan*: number of clumps and dry weight (kilograms) per clump per year, as rattan is sold by weight in this area.
- *Bamboo*: number of clumps and number of harvestable shoots per clump per year.
- *Honey trees*: number of trees, number of bee hives per tree and number of litres of honey per bee hive per year.
- *Fruit trees*: number of trees/plants and number of fruit/bunches of fruit/kilograms of fruit per year.

The number of clumps, trees or plants of each resource were counted in the field. Each resource was then quantified in the units by which it was sold in the local market. These quantities were estimated by local farmers, using their knowledge of past harvests. The accuracy of these estimates was not tested.

The community did not develop a sampling design of the type developed in the workshop inventory. Instead, individual farmers conducted a 100% enumeration of all the resources in each of their gardens. However, there was one large area which had already been cleared before the owners had had the opportunity to conduct an inventory. The quantities of resources in this area were estimated from the quantities per unit of land of the other gardens. The accuracy of this estimate was also not tested. Interestingly, the unit of land used was not in terms of land area, but in terms of the amount of rice that could be expected to be planted in it (in units of 'tins' of rice). This is the commonly used local unit, and takes into account not just the land area, but its quality (for example, in areas patched with swamps or rocky outcrops more land is needed to grow one unit of rice than in areas of well drained, deep soil). This way of perceiving land is likely to create more directly comparable units for estimating quantities of resources. However, it is based on judgments by local farmers and may not be considered sufficiently 'scientific' by the government officials from whom compensation is being sought.

The Procedure Developed for Conducting a Rattan Garden Inventory

During the course of the workshop, a procedure was developed for conducting an inventory of a rattan garden. The first three stages, in particular, should be conducted with the local people. All subsequent work should also be explained to them, even if they might not be able to participate fully in it. The stages are as follows:

- Determine the purpose of the inventory.

- Draw a sketch map of the area to be inventoried.

- Determine the data to be collected in the inventory.

- Develop a sampling design.

- Carry out the line cutting, data collection and mapping in the field.

- Draw a more accurate map, and calculate the areas of the strata and the total garden.

- Calculate the quantity of each resource, and the standard error.

Determination of the purpose of the inventory
It is important that this is discussed, and that all concerned are in agreement over the purpose of the inventory. In this case, the purpose was to assess the total economic value of all important NTFPs in the rattan garden.

Sketch mapping of the area to be inventoried
In East Kalimantan, access to government maps is often difficult, and those available are mostly on too small a scale to provide a good indication of the location of rattan garden boundaries. Accurate maps of the area may have to be made by the inventory team. An initial sketch map, drawn with the participation of the rattan garden owner(s), is useful for planning the sampling design. Following this, a more accurate map can be drawn in conjunction with the inventory itself. The more accurate map is necessary for estimating the land area.

Determination of the data to be collected in the inventory
The decisions made about the data to be collected included:

Which resources to sample? The quantity and perceived value of the resource determines whether it should be sampled or whether it should be completely enumerated. Both bamboo and rattan clumps were of sufficient quantity in the rattan garden for sampling to save considerable time and money, compared with 100% enumeration. However, in the workshop, bamboo was not considered of high enough commercial value to be worth including in the inventory, and therefore only rattan was sampled. All the (relatively few) honey and fruit trees were individually known, and were therefore completely enumerated using the community sketch map as a source of information. The accuracy of this information was checked during sampling operations in the field.

Which categories of data to record for each resource? For rattan, these categories included:

- **Species** – in the workshop, there was only one planted species, *Calamus caesius*.
- **Age class of each shoot in the clump** – as only stems with harvestable lengths over 8 m are harvested, these age classes included 'juvenile' if the shoot was stemless, immature' if the dried or harvestable part of the stem was under 8 m, and mature' if the dried part of the stem was over 8 m.

Which measurements to record for each resource? For rattan, these measurements included:

- **Number of clumps.**
- **Number of shoots of each age class per clump.**
- **For mature shoots, estimated length categories** of the dried part of the stem in 4 m length units (since this is the unit length by which rattans are sold in this area of East Kalimantan). Further details on stem length estimation and measurement in rattan are given in Box 7.6.

Following these decisions, a tally sheet should be designed to facilitate the recording of the data required.

Developing a sampling design
In the workshop inventory, one rattan garden was selected to be used as an example. Decisions were made on the following topics:

- criteria for stratification
- systematic versus random sampling
- line plot sampling versus strip sampling
- shape, size and orientation of the sampling unit or plot

Criteria for stratification. Stratification, or the sub-division of the population into strata, aims to derive parts (strata) that are each more homogeneous than the whole. If the sampling units within a stratum are similar (ie. if within-stratum variance is small) compared with the sampling units in other strata (that is, if the between-strata variance is relatively large), then the precision of the overall estimate for the whole population is enhanced. Thus, the workshop participants decided to stratify different areas of the garden by their age since burning for swidden, as this corresponds to the age of the rattan clumps and many of the trees which have been planted or which have naturally regenerated in these areas. Stratification was conducted after sampling, as there were no good maps of the location of strata in the rattan garden. Thus, the allocation of the sampling units was not optimal for enhancing precision. However, stratification was conducted as information on resource quantity at the stratum level was considered to be valuable.

Systematic versus random sampling. In systematic sampling, plots are selected according to a regular pattern, whereas in random sampling, plots are selected according to the laws of chance. Systematic sampling is not as statistically valid as random sampling, as there is the risk of bias if the sampling pattern matches or partially matches some periodic pattern of variance in the population being sampled. However, an advantage of systematic sampling is that the area can be mapped at the same time as conducting the inventory. For this reason it was chosen for the workshop inventory.

Line plot sampling versus strip sampling. These two systematic methods were both tested by participants. Line plot sampling involves cutting a line and sampling a systematic selection of plots along the line, whilst strip sampling involves cutting a line and sampling contiguous plots along it. Both methods are equally valid statistically, but workshop participants preferred the latter method. They felt that they obtained more data for the same amount of time spent in cutting the line. A study by Tandug and Lasmarias (1984) of rattan inventory in the Philippines has also found strip sampling to be more cost-efficient than line plot sampling (see also Tandug, 1978). A method is more cost-efficient if it achieves the same amount of precision (measured in terms of the sampling error) as another method, but for less cost (measured in terms of time). The lines in the workshop inventory were 100 m apart.

Shape, size, orientation and sampling intensity of the sampling unit or plot. Rattan distribution has been found to be related to topography. Thus for the same plot size, sampling rattan using long, narrow plots oriented perpendicular to the contour lines is more cost-efficient than sampling rattan using square plots, as more of the variation is encompassed in the plot (Stockdale and Wright, 1995). In the inventory workshop, the strip comprised contiguous 10×30 m^2 plots, as a 10 m width was convenient for sampling clumps 5 m to either side of a central line. Furthermore, plot sizes larger than 300 m^2 were found to be less cost-efficient than smaller plots in the study by Stockdale and Wright (1995). The orientation of the lines cut from a baseline was such that they covered as much topographical variation as possible. The sampling intensity was 10%.

Box 7.6 Estimation and Measurement of Stem Length in Rattans

Stem length is the most important measurement for rattan, as, unlike in trees, the growth of rattan stems occurs as an increase in length alone. It is not related to the diameter. The total length of a stem is not equivalent to the commercial length. Only the lower-most dried portion of the stem, where the leaf sheaths have been sloughed off, is considered to be commercially mature. For the purpose of management, both total and commercial length are important measurements. For the purpose of economic valuation, only commercial length is important. It is difficult to obtain accurate measurements of length, whether total or commercial, without destroying the resource or spending considerable time obtaining estimates.

For this reason, harvesting time would be the ideal time for sampling rattan, as the measured, rather than estimated, total and commercial lengths could be obtained at a time when the stems are being cut anyway. Not all clumps in a rattan garden are harvested at one time, as they range in age. They are first harvested at six to ten years of age, and every three (or more) years thereafter. Therefore, measurements of a particular harvest would have to be used to check, and perhaps develop a model for correcting, the accuracy of the estimates of the remaining stems.

Since the inventory workshop was not held at harvesting time, it was necessary to estimate the total length of each stem. This was done by participants on the first day, both visually and by triangulation, using a ruler as a hypsometer (as described in Stockdale and Power, 1994). Commercial length could then be estimated by multiplying the total length by 0.6 m (this was the mean ratio of commercial: total length determined by Stockdale, 1994 for *Calamus caesius* in the Kayan Mentarang Nature Reserve). Participants did not find any major difference between these two methods in terms of accuracy or difficulty, although tests by Stockdale and Power (1994) have shown mean estimates produced from the more objective ruler method to be more accurate than, although as precise as, those of the visual method.

Interestingly, the rattan garden owner proved to be very adept at visually estimating stem length of rattans, compared with non-local participants. However, he greatly over-estimated the total area of his rattan garden during the initial sketch mapping. This may have been due to his unfamiliarity with describing land in units of area (rather than the traditional method described in Box 7.5). Due reference should be made to local people's skill in estimation, but for inventory to be credible, the accuracy of local estimates should be tested against a sample of true measurements.

As both these estimation methods took considerable time, and the accuracy that they afforded was unnecessary for the purposes of seeking compensation, the participants decided after the first day that they would prefer to make crude estimates of commercial length. The crude stem length categories chosen were in units of 4 m, as this is the unit in which stems are sold in local markets.

A workshop participant estimating the length of rattan stems using a ruler as a hyposmeter.
Photograph: Sarah Cooke

Line cutting, data collection and mapping in the field

The workshop experience indicated that a minimum four-person team is necessary for fieldwork. One has responsibility for drawing the map, and the other three cut the line and then collect and record the inventory data. The person drawing the map records the boundaries of the entire garden and all strata (i.e. all areas of the same age since burning for swidden) within the garden, as well as other features of interest such as topography, streams, and the location of honey and fruit trees. The boundaries are mapped in order to calculate later the total area of the rattan garden and the area of the strata within it. The other features are mapped to check and improve the accuracy of the information on the community-drawn sketch map. Information as far as can be seen to either side of the cut line should be recorded, not just that along the line itself. After cutting an initial base line through the rattan garden, perpendicular lines are cut from it, using a compass for orientation and a clinometer to correct for slope. After 30 m of line have been cut, the three line cutters return along it to record data, before embarking on the cutting of a further 30 m. In recording data, rattan clumps were included only if the (subjectively defined) centre point of the clump was within 5 m of the central line.

Drawing a more accurate map, and calculating the areas of the strata and the total garden

Using information recorded during the inventory, a more accurate map can be constructed from the original sketch map. The map is drawn on graph paper (using one 1 x 1 cm square = 10 x 10 m^2). This enables the areas of the strata, and the total area of the garden, to be estimated by counting the squares. The locations of the topographical features and the fruit and honey trees were also redrawn on these final maps.

Calculating the quantity of each resource, and the standard error
Using standard statistics, such as may be found in Philip (1994), the mean and total quantity of the rattan resource can be estimated, as well as the standard errors of these estimates. The standard error was calculated using the formula for stratified random sampling. This assumes that the systematic selection used has resulted in an essentially random order of sample selection, an assumption which is not strictly legitimate but which was deemed acceptable in the given context.

Workshop participants felt that more than one week was needed to learn adequately the inventory methods employed.

Lessons Learned

Participants considered more discussion before fieldwork to be necessary, as well as more time for conducting the fieldwork. They also felt that more training was needed in participatory methodologies for involving local people in planning an inventory. In retrospect, the feedback discussions during the workshop and the evaluation at the end should have been more structured, including, for example, formal tests and questionnaires.

People of different cultural or educational backgrounds tend to have different strengths and weaknesses and may therefore require different types of training. This was well demonstrated in this workshop, which included participants from very different backgrounds. It is instructive to consider which aspects of the inventory were found by local village participants to be most relevant and easy, and which they considered to be less relevant or more difficult.

Planning a participatory inventory
This requires skills in:

- determining the purpose and specific objectives of the inventory
- planning and costing the logistics of the field operations
- planning the sampling design

all with the full participation of the local community.

The description of the community inventory initiative in Box 7.5 demonstrates that local people can be self-sufficient in many aspects of planning an inventory (for example, in determining objectives, and planning and costing the logistics of work in the field). This is not surprising, as East Kalimantan villagers have much experience in planning co-operative work such as rice planting or harvesting. However, they are not familiar with the concept of sampling, and they may not be confident about their ability to plan a sampling design. This may be made simpler for them by presenting a simple step-by-step methodology, rather than presenting a general outline of sampling theory and a range of options, as was done in the workshop.

Executing an inventory
This requires skills in:

- cartography (in this case, how to read and draw reasonably accurate maps)
- cutting lines with a compass and clinometer
- taxonomic identification
- resource mensuration techniques
- data capture and processing techniques
- statistical principles and analyses.

The lesson learned from the community mapping and inventory initiatives (Boxes 7.3 and 7.5) is that local people can be self-sufficient in many aspects of executing an inventory (for example, in cartography, taxonomic identification, resource mensuration, and data capture and processing). In the inventory workshop, a local farmer was found to be particularly skilled in resource mensuration (see Box 7.6). However, it must be noted that individuals vary in their skills, some of which may have been enhanced by formal education (although other skills may be unrelated to schooling). Not all members of the community participated in the community initiatives or in the workshop; in general, those who did were better educated than other members of the community.

Inventory skills which were completely new to these villagers included cutting lines using a compass and clinometer, and making statistical calculations.

Local participants found both compasses and clinometers intimidating at first, and it was not clear how well they understood the theory behind using the clinometer to adjust for slope. Nonetheless, most managed to learn how to use both pieces of equipment. This highlights the need to use equipment which is as simple and cheap as possible. Perhaps in future an alternative method might be considered, such as 'step taping', where the horizontal distance is measured out in 'steps' of a small enough size to enable two people to hold the measuring tape level. As for statistical calculations, all participants found it easy to calculate means and totals, but almost all were unable to calculate standard errors. This is hardly surprising, given that many people educated to tertiary level (in developed as well as developing countries) have similar problems. However, depending upon the purpose, and on the views of government officials to whom these data will be presented, the calculation of standard error may not be important. As long as an effort is made to sample without bias and with sufficient intensity, the estimated mean should be reasonably close to the true value, and the standard error should be reasonably small. In order to minimise bias in sampling, a system must be in place for frequent checks of accuracy. Such a system is mandatory for any inventory field team.

It appears possible for East Kalimantan villagers to conduct large parts of a resource inventory without external assistance, although this needs to be verified through further field trials. The assistance of outside organisations such as NGOs may be needed to supply equipment such as compasses, clinometers and measuring tapes, or to provide advice on some of the more difficult skills. Amongst the NGO participants attending the inventory workshop, the people with a legal aid background felt more confident about their ability to help with the planning stage, especially in facilitating the participation of the entire community. By contrast, the NGO participants with a forestry or agricultural background felt they were best qualified to provide assistance with the more difficult technical aspects such as planning the sampling design or making more complex statistical calculations.

It must be stressed that the inventory workshop was a preliminary exercise, which will need refinement in future workshops. Whether local people will adopt such inventories is a separate issue from whether they feel confident in the necessary skills to do so. Taking into consideration the lessons learned from both the workshop and the community inventory initiative, it appears that local people are only likely to adopt the inventory methodologies developed in the workshop if they feel that these sampling methods have the following attributes:

- They can be easily learned and conducted by many community members.

- The methods save time and money for the community, compared with a 100% enumeration of resources. It may be that villagers will not be receptive to the concept of sampling in rattan gardens, although in the community inventory they applied the concept when estimating losses from land that had already been cleared. In natural forest where resources are scattered over a much larger area, the argument for sampling is likely to be much more compelling.

- The approach supports and/or incorporates traditional practices. Local people are more likely to be able to conduct practices which incorporate traditional techniques familiar to them, than practices which are entirely new to them. They are also more likely to look favourably upon methods that support their traditions. Thus, it is important to understand how local people plan activities and how they measure resources or land.

- The methods are seen as credible by the 'scientifically trained' government officials who determine whether compensation for the loss of land and resources is due, and how much should be given. To be credible, the sampling methods must be objective, and result in estimates which are as accurate (with a low bias) and precise (with a low standard error) as possible.

The trial workshop developed inventory methods to assess the resources in a rattan garden for the purpose of seeking compensation. However, different inventory methods might be required for different situations. A different sampling design would have to be developed for assessing resources in natural forest rather than in a rattan garden. For example, stratification would need to be based on features such as soil type, soil fertility or topography, rather than on age since burning for swidden. The types of data recorded might change if inventory were to be conducted for the purpose of management rather than for compensation. Rather than focusing on the categories and measurements necessary for calculating the total production in one year of each resource, attention would be paid to the age/size class structure of the population, and regeneration, growth and mortality rates. Thus, younger age classes of a species might be included in the inventory, and repeated measurements made over several years at least. In the case of rattan, more accurate estimates would be needed of total as well as commercial stem lengths (refer to Box 7.6 for a discussion of estimation methods).

Future Developments in Participatory Inventory

A field manual for the participatory inventory of NTFPs is planned, oriented specifically to the needs of local people and non-governmental as well as government field workers. The manual should be flexible enough for reference in both resource evaluation and management situations. It could be used for conducting inventories of forests both in nature reserves and in timber concessions, depending upon local interest in so doing. To develop the manual, future workshops are planned with both local people and government officials, in an attempt to balance the abilities and needs of local people with the demands of government officials for scientific credibility.

7.7 Conclusion

The initiatives discussed in this chapter indicate the potential of participatory mapping and inventory methodologies for assessing forest land and resources. One aim in the development of these techniques has been to ensure flexibility, in other words to adapt the techniques to different types of communities and their different needs. For example, some communities in East Kalimantan may have well-defined territorial boundaries and/or systems of resource management. They may need maps of their traditional territory boundaries or inventories of the resources within them in order to seek legal tenure or compensation. Alternatively, they may be interested in learning mapping and inventory techniques in order to ensure that their traditional systems of management are sustainable. Other communities do not have such clear territories or systems of management. For them, maps illustrating the location and uses of different lands and resources may facilitate discussion and decision-making about appropriate territorial boundaries, resource use zones, and rules of management.

Another aim in developing the methodologies discussed has been to increase the level of participation by forest-dwelling people. It is still debatable how much outside technical assistance, whether from government or NGOs, is necessary or desirable.

A related feature of the methods discussed has been an attempt to maintain a scientific standard that will be acceptable to the government. It is hoped that this will place local people in a position of equal knowledge with government officials in negotiations or discussions on tenure, compensation or management. The political will of the government to listen to local people is still uncertain. However, there have been recent signs of recognition by the government of the necessity of community participation in forest management to ensure sustainability (BAPPENAS/Ministry of Forestry/World Bank, 1994). The government will need to recognise that the priorities of forest-dwelling communities are securing tenure and compensation for lost resources. Until the issue of traditional rights to forest land and resources is addressed, it will be difficult to advance to using mapping and inventory tools for the purpose of sustainable management.

Note

1. The 'differentiation' method requires GPS receivers to be in place at two sites, the control site and the remote site. It is essential that the control site has been independently located, thus a Dopler site with verified co-ordinates was used as the first control site. There must be co-ordination between the control and remote sites as to which satellites will be used and at what time. Optimal times for contacting satellites can be found using Magellan software which provides a daily almanac. Processing data from the satellite takes 20 minutes; as signal quality or the Position Dilution of Precision (PDOP) fluctuates during the day, five runs of 20 minutes are taken, and the run with the lowest PDOP (the highest precision) is chosen (Snel, 1993).

References

BAPPENAS/Ministry of Forestry/World Bank (1994) *Operationalising Community Participation in Forestry Development.* A workshop report. Ministry of Forestry, Jakarta.

Barber, C.V., Johnson, N.C. and Hafild, E. (1994) *Breaking the Logjam: Obstacles to Policy Reform in Indonesia and the United States.* World Resources Institute, Washington, DC.

Momberg, F., Damus, D., Limberg, G. and ST. Padan, S. (1994) 'Participatory Tools for Community Forest Profiling and Zonation of Conservation Areas'. Unpublished report for the WWF Indonesia Programme – Kayan Mentarang Project, Jakarta.

Moniaga, S. (1993) 'Toward Community-based Forestry and Recognition of Adat Property Rights in the Outer Islands of Indonesia' in Fox, J. (ed.), *Legal Frameworks for Forest Management in Asia: Case Studies of Community/State Relations.* East-West Centre Program on the Environment Occasional Paper No. 16, Honolulu.

Peluso, N. L. (1992) 'The Rattan Trade in East Kalimantan, Indonesia', *Advances in Economic Botany 9*: 115–27.

Philip, M. S. (1994) *Measuring Trees and Forests* (2nd edn). CAB International, Wallingford, UK.

Sirait, M. T., Prasodjo, S., Podger, N., Flavelle, A. and Fox, J. (1994) 'Mapping Customary Land in East Kalimantan, Indonesia: a Tool for Forest Management', *Ambio 23(7)*: 411–17.

Snel, M. (1993) 'The Use of GIS as a Tool in the Kayan Mentarang Management Plan; the First Phase, Obtaining Village Locations in the Pujungan Area with GPS'. Unpublished report for the WWF Indonesia Programme – Kayan Mentarang Project, Jakarta.

Snel, M. (1994) 'The Use of GIS as a Tool in the Management of Kayan Mentarang; Creating the Kayan Mentarang GIS Database'. Unpublished report for the WWF Indonesia Programme – Kayan Mentarang Project, Jakarta.

ST. Padan, S., Momberg, F., Damus, D. and Limberg, G. (1994) 'Pemetaan desa partisipatif sebagai pendekatan zonasi dan pengelolaan sumber daya alam di kawasan konservasi: pengalaman kegiatan di Kecamatan Krayan'. Unpublished report for the WWF Indonesia Programme – Kayan Mentarang Project, Jakarta.

Stockdale, M. C. (1994) Inventory Methods and Ecological Studies Relevant to the Management of Wild Populations of Rattan. D.Phil. thesis. Oxford Forestry Institute, Department of Plant Sciences, University of Oxford.

Stockdale, M. C. and Power, J. D. (1994) 'Estimating the Length of Rattan Stems', *Forest Ecology and Management 64*: 47–57.

Stockdale, M. C. and Wright, H. L. (1995) 'Rattan Inventory: Determining Plot Shape and Size' in Edwards, D. S. and Booth, W. E. (eds), Proceedings of the Conference on Tropical Rainforest Research: Current Issues, *Monographiae Biologicae*, Kluwer Academic Publishers, Dordrecht,The Netherlands.

Tandug, L. M. (1978) 'Sampling Methods for the Inventory of Rattan and its Distribution', *Sylvatropica Philippines Forestry Research Journal 3(3)*: 155–70.

Tandug, L. M. and Lasmarias, V. T. (1984) 'Determination of the Most Appropriate Sampling Design for the Inventory of

Philippine Rattan'. Philippine Council for Agriculture, Forestry and Natural Resources Research and Development – International Development Research Centre (PCARRD-IDRC) National Integrated Research Program on Rattan, Manila. Unpublished terminal report.

Weinstock, J. A. and Vergara, N. T. (1990) 'The Land or the Plants: Agricultural Tenure in Agroforestry Systems' in *Voices from the Field: 3rd Annual Social Forestry Writing Workshop*. Environment and Policy Institute, East-West Centre, Honolulu.

Whitmore, T. C. (1984) 'Vegetation of Malesia (map). A Contribution to the Global Environment Monitoring System, United Nations Environment Programme', *Journal of Biogeogeography*.

Zerner, C. (1990) *Legal Options for the Indonesian Forestry Sector*. Government of Indonesia/Food and Agricultural Organisation, Jakarta.

Acronyms and Indonesian terms specific to this chapter

BFL	Basic Forestry Law
BAL	Basic Agrarian Law
BIPHUT	Balai Inventarisasi dan Pemetaan Hutan (Agency for Forest Inventory and Mapping)
DGFPNC	Directorate General of Forest Protection and Nature Conservation
adat	traditional law governing community life
musyawarah	formal village assembly for discussion and decision-making
paren	hereditary class of elites

8 Forest Assessment and Monitoring for Conservation and Local Use: Experience in Three Ugandan National Parks

Joe Watts, Penelope Scott and Jackson Mutebi

This set of case studies differs from the others in describing a forest management situation in which the primary goal is conservation, with the harvesting of forest products being permitted only when this will entail minimal forest disturbance. The areas concerned are National Parks, under the control of the Ugandan Government, and local people's access to the forests is limited by law. The chapter describes how three projects, operating in three different National Parks in separate parts of the country, are approaching forest assessment as part of their overall management strategy. The case studies are: the Development Through Conservation Project of Bwindi National Park in south-west Uganda, the Conservation and Development Project of the Mount Elgon National Park on Uganda's eastern border with Kenya, and the Conservation and Development Project of the Rwenzori National Park near Uganda's western border with Zaire (see Figure 8.1). All three projects currently aim to involve local people in park management, and two are working towards joint management agreements.

Uganda contains many areas of particular value for biodiversity conservation, and has attracted much international attention and funding for this purpose. The country is exceptionally diverse in ecological terms, partly as a result of its wide range of altitude and rainfall (Harcourt, 1992). Of perhaps greater significance is its geographical position, within the overlapping zone of the ecological communities characteristic of the West African rainforest and those of the East African savanna. In the absence of disturbance by man about 20% of Uganda's land surface area would be covered with closed canopy forest. However, much of the forest has been cleared and by 1987 it was estimated that forest covered only 3% of the country's land area. The population of Uganda has risen from 3 million in 1921 to an estimated 18 million in 1990. There is inevitably considerable pressure on the remaining forest areas in the country.

Land use close to Bwindi Impenetrable National Park. This scene is typical of the heavy agricultural pressure on the land around the Park.
Photograph: Joe Watts

8.1 Forest Legislation and the Role of the Ugandan Government in Forest Management

Until the early 1990s much of Uganda's forest area was within Forest Reserves (although several reserves had dual status as Game Reserves, Animal Sanctuaries or National Parks). The management of these Reserves by the Forest Department was greatly affected by poor funding and, more significantly, the political unrest within the country between 1971 and 1986. Following political stabilisation, a new forest policy was issued in 1988. This re-introduced a 1929 emphasis that, in addition to providing wood, forests had a role in maintaining environmental values. It also restored the boundaries of the Forest Reserves to their 1963 positions – resulting in the eviction of over 130,000 people.

Under the Forest Act of 1964 local people were permitted to take unreserved forest produce (i.e. not species of tree requiring Forestry Department permission to harvest) from reserved or public forest for their domestic use. This included dead wood for fuel and medicinal plants (Struhsaker, 1987). The ecological impact of this collection of 'minor' forest products was not monitored.

With political stability and clear international interest in Uganda's biological diversity, debate grew over the most appropriate strategy and institution to manage key conservation areas. Possibilities included the areas remaining under the Forest Department (within the Ministry of Natural Resources), or being transferred to the Uganda National Parks (UNP), a parastatal

213

Figure 8.1   Location of the Three Case Study National Parks in Uganda: Bwindi Impenetrable, Rwenzori Mountains, and Mount Elgon

Source: adapted from Howard, P. C., 1991. *Nature Conservation in Uganda's Tropical Forest Reserves.* IUCN, Gland and Cambridge

organisation under the Ministry of Tourism, Wildlife and Antiquities. The Forest Department, with institutional support from the European Community (EC), embarked on developing a new category of Forest Park (later to become Conservation Forest). This status would have allowed the multiple-use zoning of the principal Forest Reserves to accommodate areas of total protection within areas of sustainable production with some element of local consultation and/or participation. However, it was the UNP that finally gained responsibility for the most important forest reserves. From 1991 to 1994 six of these (Bwindi Impenetrable, Mgahinga,

Rwenzori, Mt. Elgon, Kibale and Semliki Forest Reserves) were re-gazetted as National Parks. At the time the UNP had few staff in the relevant locations and little experience of high forest management or working with local communities. Under the National Parks Act of 1964 National Parks are administered by the Board of Trustees of UNP who are charged to 'take such steps as will ensure the preservation of the animal and vegetable life in a natural state' (National Parks Act 1964 quoted in Howard,1991).

Throughout the difficult and sometimes contentious change in status a number of internationally funded projects have been working in the areas concerned (and in other Forest Reserves and National Parks), supporting protected area management and rural development activities in the surrounding communities. This has led to considerable innovation by Project and local UNP staff to try to reconcile the demands of the local communities on the natural resources with the need for biodiversity and environmental conservation. These, largely experimental, innovations have taken place in very different biological, socio-economic and institutional environments.

The innovations are supported by the central authorities. Although initially cautious, they have undergone a major change in perspective. Their originally conservative and protectionist standpoint has now broadened to considering multiple-use of National Parks by local communities. Whilst sharing similar goals, the local National Park management (and their supporting projects) have approached work with local communities slightly differently, within their own local context and timing. This difference is also seen in the role given to local people in the collection and use of management information and in decision-making. Most notable is the decision made by the multiple-use team and the Park management authorities in Bwindi to aim towards what they term participatory resource management, rather than Joint Forest Management. The latter was their original intention, and is still the aim in the case of the other two National Parks considered here. The change to 'participatory' resource management in this context represents a reduction in the amount of control over resource use that local people will be allowed, although exact roles in future decision-making remain to be determined.

> A clear distinction should be made between the Joint Management Agreements intended under the management of some National Parks in Uganda, and approaches to Joint Forest Management (JFM) in other parts of the world, most notably India. In India, the concept is a key feature of national forest policy, and is backed in a number of states by strong legislation. It is essentially seen as a partnership between local people and Forest Department staff, under which responsibilities for the productive management of the forest are shared, as are the benefits of the harvest. In Uganda, the situation is different, as this chapter explains.

8.2 The Three National Parks

Bwindi Impenetrable National Park

Past and present forest utilisation

The Bwindi Impenetrable forest lies in the Rukiga Highlands of south-west Uganda. The forest has high biodiversity for East Africa, due to a large altitudinal range (1,160 m to 2,607 m above sea level) and the probability that the forest lay on the edge of the East Zaire Pleistocene Refuge. The forest is considered to be the richest in East

Africa in terms of tree species. Examples of both local and international importance include species with medicinal properties such as *Prunus* (syn. *Pygeum*) *africana, Faurea saligna* (used for making bee hives, *Podocarpus latifolius* (a source of good, smooth, hard timber, also used for bee hives and important for honey production), and *Polyscia fulva* (used for carving). The forest is used by local people for a variety of other purposes including fishing and the collection of products such as bean stakes (for climbing beans). A number of sites (including the hot springs) have cultural importance (particularly for the **Batwa** people). The forest also covers an important water catchment area. In addition, and of high conservation interest, the forest provides a habitat for mountain gorillas (*Gorilla gorilla beringei*) (see Box 8.1).

Box 8.1 The Mountain Gorillas of Bwindi

About 300 mountain gorillas live in Bwindi, probably about one half the world's total population of this endangered primate. This species has a very high international profile and the potential to bring substantial foreign exchange into Uganda through tourism. Already two groups have been habituated to human presence. The tourism is restricted to a small zone within the park and is strictly controlled to avoid stress to the animals and to prevent transmission of disease to the gorillas. The substantial money being paid by tourists to central government (each foreign tourist pays $120) will support park activities in Bwindi (and other, less lucrative, parks) and local development initiatives around the park. In addition, communities near the tourism zone benefit from managing a community camp-site. However, the presence of such a high-profile species, although a major factor in attracting international assistance and tourist revenue, does restrict the options for closer local involvement in forest management – as forest use needs to be controlled to avoid disease transmission.

There has been human presence in the Bwindi Impenetrable forest for many thousands of years. Initially this was in the form of very low densities of hunter-gatherer populations, whose impact on the forest would have been minimal. This changed when agricultural and iron-smelting technologies were introduced to the region some 2,000 years ago. Human populations have expanded steadily since this time, with extensive conversion of the forest to agriculture.

The forest was gazetted as Crown Forest in 1932 and underwent numerous changes of name, status and .size before becoming Bwindi Forest Reserve in 1968. During the 1970s and 1980s, increasing population pressure, combined with political and economic disruption, brought the forest under escalating pressure from legal and illegal exploitation. It has been estimated that only 10% of the reserve remained essentially undisturbed, with 61% having been intensively exploited by pit-sawers. Selective pit-sawing almost completely removed the best hardwoods from some 29% of the area (Howard, 1991). Other forms of forest utilisation included the hunting of animals for bush meat, honey collection from wild bee hives (and the keeping of hives), the harvesting of fuelwood, bamboo and building materials, and panning for gold in the river valleys. The combination of steep slopes, heavy rainfall, loss of forest cover (27% was lost between 1954 and 1990), and intense cultivation led to soil erosion, poor agricultural yields and the degradation of the local water supply.

Agricultural clearance right up to the Bwindi park boundary.
Photograph: Joe Watts

The people of the area

The area surrounding Bwindi is now one of the most densely populated in Uganda, with an average of 220 people km^2 in the three surrounding counties. The present population comprises a variety of ethnic groups, amongst whom the **Batwa** are recognised as being the indigenous group with the greatest claim to the forest. However, in negotiations with the UNP, they requested that they should not be given privileges over other groups – possibly because of fear of reprisals if they were treated exceptionally.

Community organisation is quite strong, and based on the authority of local chiefs. Decision-making is traditionally dominated by men, and the park has had to make deliberate attempts to involve women in the negotiation process. Different communities have different local/traditional structures, membership of which is mandatory. Notable amongst them are:

- **abataka** groups
- stretcher societies
- village resistance councils (established in 1986)

For example, in the parish of Mupungu, there is an organisation of about 26 stretcher societies, one in each village. The members of this society have responsibility for transporting sick villagers to the nearest medical facility (a journey that may take up to several days). In Rutugunda parish, villagers are organised in **abataka** (singular **bataka**) groups, whilst in Nteko both stretcher societies and **abataka** groups exist. One **bataka** group forms a Resistance Council, which here is a stronger organisation than a stretcher society.

In each of these three pilot parishes, the strongest local organisation has been used as an entry point to discuss forest resource utilisation (stretcher societies in Mpungu, **abataka** groups in Rutugunda, and Resistance Councils in Nteko). These organisations are then used to form broader structures such as the parish Forest Society and the recently formed Park Parish Committee (PPC), through which the Park now operates. The way in which stretcher societies have been involved in the Mpunga parish Forest Society is illustrated in Box 8.6.

> The park authorities have taken care to identify the appropriate local organisation through which to work. Clearly, this has varied in different parishes.

The development of the project
In 1986 the Impenetrable Forest Conservation Project (IFCP) began, with funding from the WWF US and USAID. It concentrated on ecological research and support to Game and Forest Department staff. A research and education centre was established, which later became the Institute for Tropical Forest Conservation (ITFC), a faculty of the local Mbarara University. The project was instrumental in the instigation of the Development Through Conservation Project (DTC) in 1988. The DTC project, which is funded by USAID and implemented by CARE-International, has a remit for rural development activities outside the conservation area and the development of sustainable in-forest resource use.

Bwindi Forest Reserve became Bwindi Impenetrable National Park, an area covering 330 km^2, in 1991. By this time nearly all local access to the forest had been stopped and there was deep hostility between the park staff and the community.

DTC is organised in four sections. The Development Section works with directly employed extension workers in all the parishes around Bwindi. The other three sections, Conservation Education, Multiple-use, and Park Management, work with local UNP staff. A central tenet of the DTC/UNP approach at Bwindi is that the park's ultimate survival is dependent on sufficient benefit from the park going to the local community. It is envisaged that such benefits will take four forms, as follows:

- The multiple use of limited areas within the Park (see Sections 8.4 and 8.5).

- The sharing of revenue. It has been agreed by UNP that up to 10% of revenues from tourism will be distributed to local development projects. Park Parish Committees (PPCs) have been formed in the 22 parishes adjacent to the park, and two workshops have been held to train PPC leaders in project design, monitoring and evaluation and the drafting of project proposals. Distribution of funding awaits the approval of submitted project proposals.

- Income from a conservation trust, which will support small-scale development projects, park management and applied research. The Global Environmental Facility (GEF) is to invest $4 million in establishing this trust.

- Development activities by DTC and to a certain extent UNP around the park.

Communication between the Park and the communities has been encouraged through the creation of a new position of Community Conservation Ranger, whose job is to serve as a link person.

The intention of the Forest and Game Departments and the IFCP was to allow the sustainable use of 'minor' forest products and the first registration of beekeepers took place in 1989. Strong requests for some access to resources were made by the community through politicians, community leaders and direct hostile action. Following a recommendation from ITFC, the Board of Trustees of UNP asked that 20% of the park should be identified as a multiple-use zone. Community leaders were then involved in drafting the park management plan, but, as described in subsequent sections, the most active involvement of local people took place at a later stage in the proceedings.

Bwindi was the first national park to embark on multiple-use and therefore the work has necessarily been of an experimental nature. A 'learning by doing' approach has been adopted (Wild, Mutebi and Cunningham, 1995). Although the approach taken towards involving local people in resource management may seem rather cautious ('permitted access' is perhaps an appropriate description), it should be seen in the context of an area of high international profile and the testing of a relatively new idea for Uganda that needed to gain the support of not only the local people but also the UNP Board of Trustees.

Mount Elgon National Park

Past and present forest utilisation

Mount Elgon is a solitary and extinct volcano lying on the border of Uganda and Kenya and reaching 4,320 m. The vegetation on the mountain consists of high moorland, high montane heath, bamboo and low canopy montane forest, and mixed montane forest. The former two categories, which lie above 3,500 m and from 3,000 m to 3,500 m respectively, are considered by Howard (1991) as the most important for species conservation. They are rich in species endemic to the higher East African mountains or even to Mount Elgon itself, such as the giant *Lobelia elgonensis* and *Senecio elgonensis*. Of the 427 tree species recorded in the forest reserves of Uganda, 112 are found on Mount Elgon (Heist, 1994). Amongst those that have a limited distribution within Uganda are *Juniperus procera*, *Stoebe kilimandscharica*, and *Pittosporum viridiflorum*.

Mount Elgon also forms an important water catchment area. There is a long history of human use of the natural resources of the mountain. This includes resident pastoralists within the forest/grassland, hunting and large-scale exploitation of the bamboo for building materials and for the edible shoots.

The Mount Elgon Forest Reserve was first gazetted in 1938. After many boundary disputes a ten-year working plan was produced in 1968 which established most of the present-day boundaries. The Park covers 1,184 km², with a 211 km boundary on the Ugandan side. Within the plan the primary objective was the management of Mount Elgon as a protection forest, with timber production as a secondary objective. During the political instability of the 1970s and 1980s there was widespread damage to the forest by pit-sawing and agricultural encroachment. Recent vegetation mapping has indicated that about 20% of the area of the Park was once under agriculture (M. van Heist, pers. comm.).

Following the new forest policy in 1988, mass evictions were conducted by the Forestry Department from the Mount Elgon Forest Reserve. In 1992 the Forestry Department, supported by the European Community, prepared an interim management plan (1992–4) for Mount Elgon proposing a zoned multiple-use system (although a 'community zone' was limited to 500 m from the boundary). However, in the same year the process of transferring the management of Mount Elgon to UNP began. This was completed in January 1994.

The people of the area

The population density in the areas surrounding Mount Elgon is extremely high. The boundary of the park is shared by two districts, Mbale and Kapchorwa, with the average population density for forest-adjacent parishes of Mbale being 512 people/km² and for Kapchorwa, 224 people/km². The communities living in the forest-adjacent parishes primarily comprise two tribes. The **Bagisu**, of Mbale district, are agriculturalists, while the **Sabiny**, of Kapchorwa district, are pastoralists by origin, who grazed their livestock on the lower plains. Because of intensified cattle rustling activities on the plains, they have steadily migrated up the mountain slopes, reduced their pastoral activities, and turned to commercial maize and wheat cultivation. Until recently, a forest-dwelling pastoral community, the **Kony**, lived in the grassland and moorland areas of the northern part of the mountain. When the forest reserve was first gazetted, they were permitted to live within it without licences (the **Bagisu** cultivators had heritable licences to live within the forest). The main activities of the **Kony** within the forest were grazing, honey collection, hunting, and bamboo basketry work. Until the 1960s, there were also a number of forest dwelling people in the southern part of the mountain, although they generally inhabited land outside the reserve.

In 1983 the **Kony** were evicted from their traditional lands, and forced to resettle further down the mountain in an excised area to the north of the reserve. As noted above, further mass evictions of all people living within the reserve took place in 1988. The present population living immediately adjacent to the park is faced with a variety of difficulties, including increasing land shortage, poor access to markets, and limited educational and employment prospects.

The development of the project

The Mount Elgon Conservation and Development Project (MECDP) began in 1987. A consortium of institutions are involved in its management, which is co-ordinated through the Department of Environmental Protection. Technical assistance is provided by the World Conservation Union (IUCN) and financial assistance by the Norwegian development agency NORAD. Originally the project was to include the forests of Kibale and Semliki in the west of Uganda, but work in these areas was delayed and they now form a separate IUCN-supported project.

The main objectives of the MECDP have been two-fold:

- To ensure the conservation of the biological diversity and ecological processes within the natural forest and maintain the water catchment services provided by it.

- To maintain the economic benefits derived from the land surrounding the forest.

The project activities have covered forest conservation, sustainable development and environmental education and extension.

During the first six years of the project thousands of squatters were evicted, and the entire reserve boundary was re-surveyed. The project supported a Task Force, under Park Management, which operated a rigorous control programme. However, it could not control the vast amount of technically illegal forest use that still continued. In addition, the project assisted the government extension service in providing conservation messages and considerable on-farm assistance to 9 out of the 58 parishes surrounding the forest. Parish-level Development Committees were also established.

In 1993, a visiting consultant elaborated on concerns expressed by an earlier evaluation mission, noting the lack of linkage between the in-forest and out-of-forest activities (Wiley, 1993). Interventions outside the forest were not focused to address the issue of forest conservation. In addition, the Forest Conservation Unit considered management only in terms of protection to be carried out by the State. It was suggested that in future, although product substitution could go some way to reduce the conflict, more comprehensive substitution could sever the link between local people and the forest. Wiley recommended 'the establishment over time of a buffer community with a vested interest in protecting the forest and a widened base of responsibility and commitment to forest conservation.' Since this report and in the future five-year Phase 3 of the project, the main emphasis has been and will be on piloting and developing collaborative management approaches on Mount Elgon.

Rwenzori Mountains National Park

Past and present forest utilisation

The Rwenzori Mountains lie along Uganda's western border with Zaire and rise to 5,110 m. The forest on these mountains is quite distinct, in terms of both flora and fauna, from that of the Bwindi and Mount Elgon forests. The Rwenzori Mountains also have the least disturbed flora of the principal forest reserves in Uganda, although the fauna are less well preserved, hunting having severely reduced most mammal populations. The natural vegetation may be categorised into five distinct zones, largely on the basis of altitude (Howard, 1991). At lower elevations, the broken montane forest is characterised by species such as *Symphonia globulifera*, *Prunus africana*, and *Albizia* spp. This gives way to bamboo forest (*Arundinaria alpina*). Above the bamboo lies tree heathland on poorer soils, and a mixture of small trees (including *Hypericum* spp.) over tangled undergrowth on better soils. Higher still, the vegetation comprises Afro-alpine moorland, up to the snow line at about 4,400 m.

Some of the most important forest products for local people are bamboo, *Smilax* spp. (a climber used for basketry), poles and fuelwood, mushrooms, and a variety of medicinal plants. Hunting is no longer very popular in the area, due to a combination of social changes (including religion, education and access to alternative meat supplies) and the low levels of animals remaining in the mountains (Penelope Scott, pers. observation). In the southern part of the mountains, hunting of the rock hyrax for their skins still occurs, but little information is available on the extent or impact of the activity.

The Rwenzori Forest Reserve of 996 km^2 was originally gazetted in 1941. The management of the area was transferred to UNP and gazetted as the Rwenzori Mountains National Park in August 1991.

The people of the area

The people living adjacent to the park fall within three districts, Kasese, Kabarole and Bundibugyo. The main tribe bordering and using the mountains is the **Bakonzo**, which is the dominant tribe of Kasese – the district to the South-East and South of the park. In Kaborole, the district to the East and North, the dominant tribe is the **Batoro**. To the North-West, in the narrow strip of land between the mountains and the border with Zaire, there is a mixed ethnic population, including the **Bwamba** and **Batwa** (a pygmy tribe). There is a history of bloody conflict between the **Batoro** and **Bakonzo**, although there have been no open hostilities since the 1960s.

The communities neighbouring the present National Park (in particular the **Bakonzo**) have a long-standing cultural affinity with the forest. It is viewed as the residence of many of the spirits that play an important role in their daily lives, and in the past sacrifices to these spirits were made regularly. Although not now common practice, sacrificial sites may still be found in many parts of the forest. The **Bakonzo** consider the Rwenzori Mountains as theirs, and despite 50 years of government management, outside managers are viewed as visitors (or intruders, in some cases). Whilst to date the Park authorities have not had to mediate between conflicting **Bakonzo** and **Batoro** interests, they are well aware of past conflicts.

The development of the project

The Rwenzori Mountains Conservation and Development Project began field activities in 1992. The project is funded by WWF-US and USAID and works with the staff of UNP at the Rwenzori Mountains National Park. In summary, the objectives of the Project are:

- To assist in the development of the management of the National Park.

- To reduce the pressure on the park by providing management alternatives to local communities and to increase conservation awareness, thus enabling informed natural resource decisions to be made.

The Project is implementing rural development activities in five pilot parishes adjacent to the Park. One significant difference between the Rwenzori Mountains and the two other case studies is that there has been no history of mass evictions or particularly rigorous law enforcement (although Park boundary disputes do exist).

A needs assessment survey was conducted by the Project in early 1993. The greatest community concerns, as expressed in local interviews with senior individuals, were for continued access to the footpaths that cross the northern section of the Park and to be allowed to continue to harvest forest products such as bamboo and medicinal plants.

It is uncertain how the lack of historical hostility between the authorities and the local communities will influence the development of future relationships. It may be a positive factor for the Park management. However, it could also be a negative factor, as there will be no goodwill generated by the cessation of hostile actions.

8.3   The Need for Forest Resource Assessment

All three case study projects have the same general aim of developing controlled access to National Parks by local communities, but each has embarked on the process slightly differently. The particular needs for forest resource assessment have likewise been perceived in different ways. In all cases information collection has been initiated by the Projects/UNP, not by the communities themselves.

Figure 8.2 Diagrammatic Representation of the Process Leading to Participatory/Joint Management Agreements in Bwindi, Mount Elgon and Rwenzori Mountains National Parks

Bwindi Impenetrable National Park

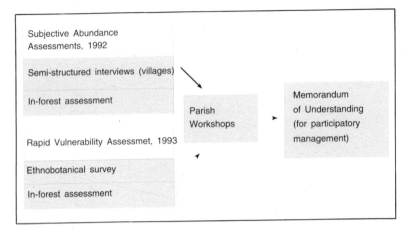

Mount Elgon National Park

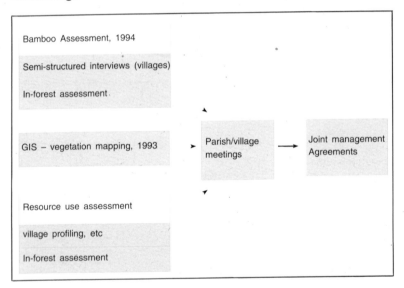

Rwenzori Mountains National Park

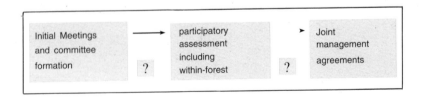

The rationale for focusing on specialist, rather than generalist, resource use within multiple-use areas was as follows:

• Generalist uses such as the harvesting of poles, firewood and bean stakes would have entailed far larger numbers of people in the forest, perhaps threatening the gorilla population.

• Unselective harvesting, removing trees of successive size classes, has potential to change the canopy structure.

• The cost of monitoring such harvesting would have been prohibitive.

• There was clear potential for on-farm substitution of many generalist uses.

The projects, their consultants and UNP have used and adapted ideas (and terminology) from experience elsewhere (both in other parts of Africa and beyond). Their activities have also been dictated to a considerable extent by the individual circumstances in which they found themselves. None of the approaches adopted may be considered ideal, at least so far, but they provide a range of interesting and potentially valuable techniques. The steps in each of the approaches are presented in Figure 8.2.

In Bwindi there had been considerable discussion over forest resource use for a number of years before any data were collected. The strategy adopted has comprised two complementary elements:

• 'low impact specialist resource use' within multiple-use areas
• on-farm substitution of 'generalist high impact uses'

This case study focuses on the former element, under which there was a clear need for forest resource assessment.

The initial suggestion of potential multiple-use areas was made by the IFCP. These were developed by Scott (1992) through semi-structured village interviews and in-forest assessment. The use of the forest resources was further investigated by Cunningham (1992), who made recommendations for sustainable forest use. Whilst these studies were being conducted, some limited forest access was permitted. Beekeeping was the first activity allowed, in early 1992. This was re-started in three parishes which had previously been allowed to keep hives by the Forest Department. Beekeepers were asked to form user groups, and meetings were held with these groups to establish rules of operation and issue identity cards. Support in beekeeping techniques and marketing was also provided. Given that there was no PRA, no joint management agreement, and no formal involvement of community leaders, this aspect of resource use has been in marked contrast to the more detailed investigation and control of extractive resource use that forms the main focus of the case study. The information gathered in the Scott and Cunningham studies, and the recommendations made from them, were used in negotiations with the local communities in three pilot parishes, leading to the signing of Memoranda of Understanding between them and the UNP. Forest-based activities permitted included a certain amount of extractive utilisation, and access to footpaths and hot springs.

In Mount Elgon, data were gathered on the vegetation (in the form of vegetation mapping and biodiversity assessment) and the use of bamboo (in the form of semi-structured interviews and in-forest resource assessment using local insights). There then followed intensive resource use assessment (in the form of gathering socio-economic data at a number of levels very rapidly, and in-forest assessment). This information will be used to launch a series of meetings with the pilot parishes. These will eventually lead to Joint Management Agreements.

The project in the Rwenzori Mountains is the last to start on the process. A series of meetings is progressing with the pilot parishes to develop a process whereby the communities are actively involved in the collection of data on the forest resource and its use before moving on to discussions on Joint Management Agreements.

8.4 The Forest Resource Assessment Process

Bwindi Impenetrable National Park

Subjective abundance assessments
Following the request by the Board of Trustees that 20% of the Bwindi Impenetrable National Park (BINP) be identified as a multiple-use zone, a preliminary study was carried out by Penelope Scott, a Masters student from the Norwegian University of Agriculture. Technical support was provided by the ITFC and DTC. Semi-structured interviews were conducted with a total of 352 households throughout the area adjacent to the Park. These focused on local attitudes to the Park and the demand for forest products. All the data collected were geographically referenced to allow mapping of the findings within a geographical information system (GIS). The work was followed by a socio-economic baseline survey in August 1992.

Scott also conducted a survey within the forest. The IFCP had previously suggested areas with potential for multiple-use collection zones within the periphery of the Park, based primarily on the presence of distinctive natural features as boundaries. Scott delineated the remaining forest fringe into similar zones – Potential Collection Areas (PCAs). An elementary vegetation survey was conducted within all the PCAs around the Park and a visual abundance assessment was made for species mentioned during the interviews. The abundance assessment was made with the assistance of a Park Ranger and a local forest guide (usually an ex-pit sawyer). Each species was given a relative weighted demand value from the combination of the existence of alternatives, the relative distribution of the species in and outside the forest, and data from the village interviews. This gave a preliminary indication of the potential of a PCA to satisfy the demand for a given species. The assessment was acknowledged to be qualitative and, to a certain extent, subjective. Nevertheless, it assisted in identifying areas that are definitely not suitable for community use – either because they do not provide resources that are in local demand, or because they are in some way biologically or geographically sensitive.

Rapid Vulnerability Assessment
A further study was carried out by Tony Cunningham (1992), Field Officer-Africa for the People and Plants Programme (WWF/UNESCO/Kew). This study built on and filled information gaps in the previous report, and included in-depth ethno-botanical

surveys with specialist user groups. It provided recommendations on the suitability of certain resource categories, and in some cases particular species, for sustainable use.

The assessment of species suitability for sustainable harvest is based on certain biological characteristics of the plant and its use. This Rapid Vulnerability Assessment is a methodology that has been developed over a number of years, and was further expanded in later work in the nearby Mgahinga Gorilla National Park (Cunningham, Wild, Mutebi and Tsekeli, 1993). It is a technique for quickly identifying a species, category of resource or even a site, that is vulnerable to over-utilisation. Site, community, species and use data are collected during small specialist group discussions and also forest visits with resource users (who thus become key informants). Questions are asked by members of the Multiple-Use team (researchers, UNP and DTC staff). Data are also collected from forest plots and (if available) secondary sources. Through progressive refinements of the information, vulnerable species/categories/sites are identified.

Key information collected is summarised in Box 8.2.

Box 8.2 Rapid Vulnerability Assessment

The key questions asked are summarised below:

1. Is the resource concerned used in high, medium or low volume?

2. What numbers of people would be involved?

3. Who harvests the resource? What other impacts may result? (e.g. harvesting by women represents a lower risk of hunting taking place under the cover of a plant harvesting activity).

4. Is harvesting a result of general demand (fuel, building materials, etc.) or special activities?

5. Is there size-class selection or do traditional conservation practices apply?

6. Does commercial harvesting take place?

7. What numbers of species are involved?

8. What parts of the plants are used? Does the species have habitat-specific requirements or not? What plant life-forms are involved and what is their population biology? (e.g. Are they slow growing and slow reproducing, or fast growing, fast reproducing? The latter are more resilient to harvesting pressure.)

10. Does the harvesting take place in complex habitats? (The higher the species diversity, the higher the number of plant uses and users to be expected. Management in such circumstances becomes extremely complicated and difficult.)

Source: Cunningham *et al.* (1993)

Field forms are completed in the field, while working with specialist groups of informants. Species summary forms are completed later, and include the following information:

- estimated species population size and quantities within the Multiple-Use area
- species ecology
- parts of species harvested
- reproductive capacity of the plant
- quantities harvested and harvesting season(s)
- community demand for the species

From the information collected, species may be categorised into those having high potential for sustainable harvesting, and those with low potential, as indicated in Box 8.3. Clearly few species satisfy all the criteria for low or high potential, but the classification can give a valuable indication of the relative position of a species.

Box 8.3 Criteria for Assessing the Potential of a Species for Sustainable Harvest

Ecological criteria	
High potential	Low potential
High abundance Fast growth Fast reproduction Vegetative reproduction Habitat non-specific Low habitat diversity Low life form diversity	Low abundance Slow growth Slow reproduction Sexual reproduction only Habitat-specific High habitat diversity High life form diversity

Life form criteria
Use of grasses and forbes is likely to be more sustainable than trees.

Parts used
The use of leaves/fruit/stem is more sustainable than of the roots (if damaging) or the whole plant.

Method of harvesting
Potential for sustainable harvesting is higher if size/age classes are not selected.

Source: Cunningham (1992)

Resources with low potential for sustainable harvesting are targeted for the development of substitute or alternative resources outside the forest. The decisions concerning the categories for which harvesting is permitted, and broadly who is permitted to harvest them, are largely taken by the UNP/DTC. The main issues negotiated with the communities are which species within these

The draft BINP multiple-use plan states that 'the decision whether to use a species is based on the availability of the resource and not the demand of the community' (Wild and Mutebi, 1994). This principle is one that should obtain in all sustainable management practices. However, the level of local people's participation is determined by the extent to which they make the decisions (based on information collected by or with professionals). A comparison may be made here with the approaches described in Chapters 2 (Nigeria) and 5 (Ghana).

categories should be harvested, how much, from where, and by whom exactly, and who should manage this activity.

Once decisions have been made over what harvesting permission is to be given, further more detailed work can be conducted on the species/resource categories of focus. Quantitative assessments with regard to specific more vulnerable resources are made with local resource users. Examples include the quality and quantity of mature bamboo culms [stems] (*Arundinaria alpina*) for building purposes, and the assessment of the stocking of trees suitable for beer-boat manufacture. This use of local insights corrected an earlier assumption that the nearby Echuya Forest could be an alternative site for bamboo collection. In addition to the distance from the villages, the form of the bamboo was not suitable for basketry.

The approach adopted in the BINP was influenced both by political necessity and concerns of sustainability. A further issue is cost. Cunningham *et al.* (1993: 50) warn of the difficulties of trying to manage the complex and poorly known Ugandan forests for multiple-use and recommend that

> although local needs need to be taken into account as much as possible through resource sharing arrangements that help to reduce land use conflicts, in the long term resource over-exploitation benefits neither the park or the local community. For this reason, resource sharing recommendations focus on low impact uses and specialist user groups.

***Arundinaria alpina* being removed from Bwindi forest for planting on homesteads.** This species of bamboo is highly favoured by local people and has many different uses.
Photograph: Joe Watts

Parish workshops

The information collected, and the recommendations made in the Scott and Cunningham studies, provided the basis for starting negotiations. This work began in three pilot parishes. The aim was to develop agreement on previously identified multiple-use areas adjacent to these parishes. The main activity was a series of week-long workshops held at parish level. These used participatory rural appraisal (PRA) techniques adapted from community development approaches and the experience of Joint Forest Management in India. Issues covered included the use of the forest, resource and population trends, various community organisations and the nomination of specialist resource users.

During the workshop, maps were drawn on the ground in participatory mapping exercises which located and prioritised key resources. These maps were transferred to paper, and data from Scott's survey and available topographical maps were incorporated. The maps were then taken into the forest with nominated resource users for further ground truthing. During these forest visits, names for forest areas and resource use areas were agreed, and the boundaries of the multiple-use zone were identified or confirmed.

At later meetings the most appropriate organisation to work with the National Park for the management of the multiple-use zones was discussed and developed, as well as the form of any agreement, and its administration and monitoring (see Section 8.5).

Training

The training of personnel involved in the management of the Bwindi Impenetrable National Park has been at three levels – training for local people, for local Park staff, and for CARE-DTC staff. As indicated in the discussion in the following section, local people have been trained in community monitoring and record-keeping procedures. The Park Warden, Community Conservation Rangers, and Patrol Rangers have all received training in communications skills, and in the PRA techniques used in village meetings. Patrol Rangers are also trained in monitoring and record-keeping procedures. In both cases, this training has been provided locally, by CARE-DTC staff and certain hired resource persons. As far as CARE-DTC staff themselves are concerned, training has been both local (in communications skills and PRA techniques) and overseas (a course on Joint Forest Management in India).

Mount Elgon National Park

Resource use assessment

Resource use assessment on Mount Elgon was instigated as a result of Wiley's (1993) recommendation. It was conducted in six parishes around the mountain, and aimed to follow the five stages set out by Wiley for a 'community-based approach to forest management', set out in Box 8.4. The six parishes were selected to represent a geographic range around the reserves and to cover specific issues that needed to be addressed. Initial work covered stages 1 to 3 in the approach recommended by Wiley (see Box 8.4). Stages 4 and 5 have yet to take place in all the parishes (see Section 8.5).

Box 8.4 The Five Stages for a Community-based Approach to Forest Management, as Recommended by Wiley

1. Initial consultation – at parish level involving a meeting and a walk (1 or 2 days)

2. Village-level resource assessment – involving a meeting with representatives from all villages (1day), a village profile (0.5 to 1 day) and walk with representatives from selected villages (0.5 to 1 day) and selected household interviews (3 days)

3. Resource assessment in forest with parish representatives (1 to 2 days)

4. Planning of a forest management plan – with some form of locally elected forest management committee (2 days)

5. Drafting and agreement of trial Joint Management Agreement (1 day plus)

(The expected time required for each parish is given in brackets, although it will vary to some extent according to circumstances).

Source: Wiley (1993)

At the introductory meeting held at parish level, the new approach towards forest management was introduced. This maximised transparency from the beginning regarding the reasons and need for collecting information. It was followed by a general information-gathering meeting at parish level (parish-level profile), and then more detailed information collection through meetings with selected villages (village-level profiles) and specialist users. Quantitative data capable of extrapolation were obtained from interviews with opportunistically selected households (household-level). Data from each level could be cross-referenced to assess their validity. A short-cut version of this procedure can be conducted in other parishes in the future.

The method generated a large amount of data, incorporating socio-economic and spatial considerations such as wealth, gender, household composition and distance from the forest boundary. A distinction was made between households using, collecting and selling forest products, for a deeper understanding of the nuances of forest utilisation. Each detailed parish profile provides a basis on which management discussions with these particular communities can be initiated in the future. In addition, the results have been extrapolated to the entire forest-adjacent community, to offer an indication of forest use for the entire National Park. For example,

An important component of the resource assessment was to encourage the communities to begin thinking as *managers* rather than simply *users*, through activities such as community evaluation of the level of damage caused by their activities, and the level of control necessary, in a future management regime, to ensure sustainability.

the net monetary value of extractive resource use to all communities adjacent to Mount Elgon was estimated at between $US 1.5 and 1.7 million, seven times the value of the sustainable timber harvest.

Following village profiling, forest walks were held over a period of four days with selected resource users. During these walks information was collected on previous management regimes; particular areas were mapped and scored for various resources; and herbarium specimens were collected with information on the harvesting method and population biology (as far as was known) of the plants. (This was used for later assessment of their suitability for sustainable harvest.)

Biodiversity inventory and vegetation mapping

A biodiversity inventory and vegetation-mapping exercise was carried out on Mount Elgon in early 1993. A GIS was used in collating the map, which was produced the following year (Heist, 1994). The exercise was a major undertaking that has produced a useful source of reference. In particular, the use of GIS will allow linking of the resource use data to the maps; and, the map may be useful in the strategic planning of the use of certain vegetation types.

However, the intended use of the data collected under the mapping exercise could have been more effectively defined at the outset. In particular, the following points may be noted:

- The map scale may not be appropriate for detailed village discussions (this reflects the fact that there was no clear linkage from the start between the mapping exercise and the resource use assessment).

- Unless the GIS is used with care, this method of data collection could alienate the local community from the information collection and decision-making process.

- The exercise has not produced adequate data to act as a ecological base line for monitoring the impact of joint management.

Training

Different MENP Wardens and several extension staff from the Ministry of Agriculture, Animal Industry and Fisheries have been involved in the discussions and subsequent negotiations with the communities. This represents a certain level of on-site training. Once the approach to the management of resources within the Park has been confirmed by both UNP and the communities concerned, it is envisaged that an extensive training programme for both MENP staff and resource users will be developed.

Box 8.5 Mount Elgon Bamboo Assessment

Bamboo (*Arundinaria alpina*) forest covers about 21% of the Mount Elgon National Park and is one of the most important forest resources for the forest-adjacent communities, providing edible shoots, construction poles and basketry materials. A survey was commissioned by the project to:

- assess the use of bamboo by forest-adjacent communities
- assess the bamboo resource (from an ecological and utilisation perspective)
- make recommendations on the future management of the bamboo forest

The fieldwork had two components, one village-based and the other within the forest. The village study was conducted in 14 parishes in the form of semi-structured interviews with particular emphasis on bamboo product information to give an indication of the type and scale of demand.

The within-forest study was designed to correspond to the vegetation-mapping exercise that was being carried out simultaneously. Three of the major bamboo areas were selected with reference to both geographical distribution and the variation in the nature of use by communities. 170 plots were surveyed. In addition to standard site descriptions, various quantitative and qualitative assessments were made of the bamboo. The level of harvesting was established (by counting the number of cut culms) and a record made of the likely purpose to which harvested culms had been put. Each plot was scored in terms of its popularity (access and quality combined) and bamboo quality. Local bamboo users, who were integral members of the in-forest team, played a key role in this work. In particular, the local users' assessment of shoot harvesting popularity formed the basis for estimating the relative levels of shoot collection – data which were otherwise impossible to collect through a static assessment. All the trails within the three bamboo areas were walked and then the area mapped, together with more general user assessments of the popularity and quality of the bamboo.

The involvement of the bamboo users in all aspects of data collection led to a greater local understanding of the research. After an initial period of training, much of the quantitative data were collected by the harvesters themselves. Their proven ability to take an active role in this scientific process highlighted their potential for future participation in monitoring/research activities.

Using Cunningham's Rapid Vulnerability Assessment (see Boxes 8.2 and 8.3), bamboo was found to have high potential for harvesting. The extent of the resource on Mount Elgon (approximately 21% of the National Park, or 230 km^2) provides a further indication that some harvesting is likely to be sustainable, particularly given that less than 50% of the bamboo forest is accessible. This means that a large, natural protection area exists. This will be an important component of a zoning regime and will represent a control area for monitoring the impacts of utilisation elsewhere.

The overall conclusion of the research was that, even when only the effective harvesting areas are considered, current levels of harvesting are sustainable. As long as harvesting is well managed, most community needs can be satisfied from the forest.

Source: Scott (1994b)

Rwenzori Mountains National Park

UNP approval was given in 1994 for this National Park to pilot joint management in two parishes. The pilot parishes were selected in one district, the selection being based on ease of access and reasonably good relations between the Park staff and the communities. Concentrating initial activities in one district also means that, through extending activities to neighbouring parishes, an entire pilot area may be created in the future.

Since the Rwenzori Mountains National Park embarked on the process towards management agreements after the BINP and Mount Elgon, this has allowed some reflection on, and adaptation of, the earlier approaches. The intention is to develop joint management in parallel with the assessment of the resource and its use by local people. Considerable emphasis is being placed on the *process* used to achieve this. An important element of the process is that of training, to develop the management capacity of both the local UNP staff and the communities. As part of this training of project staff, intensive meetings are held before work in a parish begins, to discuss the objectives of village meetings, and what they are intended to achieve. Emphasis is placed on capacity building at each stage of the discussion, and care is taken that matters do not proceed to a later stage until adequate capacity is achieved. A further important feature is that, to ensure that local people are as fully involved in decision-making as possible, they are asked to define the information that they think should be gathered. They then have a greater sense of ownership in its collection, analysis and end use.

In the two pilot parishes, the UNP Warden (for Community Extension Education) held introductory parish meetings where he explained the concept of joint management. As always, the boundary of the discussion was also presented, in terms of certain issues on which the UNP will find it hard to compromise (for example, hunting), and other issues on which the community may find it hard to compromise (such as the collection of medicinal plants). Further meetings were held where the form and geographical remit of future management committees was discussed. Later, members of that committee were elected to represent various elements of the community and resource user groups. The committees also decided that they would prefer to be directly involved in collecting the information they would need to take management decisions, rather than to have 'experts' provide the information later.

Aerial photographs proved to be a useful tool for stimulating discussion on resource use in the two pilot parishes. They were scanned into a computer and printed (on a scale of approximately 1 km to 30 cm), in which form they can be joined to show the position of the settlements, farms and the forest. Local people readily identify obvious landmarks on the photographs. Information collected in community mapping exercises and during

The use of aerial photographs to clarify maps drawn by the community may be compared with the use of Global Positioning Systems for a similar purpose in Chapter 7 (East Kalimantan).

in-forest assessment has been transferred to the photographs, which have been laminated to facilitate drawing on them with overhead pens. Their main purpose is to serve as a check between community mapping and zoning and the official maps available (for example, in locating very small streams and other landmarks in the forest which local people identified as an appropriate boundary). It is vital that there is common agreement about the position of the boundaries of the various use zones.

Training

The process approach adopted has an inherent capacity-building/training component, involving all stakeholders. The focus has been on developing the capacity of local people to make decisions within the framework of the Park's management objectives. As someone with a key role, the Warden (for Community Outreach) has been intimately involved in this, his training taking place through working closely with his external adviser and the communities concerned. Two Community Rangers have also been involved in this process from the outset. As far as local communities are concerned, training has taken the form of providing opportunities to express and apply their knowledge of resource management. There has been little technical input to date; if this does prove necessary once management details have been agreed, the need will be addressed then.

8.5   Current and Future Developments

Bwindi National Park

Progress towards participatory management

Memoranda of Understanding have been signed in all three pilot parishes. The Memorandum is the main document recording the outcome of months of discussion and negotiation between local UNP staff (assisted by DTC) and the individual parish concerned. Mpungu parish is almost surrounded by the National Park and was the first parish to embark on the multiple-use negotiations. Discussions began in June 1993, the Memorandum of Understanding was signed in April 1994, and the first community harvest took place in June 1994. The form of the Memorandum of Understanding for Mpungu parish is indicated in Box 8.6. Each agreement will follow the same basic format, whilst of course differing in regard to the name and composition of the forest society, the species and quantities permitted for harvesting, etc. However, it may be noted that, after all the negotiations, the local community will only effectively participate in the management of 20% of the Park, the rest being managed solely by the UNP.

> # Box 8.6 The Memorandum of Understanding between Uganda National Parks and Mpungu Parish
>
> The agreement notes that the communities' access to the National Park is a privilege, not a right. The bilingual document (English and Rukiga) specifies the establishment of a community and resource users' organisation, the *Forest Society*. The committee of the society is made up of 42 people representing each stretcher society (25), representatives from the resource users (4), representatives of local administration from RCs (3), religious leaders (2), chiefs (3) and women (2). From UNP there is the Patrol Ranger and Community Conservation Ranger and from DTC, a Conservation Extension Agent. The aims of the society are, *inter alia*, to:
>
> - Conserve Bwindi Impenetrable National Park.
> - Act as an information link between the park and the community.
> - Control the nominated resource users.
> - Participate in the management of the multiple-use areas.
>
> The society is to meet three times a year and at the Annual General Meeting the memorandum and its implementation will be reviewed. Off-take from the forest is to be recorded by the communities, with the monitoring of species use being the responsibility of UNP (with ITFC). The Society has the responsibility of compiling the records collected by the individual stretcher societies on resource use or infringements. Resource assessment is to be a joint activity.
>
> Collection from the forest is limited to within multiple-use areas for community-nominated specialist herbalists and basket-makers (all issued with identity cards) collecting specified species according to given quotas. For example, the annual quota for a given collector of the tree fern (*Cyathea manniana*) is six handfuls of leaves and six palmfuls of bark. The choice of species to be harvested and a suggested harvesting quota were partially governed by the botanical qualities and utilisation of each species, as well as community requests. This information was collected during workshops with specialist users where the expected rate of recovery of the species to be harvested was discussed. The information was then considered by a committee of UNP, ITFC and DTC staff who made recommendations to the Director of ITFC and the UNP Warden in Charge.
>
> Following the joint monitoring programme, changes to the quotas may be made. The agreement with Mpungu parish specifies 7 species for basket making and 17 species for medicinal purposes. It also permits the use of footpaths in the Park. The multiple-use areas covered by the agreement are smaller than the areas originally identified by the IFCP and Scott, and reflect the Forest Society's own assessment of its management capacity. The Society also felt that it should only use a part of the potential collection area to allow for 'fallowing' if the resource began to decline in the area actively used.
>
> Source: UNP (1994)

Monitoring

The monitoring of the participatory management agreement is to cover illegal activities, utilised species, general impact on the ecosystem, user presence and community attitudes. It is planned that such information will be collected from three sources:

- the resource users/Forestry Society
- the patrol rangers
- formal ecological monitoring

At the level of the resource users and the Forest Society, information will be collected (with assistance from the Community Conservation Ranger) on resource off-take, illegal activities and the state of the resources. Emphasis is put on self-monitoring by the communities. In one area of the Park, newly gained access to keep bee hives in the forest was followed by an increase in the number of hunting snares. The community was threatened with losing the privilege of keeping bees and now the area is said to have the lowest level of snares in the Park. Although performance, measured by the local level of protection given to the Park, should ideally be linked to the immediate reward of the safeguarding of a local resource, it may also be necessary to link it to other incentives. Development funds would be an obvious example, but they have not been used in this context to date. UNP Rangers can also collect information within patrol reports and from records of community harvesting days (see Box 8.7).

Monitoring the harvest of *Smilax kraussiana*, Bwindi Impenetrable National Park
Photograph: Joe Watts

At a more formal level the ITFC and UNP have a role in the ecological monitoring of the impact of the controlled harvesting and the evaluation of additional species requested by the communities. So far, 22 permanent sample plots (PSPs) have been demarcated. The intention is that they will form part of a network of such plots for (as yet unspecified) ecological monitoring.

Recommendations for future research and monitoring in Bwindi are currently being prepared by the ITFC and DTC. This is an area where there is a need for additional inputs, including ecological baseline studies.

Box 8.7 A Community Harvest: Rutugunda Parish, Bwindi Impenetrable National Park

This was to be the first harvest in Bwindi Impenetrable National Park under the Memorandum of Understanding with the people of Rutugunda Parish. The six staff from UNP, DTC and ITFC met with the 18 nominated resource users at mid-morning by a church on a hill looking down on farmland and towards the forest boundary. After greetings and introductions the users were issued with identity cards bearing their photographs. The party moved off together along the path through coffee and food farms and reached the forest boundary within half an hour. They then divided. The seven women collectors went to harvest material to weave winnowing baskets, about five men dispersed to collect medicinal plants and the rest of the men focused on collecting the liane **Enshuri** (*Smilax kraussiana*).

The **Enshuri** monitoring team followed the resource users as they darted around the forest collecting the vines. The ground runners are harvested as they are more flexible than the vertical shoots. This is the traditional method, which is apparently sustainable. The plant grows in patches which the collectors had learnt of from their fathers, and they reported no change in extent. On observing the harvesting site, the monitors marked its position with a red flag noting the date and the product harvested. If a sizeable amount is harvested from an area, a 20 m x 20 m plot will be marked out to monitor exploitation of the species.

A sample bundle of coiled **Enshuri** was unwound and the UNP/DTC staff measured the length of the vine, as well as the number of nodes and the middle diameter. Unfortunately heavy rain began to fall and everyone ran back to the village. When all were assembled at the original meeting point, each product collected was weighed and noted alongside the collector's name. As the harvest had been interrupted by the weather and the next programmed harvest was in six months time, a new date was set to complete this harvest's quota.

It is not intended that detailed monitoring of harvests and plots should be carried out indefinitely, or at all sites. Measuring off-take is as important for developing communities' own monitoring skills as for the information gained *per se*. Although the intensive measuring of the harvest may set a useful precedent, the laborious methods could also have a negative impact. This is further compounded by recent interviews indicating that previous off-take rates may have been significantly higher than those suggested during the PRAs from which the quotas were set. Either the communities' respect will decrease for a system that appears to present unreasonable quotas or unnecessary complications to harvesting, or they may simply continue to harvest as normal in the periods between official harvests and go through the act of the official harvest as a price to pay for peace with the Park. It is hoped that the growing communication between the Park and the communities will eliminate this problem.

Harvesting *Smilax kraussiana.* A member of the Rutugunda Parish harvesting team at work in Bwindi Impenetrable National Park.
Photograph: Joe Watts

The UNP/DTC staff have intentionally designed the system to be one of action research, acknowledging the experimental nature of the monitoring yet immediately addressing the needs of the communities. In the longer term there may not be a need to measure the harvests (which are set at conservative quotas for resources that were originally selected for their potential for sustainable exploitation). However, there is a need to move on from this, albeit valuable, initial stage and establish effective and realistic monitoring that on the one hand will appear rational and maintain the support of the resource users, and on the other hand present rigorous ecological monitoring (at a level that is practical in the longer term) that will satisfy the wider conservation community (including the essential support from the Board of Trustees of UNP). Pragmatically, even if the ecology of the multiple-use zone is altered, if, by its use, the protection of the core (80% of the Park) is assured, perhaps the process of multiple-use is still justified. It may be more realistic to monitor impacts on the resource (such as evidence of over-stripping of bark of species such as *Prunus africana*) rather than the 'official' harvest, which may not be all that is harvested.

In the long term there is the intention to encourage much closer links between the communities and their environment (with the work of the DTC's new Community-Based Environmental Management Section) and the development of community groups to consider the problems of the exploitation of individual species themselves.

Weighing the *Smilax kraussiana* harvest. A bundle of coiled liane is weighed by UNP/DTC staff.
Photograph: Joe Watts

Women collectors of Rutungunda Parish. Forest products gathered by the women are weighed by UNP/DTC staff.
Photograph: Joe Watts

Mount Elgon National Park

Following the resource use assessment conducted in six parishes (Wiley, 1993; Scott, 1994a), the Director of UNP approved the piloting of Joint Forest Management in two parishes. Within these two parishes, meetings were conducted in each village bordering the National Park. The main objective was to increase public awareness about the approach being adopted towards Park management, and to obtain an input from all those concerned. Each village was then asked to elect members from amongst the primary resource collectors to represent it on a Forest Use Management Committee. The final monitoring and control of forest use are along individual user trails that lead up to the bamboo area of the mountain.

As in the BINP, the boundary of the discussions (regarding the main threats to the ecosystem) is set prior to the meetings, in terms of no hunting or pit-sawing. These controls are in fact similar to those the communities recommended during the resource assessment.

The context of the management discussions on Mount Elgon is slightly different from that under the BINP. The forest area is far greater, as is the adjacent human population. Thus it appears that the project is faced with a larger forest user base, without the promise of significant revenue-sharing schemes. At this stage it is felt that future access to the forest resources needs to be wider than specialist users only, in order to achieve a sufficiently wide beneficiary base and 'human buffer' for the forest. Therefore more extensive and intensive use of the forest is being discussed, including bamboo harvesting and some level of grazing (perhaps as a temporary measure). There will probably be less emphasis on quotas for resources of low potential conservation concern and more emphasis on the community monitoring of illegal activities. The focus will be more on the forbidden and less on the permitted. There may be considerable scope for participatory monitoring of the resource – particularly with bamboo, which is a relatively simple and widespread resource to manage. All issues (and all resources) are being discussed at the same time. This contrasts with the more cautious, sequential resource use discussions under the BINP.

These ideas may represent an additional step towards the decentralisation of forest management. The possible implications of these meetings will therefore be built into a 'mock' joint management agreement, which will be submitted in order to gauge the support of UNP headquarters (which has already sanctioned the joint management pilot initiatives). This is important as UNP staff need reassurance regarding the direction of their management as much as the local populations; the process involves risk for both parties.

> It is important that the results of the resource assessment are visibly returned to the communities, where they can be used as a base for further discussion. If the communities' earlier work and suggestions are not used, there is a risk that local confidence in the process may be undermined.

Rwenzori Mountains National Park

It is intended that the community will be actively involved from the start in all stages of information gathering and, later, monitoring. Sustainable harvesting levels can be assessed and readjusted more effectively in conjunction with users who are fully aware of the resource and the impact of their practices. This *process* approach is based on the assumption that a future Joint Management Agreement and its implementation will be as meaningful to the community and to UNP as the process which it formalises.

There may be problems with this as yet untried approach. It requires reasonable understanding and agreement at each stage of the process, and therefore may take considerably longer than the more structured approach followed under the BINP. If the process takes too long, frustration may develop (within the communities, UNP or donors), whereas, under the BINP, the process is being refined within a working system.

At the beginning of the discussions the UNP/Project negotiating team is only minimally informed about the conservation priorities and resource use, and therefore may be negotiating from a position of weakness. However, the parity of the lack of knowledge at the beginning and the development of that knowledge together may produce franker, better informed and more balanced negotiations in the long term. The committees have contained representatives of all resource users as the communities have perceived them. For example, herbalists were identified and represented as a single group whereas experience from elsewhere (Tony Cunningham, pers comm.) may indicate that sub-groups such as traditional birth attendants may have very different needs and uses of the forest.

> It is hoped that the approach being adopted in the Rwenzori Mountains will provide an indication of the potential of communities in Uganda to take a much greater role as managers of the resource.

8.6 Conclusion

The case studies illustrate that it is just as important to consider the *way* in which forest resource information is collected as *what* is collected. The nearer and more comprehensible that process is to the people involved in management (both resource users and UNP staff), the more likely they are to understand and have a sense of ownership of the resource. This process has begun to happen in all the case study projects, although via the use of different techniques – resource assessments using local insights, PRA exercises, and village profiling. There is obviously a difference in approach between the sequential method adopted under the BINP, where information is gathered and then management is cautiously started, and the more aggregated approach on Mount Elgon (and to a greater extent in the Rwenzori Mountains) where wider debate, information collection and initial access to the resource are envisaged which will be developed as more information becomes available. There is also an apparent difference in the intended level of local people's ultimate participation in resource management. This, however, has still to be clarified.

Clearly there is a certain hesitancy amongst all parties to embarking on the new idea of participatory or joint management. The local community may fear to ask too much, the UNP headquarters/ Board of Trustees may fear to give too much, thus risking the integrity of the Parks, whilst local UNP staff may feel caught in the middle. Ensuring that the information gathered is accessible at all levels should be one way of increasing the

Having the responsibility to use and assess information is part of the process of developing the capacities of, and giving greater responsibilities to, the forest-adjacent communities and local UNP staff. The work in the Rwenzori Mountains should provide a useful insight in this regard.

confidence of all parties. This should help contribute to more open, balanced and informed debates, leading to a greater sense of understanding and ownership of any agreement reached.

A major issue (raised by Cunningham *et al.*, 1993) is the cost of long-term monitoring of certain forest resources. This could be so high as to threaten ensuring their sustainable exploitation. However, it is argued by BINP and DTC staff that, through the selection of the least vulnerable species for harvesting and monitoring, monitoring costs should be minimalised and may be low enough for the community to cover by themselves in the future. An additional potential problem is the lack of adequate ecological baseline data. Monitoring systems are being developed in Bwindi but the complexity of the vegetation renders it a difficult task. Nevertheless, the forest is far better known as a result of the studies conducted under the project. These have generated a wealth of data, and perhaps a greater problem is the processing, storage, and appropriate dissemination of all this information. It is unclear whether UNP or donors are willing to bear the cost of monitoring, but clearly the cost cannot be simply balanced with the cost of the resources extracted – the value of local people's co-operation goes much further than the vines or medicines harvested.

The flexibility of management under the UNP Board of Trustees has greatly contributed to the innovative approaches adopted within the three National Parks. It is important to maintain such momentum and to keep all the interested parties (local resource users, local UNP/Project staff, UNP – Headquarters and Board of Trustees, and donors) informed.

References

Cunningham, A. B. (1992) 'People, Park and Plant Use – Research and Recommendations for Multiple Use Zones and Development Alternatives around Bwindi Impenetrable National Park, Uganda'. Report prepared for CARE-International, Kampala.

Cunningham, A. B., Wild, R., Mutebi, J. and **Tsekeli, A.** (1993) 'People and Wild Plant Use: Mgahainga Gorilla National Park – an Investigation into Past, Current and Possible Future Utilisation of Wild Plants, and Appropriate Resource Substitution around Mgahinga Gorilla National Park, Uganda'. Report prepared for CARE-International, Kampala.

Harcourt, C. (1992) 'Uganda' in Sayer, J. A., Harcourt, C. S. and Collins, N. M., (eds). *The Conservation Atlas of Tropical Forests. Africa*. Macmillan, London.

Heist, M. van (1994) 'Land Unit Map of Mount Elgon National Park'. Unpublished Technical Report No 13. Mount Elgon Conservation and Development Project, Uganda.

Howard, P. C. (1991) *Nature Conservation in Uganda's Tropical Forest Reserves*. IUCN, Gland, Switzerland and Cambridge, UK.

Scott, P. J. (1992) 'Fringe Benefits: Minor Forest Product Collection Within Buffer Zones as a Potential Tool for Conflict Resolution in The Impenetrable (Bwindi) National Park – Uganda'. Unpublished M.Sc. Thesis, Agricultural University of Norway.

Scott, P. J. (1994a) *Assessment of Natural Resource Use by Communities from Mount Elgon National Park.* Technical Report No. 15, Mount Elgon Conservation and Development Project.

Scott, P. J. (1994b) *Bamboo: Potential for Utilisation by the Communities Surrounding Mount Elgon National Park.* Technical Report submitted to the Mount Elgon Conservation and Development Project. November.

Struhsaker, T. T. (1987) 'Forestry Issues and Conservation in Uganda', *Biological Conservation* 39: 209–34.

Uganda National Parks (1994) *Memorandum of Understanding between Uganda National Parks – Bwindi Impenetrable Forest National Park and the People of Mpungu Parish: an Agreement Concerning Collaborative Forest Management at Bwindi Impenetrable National Park.*

Wild, R. and **Mutebi, J.** (1994). 'Bwindi Impenetrable National Park, Multiple-Use Plan'. Draft report to Uganda National Parks.

Wild, R., Mutebi, J. and **Cunningham, A. B.** (1995) 'Networks to Enhance the Conservation of Bwindi Impenetrable National Park'. Networks and Nature Conservation. CSIRO, Australia.

Wiley, L. (1993) *Report on Short Advisory Input: to Prepare a Programme to Assess Forest-use and the Potential for Community-based Forest Management.* Technical Report No. 10, Mount Elgon Conservation and Development Project.

Acronyms specific to this chapter

BINP	Bwindi Impenetrable National Park
DTC	Development through Conservation
IFCP	Impenetrable Forest Conservation Project
ITFC	Institute for Tropical Forest Conservation (a faculty of Mbarara University, Uganda)
MECDP	Mount Elgon Conservation and Development Project
IUCN	World Conservation Union
PCA	Potential Collection Area (in Bwindi Impenetrable National Park)
PPC	Park Parish Council (in Bwindi Impenetrable National Park)
UNP	Uganda National Parks
USAID	United States Agency for International Development

9 Discussion: Advancing along the Learning Curve

The case studies described in the preceding chapters are diverse, and in many ways reflect their individual circumstances. Nevertheless, certain experiences are shared by all or a number of them. This penultimate chapter examines some of the common themes and potential lessons that may be drawn from the case studies, where possible placing these in the perspective of wider field experience. The discussion is structured around the following topics:

- social and institutional aspects
- practical aspects of fieldwork
- forest assessment for management: the limitations of silvicultural knowledge
- economic viability
- local participation re-examined

9.1 Social and Institutional Aspects

There is already a substantial body of literature discussing the social and institutional conditions under which participatory forestry is more or less likely to succeed (Cernea, 1991; Fox and Fisher, 1990; Thomson, 1992; Britt-Kapoor, 1994; Carter, Connelly and Wilson, 1994; Hobley, 1996). In the context of forest resource assessment, the following key points may be highlighted for discussion:

- government attitudes and supporting legislation
- forest ownership
- working with the community

Government Attitudes and Supporting Legislation

The best known examples of successful community or participatory forestry initiatives occur in countries such as Nepal and India. These countries have adopted policies and legislation giving local people rights to control and/or manage forest resources (although in India, legislation varies on a state-to-state basis). Countries with such a background might also be expected to provide the most complex and well developed examples of participatory forest assessment techniques. In fact, the link is not so straightforward. The case study from Nepal described in Chapter 6 provides an interesting example, but is far from being the most technically advanced form of forest assessment described. For reasons made clear in the chapter, technically complex forest inventory procedures would be inappropriate and are not demanded by the government. Of the case studies documented in this book, the greatest technical complexity may be ascribed to the Quintana Roo Forestry Project in Mexico, which has developed against a mixed background of government and legislative support. In the East Kalimantan case study, government attitudes to local people controlling and managing areas of forest themselves are the least favourable of any of the case studies. However, this has actually served as a catalyst to arouse local people's interest in forest resource assessment.

The development of interesting participatory forest resource assessment initiatives is thus not necessarily related to supporting government attitudes and policies. Indeed, an important use of forest resource assessment is to formalise issues of forest control between local people and government authorities, whether at the level of ownership or rights of management. Maps, surveys and inventories are all tools used by governments to quantify resources and, in the process, exercise control over them. As the case study from East Kalimantan argues convincingly, local people's interest in adopting such tools may be to 'translate' their claims and knowledge systems into terms which government bureaucracies will accept.

Where political and legislative support exists, participatory forest resource assessment has an important role in the institutionalisation of participatory forest management. Maps, surveys and inventories can in this case serve to demonstrate to the authorities a commitment on the part of local people to planned, rational forest management. Governments have a responsibility to ensure the maintenance of a permanent forest area (although its extent will clearly depend on national forest policy). Without a clear demonstration of planned forest management, a government might be justified in refusing to sanction or support (by financial or other means) forest operations by local people. This is especially the case if it entails the handing over of forest land currently under State control (as in Nepal). The key feature, of course, is what form of forest assessment different governments choose to accept as proof of commitment to planned forest management, and then how they monitor and evaluate its implementation. Here the forest inventories of low sampling intensity demanded as a formality in some Latin American countries contrast with the theoretically much less accurate, but arguably in practice far more meaningful, form of forest assessment conducted by Forest User Groups (FUGs) in Nepal as a part of their Operational Plan. The willingness of the government of Nepal to recognise formally a system of forest assessment that has a greater qualitative than quantitative element may be seen, therefore, as a demonstration of its strong support for community forestry.

Forest Ownership

Local people's willingness to devote time and money (either directly or indirectly) to conducting any form of resource assessment is likely to depend on a strong sense of ownership. However, this ownership may not necessarily be recognised in the national law of the country concerned. Legal security of tenure over the forests in the case study chapters varies, but in all cases local people *perceive* the forest concerned to be theirs.

The conclusion that legal security of land tenure is not a prerequisite for participatory forest resource assessment cannot be applied universally. In some countries legal security of tenure is required for any form of formal forest management, including assessment, by local people. This is illustrated by the example of Costa Rica, given in Box 9.1.

Working with the Community

Two broad points may be made about the development of working relations between outsiders and local people, and amongst local people themselves. Specific aspects about working with local people in participatory forest assessment are covered in the relevant sections (most notably Section 9.2) of this chapter.

All the case studies in this book indicate the importance of outsiders gaining an understanding of local community dynamics before initiating any forest assessment activities, although the methods used for gaining such information have not been discussed in detail. Any individual outsider, project or government official working with local people must develop their trust and respect if s/he is to establish a working partnership with them. This is particularly the case when suggestions for forest assessment are initiated by outsiders, rather than by local people themselves. Good relationships with local people can be particularly essential when matters do not go according to plan and, for example, difficult and unexpected forest assessment decisions have to be taken. This is well illustrated in the development of the inventory design in the Quintana Roo case study, and also in the Ghana case study, where a number of time-consuming attempts had to be made before a satisfactory survey and mapping method was achieved.

Box 9.1 Participatory Forest Resource Assessment for Forest Management in Costa Rica: The Importance of Secure Land Tenure

The scope for participatory forest resource management in Costa Rica appears more limited than in other countries within the region, because of a number of social and historical factors. A number of initiatives have been attempted using forest resources that are perceived to be communally held, or by combining a number of individually owned forest blocks into a single unit for management purposes. Some external assistance has invariably been necessary as, by law, a registered professional forester must supervise the inventory/stock survey, prepare the management plan and monitor logging activities. The success of the various initiatives has been mixed, but it is clear that an important prerequisite is security of land tenure. Where a land holding has not been inscribed in the Public Register of Property, permission to harvest timber will not be given by the **Dirección General Forestal** (DGF – the State forestry service), nor will state forest management incentives be granted. Legally recognised ownership is a common feature of two of Costa Rica's more successful examples of natural forest management by local communities, Coope San Juan on the San Carlos plains and ASACODE in Talamanca.

The tenure requisite is complicated by the fact that many of the communities where participatory forest management is a potential option are **asentamientos campesinos** (State-funded settlements for small farmers). These **asentamientos** are often large farms that have been purchased by the State through the Agrarian Development Institute (IDA) and divided into small lots for distribution amongst landless people. Although the land title is initially held by IDA, it will eventually be passed to the **campesinos** who purchase their lots over a ten-year period.

The only exception to this process concerns any areas of forest within the **asentamiento**, control of which passes automatically to the DGF, thus being incorporated into the public forest estate (comprising forest reserves, protected zones, national parks, etc.). In fact, management of State forest reserves for timber production is permitted through a concession agreement, and **campesino** groups are able to claim exoneration from the normal stumpage and concession fees. However, few, if any, **asentamientos** have had the technical and legal advice necessary to give them the confidence to act on this. Two projects (Proyecto Chortega in Guanacaste and Proyecto de Manejo Integrado del Bosque Natural on the northern Atlantic plains) are currently working with a number of **asentamientos**, State and non-governmental bodies to facilitate this transfer of usufruct rights.

(continued/...)

Box 9.1 *(continued)*

The Coope San Juan perhaps provides an indicative model for the successful development of other participatory forest management initiatives in the future. It is a communal farm in Northern Costa Rica which includes 212 ha of natural forest. For the last three years the community has been managing this forest, which belongs to them, under a State-sponsored forest management incentive programme. Assistance with technical operations has been limited to periodic advice and training from one professional forester (funded through GTZ, the German Agency for Technical Co-operation) and the State-funded National Learning Institute (INA). A number of individuals have been trained as **paraforestales** (local forest technicians), learning resource assessment techniques, harvesting, extraction and silvicultural treatments through on-the-job instruction. Features key to the success of the initiative are:

- Secure land tenure.

- A natural organisational unit (the co-operative).

- The community directing the professional forester rather than the other way round.

- The introduction of **paraforestales**, reducing the cost of technical operations and creating some employment.

Source: Stewart Maginnis (1995, pers comm.)

The success of any participatory forest resource assessment initiative is also dependent on a common commitment amongst local people. Although often this is more readily found amongst communities of a uniform ethnic, caste or religious grouping, such uniformity is by no means essential. It is possible for communities of quite diverse composition to work together, if they perceive the need. Thus, for example, in Nepal many successfully functioning Forest User Groups (FUGs) comprise members of a variety of ethnic groups and castes. Their adequate and fair representation on the FUG committee is essential, and many existing committees demonstrate that this can be achieved. Strong local organisations are a key feature in developing a participatory approach to forest assessment and management, as demonstrated in many of the case studies – from the **Societales Civiles** of the **ejidos** in Mexico to the **abataka** groups and stretcher societies in Uganda.

9.2 Practical Lessons of Fieldwork

This section considers working in the field with local people from a wide variety of perspectives. Issues discussed include:

- recognising local people's strengths and weaknesses

- building on local knowledge
- species identification
- systematic, planned data collection
- statistical aspects
- training

Recognising Local People's Strengths and Weaknesses

A participatory approach to forest resource assessment requires sensitivity to local people's information needs and capabilities. Such capabilities will vary both between communities and within a given community – between different groups and between individuals.

Differences between communities

The local people participating in the case studies described in this book are from very different cultural backgrounds with different locally-based knowledge systems. They have been exposed to different levels of formal education, and have different reliance on cash versus subsistence economies (largely as dictated by access to markets). Thus a forest resource assessment method that has been adopted successfully by local people in one area will not necessarily be readily adopted by people elsewhere.

Where systematic forest resource assessment methods are to be used by people who are barely literate and/or have limited numeracy, particular explanation, modification and adaption will be required. The technician introducing new concepts and techniques should be responsible for explaining them in a comprehensible, unambiguous manner. The onus should not be on local people to understand – and be labelled as stupid if they do not.

A few tentative conclusions may be drawn about technical aspects of forest resource assessment which local people may find particularly difficult to conceptualise. Given the now wide experience in participatory mapping in many different countries, map making does not generally appear to be a difficult concept for local people, perhaps because two-dimensional pictorial representations of the three-dimensional environment are common to many societies. However, *accurate* mapping demands a different level of comprehension and an understanding of scale – that, for example, 1 cm on a map represents 10 m on the ground (if this is the scale used). The situation is further complicated if the area to be mapped is of rugged terrain and corrections for slope are necessary. For example, a specific difficulty in understanding the use of clinometers to correct for slope was reported amongst trainees in both the case study from Ecuador and in the NTFP inventory workshop described in the Indonesia case study. At the level of field measurements, local participants in the case studies from Nigeria, Ecuador, Ghana and Indonesia all found difficulty in maintaining compass bearings to cut a straight survey line.

Levels of formal education are not synonymous with capability. However, techniques used for accurate mapping, surveying and inventory are all based on concepts taught in formal education and are thus likely to be more readily grasped by those with such an education.

250

However, the extent to which this reflects a conceptual as opposed to practical difficulty is uncertain.

As far as forest inventories are concerned, the concept of sampling may prove to be an especially difficult one, even for people who have received some formal education, as in the Quintana Roo case study from Mexico. (It may be recalled that the statistical validity of sampling was still being debated amongst learned mathematicians at the beginning of this century.) In this respect, 100% stock surveys have a definite advantage, although if the area of forest to be inventoried is very large, they may not be practicable. Advancing further into statistical theory, the authors of the case study from Indonesia note that the local people had difficulty with the concept of standard errors. Given that this is an experience common to many university students, this is hardly surprising. Brief comment on the statistical aspects of participatory resource assessment is made in a specific sub-section later in this chapter.

Differences within communities

The different skills and knowledge base of different groups within a community (as determined by, for example, gender, age, ethnic origins, and caste) have been made clear in a number of the case studies. Individuals within any community also vary in their interests, skills, education and experience. Much can be achieved by working closely with those whose abilities are particularly suited to forest resource assessment work. Forest users with particular knowledge and expertise about plant identification and uses are an obvious example, but there may also be people in the community whose past work experience means that they have other pertinent skills. For example, in the Ghana case study certain key individuals were formerly employed as clerks or, in one case, as an agricultural extension worker. They could thus readily conceptualise the taking of records along transect lines and map making. In parts of Nepal, retired soldiers are often exceptionally innovative individuals. Their overseas work experience in the army may have given them a marked interest in trying out new ideas, and/or provided specific experience in, for example, record keeping and conducting surveys.

Whilst certain individuals may make a particularly valuable contribution to a community forest assessment exercise, it is also important that they do not dominate the process to the exclusion of others. Here careful facilitation may be necessary to try to ensure the participation of all interested parties.

Building on Local Knowledge

Building on local knowledge and experience follows from the above discussion. It is an important aspect of participatory forestry which is given limited coverage in the case studies – largely because the collection of such information is a part of good

251

preliminary investigations, which have not been a focus of the book. Some of the case study projects have clearly made greater attempts to build on local knowledge and experience than others, the most serious attempts being demonstrated in the examples from Ghana, Nepal, East Kalimantan and Uganda. Where there is a particular focus on NTFP assessment rather than on timber species, there appears to be more likelihood of local people's knowledge being actively sought. This may reflect, amongst other issues, the lesser knowledge on the part of many foresters about non-timber uses of forest species (see Section 9.3).

There is a large body of evidence of traditional/indigenous forest management systems in many countries, although in a number of cases such systems may be breaking down owing to changing circumstances and pressures (for example, Gomez-Pompa and Kaus, 1990; Redford and Padoch, 1992). Amongst the countries in which case studies were conducted, Nepal has a particularly rich variety of local forest management systems (Fisher, 1989; Tamang, 1990). Wherever new forest management initiatives are planned, any existing or past indigenous forest management systems should be thoroughly investigated. Their incorporation into new assessment methods and management plans, where possible or appropriate, should then be considered. This is, in fact, the case in the preparation of forest user group Operational Plans in Nepal.

The use of local knowledge with regard to plant identification and uses, particularly concerning NTFPs, is an aspect discussed in many of the case studies. Species identification is an important issue, and merits separate discussion.

Species Identification

Problems with species identification through confusion over local and botanical names are common to a number of the case studies (most notably in Ecuador, Mexico, and Ghana). It is often assumed, particularly early in a participatory forest management initiative, that if forest assessment is to be for and by local people, local plant names are sufficient for identification purposes. In practice, there are a number of difficulties with this assumption, most notably as follows:

- the scientific concept of a species is not necessarily synonymous with the local concept; and
- local people may have several names for the same species.

Local people, and certain individuals in particular, often have a very detailed knowledge of forest plants and can identify numerous species. However, their differentiation of plants into species or types may not correspond with botanical definitions, and is often dictated more by their uses of the plant than by morphological or phenotypical characteristics. Local people may

The recognition of differences between local and scientific concepts of species does not imply that one is better or more precise than the other. In fact, there is currently no universal agreement on the scientific concept. Furthermore, botanists recognise that the taxonomy of many tropical forest plants has been poorly investigated and is in need of revision. The major advantage of the international system of scientific classification is that it provides a standard reference – which nevertheless can be revised if appropriate.

distinguish several types or 'species' where botanists recognise only one, and indeed have a different name for each. Conversely, they may use the same name for a number of plants that botanists consider to be several distinct species. They may also tend to use a generic name for a group of plants, and only differentiate them into 'types', which botanists would consider to be separate species, when specifically asked to do so. This is illustrated with specific examples in Box 9.2, for Nepal.

In some circumstances, both botanists and local people may recognise a single species, but it may have more than one local name. This may not be surprising if members of different ethnic groups are living in the same area, and each group has its own language and system of plant names. Even where one common language is spoken, plant names may differ on a regional basis, or several may have become assimilated into common use. For example, many common plants in England have more than one name. Thus *Prunus avium* may be known as Common Wild Cherry, Gean, or (less commonly) Mazard. Different names may reflect regional dialects and the influence of past invading peoples, but, given the mobility of the current English population, any of the names may be used by different individuals now living in one part of the country.

Box 9.2 The Concept of Plant Species in the Middle Hills of Nepal

The nearest equivalent Nepali word for species is **jaat**, a word also used to distinguish the ethnic group or caste of people. In some cases, one plant **jaat** is categorised into different types, **khalko**. Often a plant **jaat** corresponds with a botanically recognised species, whilst a **khalko** of that **jaat** corresponds with a sub-species or variety. However, this is not always the case, as illustrated by the examples below.

Local recognition of types within a single botanically recognised species

Until recently, botanists only recognised *Ficus semicordata* as a single, uniform species. However, local people in Nepal widely recognise two types, **khalko**, of the tree. These are known locally as **khasro khanyu** and **rai khanyu**. Investigations into this local distinction led botanists to recognise two distinct sub-species. Local people distinguish the trees primarily in terms of their leaf fodder attributes (one is considered a far better fodder than the other), while botanists choose morphological criteria, but a distinction is clear (Amatya, 1989).

Botanical recognition of different species within a single jaat

The two species *Machilus duthei* and *M. odoratissima* are both referred to as **kaaulo** by local people. However, if specifically asked, they state that the **jaat** is of two types (**khalko**). These are described as **kaalo** (black) **kaaulo** (*M. duthei*) and **seto** (white) **kaaulo** (*M. odoratissima*). They are regarded as having broadly similar fodder, timber and fuelwood properties. (Carter, 1991).

It may be seen from this discussion that there is considerable potential for confusion if only local names are used in a survey or inventory. The greater the number of species that are included in records, the greater this potential. Limiting the species recorded to those considered to be the most important may be advisable, although the decision will largely depend on the purpose of the assessment. Local names must be used in record-taking if local people are to feel a sense of ownership over the data, but checking the botanical identity of all plants can greatly increase reliability. Indeed, through such checking, additional information may be learned about local definitions and plant uses.

> Scientific and local systems of species identification are not, and should not be seen to be, mutually exclusive. Ideally, they should be used to complement each other.

Systematic, Planned Data Collection

The detailed development of a forest assessment system for a particular set of circumstances can only be achieved through practical experience. Nevertheless, much can be learned from practical texts already available (such as Freese, 1984; Philip, 1994). The experience of the case study projects indicates a number of potential difficulties which may be avoided by the careful planning and sequencing of activities. Points to consider particularly when adopting a participatory approach to forest assessment include those listed below.

- Decide exactly what information is required, as dictated by the broad purpose and specific objectives of the assessment exercise. Ideally, the decision should be made collectively by all the local people involved, and be arrived at through a series of preliminary investigations, village meetings and discussions. A balance must be struck between trying to collect too much information, creating an unwieldy data set that is complicated to use, and too little information, which may entail a costly re-assessment exercise at a later date to gain vital information missed the first time. A particularly important decision is which species should be included in the assessment.

- Think widely and discuss the different methods of forest assessment that may be appropriate before making a choice. If several methods seem possible, consider conducting a small trial run of each with local people to gain their opinion on which is most suitable. Try different measuring techniques to determine what is most appropriate. Beware of sacrificing accuracy for simplicity; for example, local people may not need much time to learn how to use a tape measure or chain, which can be far more accurate than pacing.

- Consider carefully how data should be recorded, stored and processed to maximise local people's involvement, understanding and ownership of the information. This point should be addressed before any assessment work begins. In some cases, pictorial representations of the data in the form of maps and diagrams may be most appropriate. In other cases, a written account in the local language may be best, and in still others, a factual presentation of summarised calculations. The presentation of data is clearly linked with the issue of local people's participation in its ultimate use – discussed in Section 9.5 below.

- Draw up a list of local names of the species selected for recording. Seek professional advice on the scientific identification of these species (animal as well as plant, if appropriate), and verify their scientific names before starting data collection.

- Plan the sequence of activities logically, and try to adhere to the order even if unforeseen circumstances arise (such as changes in the availability of outside experts, unexpected weather conditions, etc.). It may be better to delay operations than to conduct them in a haphazard fashion.

- Ensure that the need for and value of accuracy is fully appreciated, and formalise a system for checking data collection that can be implemented by local people. For field measurements collected in surveys and inventories, it is usually adequate to do this on a subsample no greater than 10%. It is also advisable to have a system of checking record sheets for any obvious mis-recordings or inaccuracies before handing them over for processing.

- Give attention to data security. Instigating a formal system of responsibility for record sheets or forms can help minimise the risk of mislaying or losing data. Data storage should also be given careful thought in this respect.

Two further general points may be made, which are discussed in separate sub-sections below. These are:

- Seek professional advice if any statistics are involved in data collection and analysis.

- Invest adequate time in discussions, explanations and training.

Statistical Aspects

Where there is a need for statistical validity in forest resource assessment, the importance of seeking professional statistical advice cannot be over-emphasised. This book does not attempt to provide guidance on this complicated subject, beyond a few brief observations arising out of the experience of the documented case studies. Further information may be sought from references such as Freese (1984); Philip (1994); Alder and Synnott (1992); Schreuder, Gregoire and Wood (1993).

If options for different inventory methods are presented in an uncomplicated and meaningful way, local people may be able to participate in decisions which are adopted for assessing their forest (see Section 9.5). Evidence from the case studies indicates that there are strong practical advantages in keeping designs and layouts as simple as possible. Since sampling can raise conceptual difficulties, 100% enumerations may be most appropriate.

Where the area of forest to be inventoried is too large for 100% enumeration, and information is required for the whole forest, some form of sampling will be necessary. The cut-off point at which an area becomes too large depends on individual circumstances such as the detail of information required (species to be included, minimum size of individual trees/plants to be recorded, etc.); the nature of the terrain and the amount of labour and time available. Once a decision to sample has been made, the next decisions on the number of plots, their size and shape and the overall sampling design are crucial. This is arguably particularly so in participatory forest management, since early mistakes can have a highly demoralising effect on participants. The decision over the number of plots that are sampled, and hence the sampling intensity, is often a balance between what is theoretically ideal and what is practically feasible in terms of costs, with legal requirements sometimes also being a necessary consideration.

A number of the case studies illustrate the problems that may arise from conducting crude initial assessments that provide insufficiently accurate data. A particular danger is of overestimating the standing volume, and thus over-cutting (as illustrated by the early inventory conducted in the Quintana Roo case study, and the Lomerío project outlined in Chapter 1, Box 1.3). An ideal design for a participatory inventory is one which is simple, but can be developed into a more complex form of assessment if and when local expertise and demands for accuracy increase.

Sample plot shape and size is one aspect of sampling that may be given particular attention to facilitate local people's participation. Lines (transects) appear to be easier than plots for local people to set out in a forest (problems with compass reading notwithstanding), and the easiest to conceptualise. They may be the most appropriate means of sampling in many cases, for both trees and other plants (see also the comments in Section 9.3 below on sampling NTFPs). Experience with square, rectangular and circular plots appears mixed. In Nepal, rectangular plots were found to be the simplest to lay out in the forest. Circular plots tended to be highly unsatisfactory, being readily distorted on steeply sloping terrain (Peter Branney, 1995, pers. comm; Kleinn, 1994). By contrast, in the Quintana Roo case study (where the terrain is largely flat), circular plots were found to be the most convenient for the inventory brigades. Furthermore, the optimum plot size was determined by the brigades themselves – the total number of plots necessary to attain the desired sampling intensity then being fixed accordingly.

The choice of sampling design and layout is often influenced by the views and experience of experts advising the project, as well as by what is found to be feasible for local people to conduct in the field. Whilst it is possible to make incorrect decisions in the choice of sampling method, leading to inaccurate estimates of harvestable volume, at the same time there is often no single 'correct' method. The sampling method developed by a project should reflect the individual management objectives, type of forest, and local people's capabilities as well as sound statistics. The Quintana Roo experience well illustrates this point.

Training

Any participatory forestry exercise is likely to necessitate a considerable amount of training at all levels, both for staff of the outside agency or agencies and for local people. Indeed, if participatory forestry is a new concept, considerable effort may need to be spent first in a process of Forest Department/project staff reorientation (Gronow and Shrestha, 1991). As far as forest resource assessment is concerned, the fact that it often entails concepts and methods that are completely new to local people means that they may require quite intensive training. Amongst the case studies documented in this book, training has been given different emphasis and priority. In part this reflects varied needs, but it also reflects a difference in the intended mode of local people's participation in activities.

The emphasis placed on training is likely to increase with increasing levels of local people's participation as well as/or the sophistication of techniques to be used.

Where local people's intended role is one of collaboration or co-learning, training should be discussed at the outset with the different parties concerned. As a result, a tentative training programme should be drawn up, on the basis of perceived needs. The programme should be flexible, allowing for modification as experience progresses and particular needs become apparent. Aspects to consider in developing an initial programme and in making subsequent modifications are outlined below.

- What are the training needs? These should be assessed according to the strengths and weaknesses of the different key players (staff and local people), and bearing in mind the potential for mutual learning.

- Who should be trained? Key groups or individuals may be identified. Where this entails selection, the community should at least play a part in the decision of who amongst themselves should be trained. This may be a group decision, or may be taken on their behalf by the local leader(s) (as, for example, in the case studies from Nigeria and Ghana).

- How should training be conducted? Training may take very different forms – from formal classes, providing a theoretical background, to practical fieldwork. Workshops, group discussions and study tours may also be considered. All may play a part in an overall training programme.

- Who should conduct the training? Some training may be largely one-way, entailing the imparting of skills from one or more individuals to others. In other cases it may be reciprocal, possibly co-ordinated by a facilitator. Appropriate personnel should be identified as trainers/facilitators and, if necessary, first trained themselves (for example, a technician skilled in forest inventory may require training in communications skills before s/he begins training local people).

- When will training be necessary? A broad schedule should be drawn up, so that training is tailored to intended activities and resource persons are made available at appropriate times. Whilst recognising that much training is imparted through actual work experience (see, in particular, the Rwenzori National Park case study from Uganda), the potential need for 'refresher courses' should also be addressed.

Learning how to take a compass bearing. Members of the Arenales community in Ecuador taking part in a workshop on forest inventory techniques. Photograph: Leonel Quiñónez

9.3 Forest Assessment for Management: The Limitations of Silvicultural Knowledge

Over the last century or more, foresters have built up a considerable body of knowledge and expertise in the systematic management of tropical forests (see, for example, Troup, 1922; Dawkins, 1961; Wyatt-Smith, Paton and Mitchell, 1964). However, as noted in Chapter 1, this experience largely focused on timber production – and on the limited number of species then in demand on local and international markets. The increased interest in managing forests for a wide range of species and forest products is not limited to participatory forestry. However, it is in such initiatives that the greatest silvicultural challenge may be envisaged. This section considers two important aspects of forest management that have been mentioned in the documented case studies: the gap theory, and management for multiple non-timber forest product (NTFP) production.

The Gap Theory

The rationale behind using gap theory to dictate forest management practices is that, in mimicking natural regenerative processes, the likelihood of achieving sustainable production is increased.

The theory that gaps in the forest canopy have a profound effect on forest dynamics and species composition is an important ecological concept with major implications for forest management. Developed by ecologists, the 'gap theory', as it has come to be known, was first deliberately applied to the management of tropical forests in the 1980s (Hartshorn, 1989). One well-known example is the Palcazú Project in Peru (briefly outlined in Chapter 3, Box 3.2), which influenced the development of the original management plans drawn up for the forests of El Pan and Arenales.

The gap theory is based on the recognition that in all forests there is a cycle of growth initiated by disturbance. Such disturbance may be caused by a variety of natural phenomena such as tree death and decay, high winds or hurricanes, fire, volcanic eruptions, or earthquakes. It may also, of course, be initiated by man. The phases of gap creation, building, and maturity may be arbitrarily recognised within the forest cycle, with the first driving the process (Whitmore, 1989). Very small gaps may be filled by the lateral ingrowth of surrounding trees, but more usually they provide an opportunity for natural regeneration, with seedlings growing and developing into mature trees. A fourth degenerate phase may follow maturity, as trees reach the end of their natural lifespan, but often they are destroyed by some disturbance before this stage is reached. The size of gap in the forest canopy influences the species composition in the next cycle. Two broad categories of forest trees are recognised in this regard (*ibid*), the essential difference between them being their response to light at seed and seedling stage. This results in the regeneration of different species according to the size of gaps in the forest canopy. The terms most widely used for the two groups of trees are *pioneer* and *climax* (or *non-pioneer*) species.

Pioneer species have seed which germinates only in the open, in full sunlight; they thus colonise large gaps in the forest. *Climax* species have seedlings that become established in the shade of closed forest and are released (start active growth) when exposed to low light intensities. They thus tend to colonise small gaps in the forest. There is considerable variation in response to light within the two categories of trees, but they may always be distinguished by their vital capacity for germination and establishment beneath the forest canopy.

Whilst the fundamental principles of gap theory appear to hold in most if not all forests studied, numerous complicating factors may be identified (see, for example, Brokaw and Scheiner, 1989; Veblen, 1989; Poulson and Platt, 1989; Martínez-Ramos, Alvarez-Buylla and Sarukhán, 1989). Certainly much remains to be learned about the growth dynamics of different types of forest; the establishment of permanent sample plots (PSPs) for monitoring long-term changes in forest composition has an important role in this respect.

As far as forest management decisions in the short and medium term are concerned, gap theory suggests a number of desirable practices, not all of which are new silvicultural techniques. For example, tropical foresters have long been aware of the potential need to remove woody climbers after harvesting, and in enrichment planting to select only vigorous light-demanding species and plant them in lines cut East-West for maximum sunshine (Dawkins, 1961). Important silvicultural practices related to the gap theory, and their implications for participatory forest resource assessment, are summarised in Box 9.3.

Box 9.3 Important Silvicultural Practices Related to Gap Theory, and Implications for Participatory Forest Resource Assessment

Practice	Comment	Implications for participatory assessment
Harvesting of trees of a variety of size classes	This creates complete gaps in the canopy. The ideal size of the gap will depend on the characteristics of the species identified as being of greatest importance in forest management. Unfortunately, for many species such characteristics are not known.	Long-term monitoring is likely to be required for determining ideal gap sizes. In the short term, there may be potential for building on local people's knowledge and observations in determining the gap size to create in harvesting. The economic viability of harvesting many size classes may rest on local markets. *(continued/...)*

Box 9.3 *(continued)*

Harvesting of only selected mature trees of each species (selection felling)	A number of medium-sized and mature specimens should be left to retain a mixed forest structure. Seed trees are particularly important.	This implies selection of trees to be harvested, ideally after a stock survey. Local people should have the opportunity to dictate the selection procedure. The overall economic viability of leaving marketable timber unharvested should be assessed, and practice decided by or with local people.
Harvesting of a wide variety of species	Operations should not focus solely on one or two species, but cover as wide a species base as possible.	The subsistence and market potential of all species (for NTFPs as well as timber) should be fully explored. All species with potential value should be included in the assessment process.
Monitoring of coppicing ability	In the Palcazú Project, it was found that the system of clear-cutting in strips promoted vigorous coppicing of a number of species, including some premium timber species purported to be slow growing (Hartshorn, 1989).	The monitoring of coppicing may be included in records taken in permanent sample plots. It could also be assessed by local people through post-harvesting observations.
Removal of woody climbers	In some tropical forests, large gaps may be invaded by woody climbers that arrest the growth cycle (Whitmore, 1989). They may therefore need to be removed (Salick, 1992), preferably prior to harvesting so that felling damage is also reduced.	The growth of climbers following harvest may need to be monitored, and appropriate action taken.
Enrichment planting on a limited basis	If gaps are well managed, the need for enrichment planting should be minimised. However, if it is necessary, the broad characteristics of the species (pioneer or climax) should, at least, be known and taken into account at establishment.	Enrichment planting is an activity that local people may conduct spontaneously (see Chapters 3 and 6), and their knowledge of species characteristics may enhance survival rates. Records should be kept on survival rates, to determine whether enrichment planting in the given circumstances is effective.

Forest Assessment and Management for Multiple NTFP Production

People living in or around forests commonly use and value a wide variety of NTFPs, for both subsistence and commercial purposes. As noted in the introductory chapter, such products include game (bush meat), bamboos, canes (rattans), fruits, honey, mushrooms, fodder for livestock, medicines and spices. Assessment and management activities must usually focus on a limited number of the most important of these, for obvious practical reasons. This section focuses on NTFPs derived from forest plants.

Qualitative assessments

Indigenous knowledge about the growth habits, phenological characteristics, general distribution and perceived quality of plants yielding locally valued NTFPs is often considerable. This may form important baseline information for designing a systematic assessment of the resource, as illustrated by the case studies from Ghana (Chapter 5) and Uganda (Chapter 8). Although not detailed in any of the case studies, ranking techniques used in Participatory Rural Appraisal (PRA), in particular pairwise ranking, can be an effective means of qualitative assessment based on local knowledge (documented examples include Rusten and Gold, 1991; McGregor, 1991).

Quantitative assessments

A number of the technical and practical challenges in assessing and managing forests for multiple NTFP production are well illustrated by the national NTFP inventory in Ghana (see Box 9.4). This was established in 1990 to collect baseline information for national and regional-level planning but incorporating an element of local knowledge about NTFP use and importance. The particular sampling problems which may arise in NTFP surveys and inventories have already been outlined in the appropriate sub-section of Section 9.2. Some of the other challenges in quantifying plant-based NTFP resources include those outlined below. In many cases, the solutions remain unknown.

Deciding what to quantify. Plants yielding NTFPs may be of virtually any growth habit – from large trees with a single bole to small, multi-branched bushes; from woody climbers high in the forest canopy to small herbs on the forest floor. Furthermore, NTFPs may be derived from different parts of different plants – from the roots, leaves, shoots, stems, bark, flowers, etc. An assessment of the resource may be based on a quantification of either the whole plant, or the part of the plant of interest. It may entail destructive or non-destructive sampling – the former sometimes being necessary to determine suitable parameters for future non-destructive assessment. For example, techniques for woody biomass assessment are well developed, and biomass tables exist for certain species (Stewart, Dunsdon, Hellin and Hughes, 1992; Applegate, Gilmour and Mohns, 1988). Quantification may be by measurement, weight, volume, or an index based on calculations made from multiple measurements. If possible, the unit of measurement used should reflect locally used measurements since these will be more meaningful to local people. Thus, for example, the rattan inventory developed in the East Kalimantan case study quantified rattan length in 4 m units, since this is the unit used in local markets.

A further means of quantifying NTFPs is through economic evaluation (see the example given in Chapter 7, Box 7.5).

Full discussion of different methods for quantifying NTFPs is beyond the scope of this book, but a useful introductory reference is Peters (1993). In many cases, highly accurate information may not be needed. Decisions on what to quantify in assessing NTFP resources should be based on the intended use of the information, and what is practicable. For example, in monitoring forest condition over time, counts of the number of individual plants of a given species may be adequate. By contrast, assessment to provide an indication of yields (see Chapter 10, Section 10.3) may need to be far more detailed.

Determining size/age classes. It is often useful to group plant populations in size or age classes, since this provides an indication of the health of the population (Peters, 1993; see also Chapter 10, Section 10.3). In trees, the measurement of dbh provides a convenient mechanism, but difficulties arise in classifying many NTFP-yielding plants on the basis of size or age. Reasons include the following:

- **Identification problems**: positive field identification of the juvenile form of many NTFP-yielding plants is not easy. For example, the NTFP inventory team in Ghana found that for young canes (rattans), it was impossible to distinguish in the field between the species and other palm seedlings of similar morphology. As a result of this no data were collected on cane regeneration (seedlings).

- **Poorly understood growth patterns**: this means that relating the size and form of a plant at a given point in time to its age may be difficult. Detailed study may be necessary to determine the optimum parameters for assessing plant age for any given species. For example, in canes (rattans), stem length is the most important measurement of growth, and is not related to diameter.

- **Harvesting alters plant size:** the removal of some or all of the plant in harvesting may drastically alter its size from one point in time to another. The recorded size may therefore not necessarily provide any indication of plant age or future harvesting potential.

Since the growth dynamics of many non-tree NTFP-yielding plants are not known, it is also uncertain what constitutes a normal size-class distribution of their populations.

NTFP enumeration. A Technical Officer of the Ghanaian Forest Department enumerating NTFPs in a sample plot within a forest reserve. The plot is thick with undergrowth.
Photograph: Jane Carter

Assessing productive potential. Local people can often provide effective classification mechanisms for assessing the productive potential of plants yielding NTFPs that they regularly use. These should be carefully investigated. For example, both in Ghana and East Kalimantan a distinction is drawn between green, immature canes/rattans and mature canes/rattans from which the leaf sheaths have been sloughed off. Only the latter are harvested. Similarly, local people often know, for example, how many years particular fruit-bearing trees take to reach production, or at what size they can begin harvesting tree leaves or bark without risking damage to the tree.

Developing an appropriate sampling strategy. Conducting a 100% inventory of even a limited selection of NTFP-yielding plants occurring in a given forest is rarely feasible, since many such plants are smaller and more difficult to enumerate than trees. The appropriate shape and size of sampling unit for a given species will depend on its pattern of distribution. For example, for a species which has a distribution clearly related to topography, it is more efficient to sample in transects running at right angles to slope contours than to use square plots, as more variation will be encompassed by the transects (Stockdale and Wright, 1995). A species with fairly even distribution may be better sampled in square or circular plots, and if it is of extremely frequent occurrence the plot size may be smaller than if it is found only rarely (the total number of plots sampled is obviously also important). Forest walks and discussions with local people may provide sufficient information to determine broad distribution patterns of species. Once they are known, it is quite likely that sampling units of different shapes and sizes will be considered most appropriate for different species. Unless there is a need for statistically accurate and precise data, and the financial resources to fund their collection, a compromise between what is statistically ideal and what is practicable may be needed. Although the designers of the national NTFP inventory for Ghana were operating in a considerable information vacuum when the inventory was initiated, it provides a good example of such a compromise.

Box 9.4 The Design and Development of the National Non-timber Forest Product (NTFP) Inventory, Ghana

The need for a national inventory of NTFPs was initially identified through a survey of NTFP harvesting, use and trade, which highlighted their importance to the local economy. An inventory procedure for selected NTFPs in temporary sample plot (TSP) enumeration was designed in 1990. It was initially based on canes (*Calamus* spp. and others), and was quickly expanded to include a variety of climbers and herbaceous plants. The general objectives of the inventory were to:

- Provide an overview of the distribution of the selected NTFPs across forest types within the High Forest Zone (HFZ).
- Assess the relative abundance of the selected NTFPs across forest types in the HFZ.
- Provide basic information on the NTFP resource base for future management decisions.

In addition, the inventory team wished to gain specific information on canes with regard to:

- The impact of logging on the resource base.
- Current exploitation levels in different areas, related to the location of roads and settlements.

Designing the inventory was not easy, as the team was operating with very little information. Key considerations included the following:

- Lack of information at the time to the inventory designers about inventories of non-tree resources elsewhere.
- Uncertainty over appropriate plot shape and size.
- Verification of species identification (only local names had been used in a preliminary study of NTFP use by local people).

(continued/...)

Box 9.4 *(continued)*

- Lack of knowledge about cane growth habits (notwithstanding certain useful information provided by cane gatherers and weavers).
- Uncertainty over appropriate parameters to measure (particularly in canes, due to the poor understanding of growth habits).

Sampling design – plot size and shape

Various sampling designs were considered, including a plotless method (under which an area is inspected in detail and all NTFP species collected and identified, until further inspection reveals no un-sampled species), and line sampling using transects. However, it was logistically easiest to sample at the same time and in the same way as the national (timber tree) inventory, under which 1 hectare rectangular plots (20 x 500 m) are enumerated at a 0.25% sampling intensity (see Chapter 1, Box 1.7 for the plot layout). Although the use of such plots was known to provide a statistically reliable sample for trees, it is not known whether the same plot size would be adequate or appropriate for NTFPs. This will only become apparent once all data analysis has taken place.

Choice of species to be included, and problems of species identification

The NTFPs included in the inventory were chosen largely on the basis of their economic importance to local households. A provisional list comprising several climbers, bamboo, herbaceous plants, mushrooms, snails and tortoises was drawn up using the results of the earlier survey of NTFP harvesting and use. Inventory work began with the assistance of a forest botanist who was particularly skilled in NTFP identification. This officer assisted the inventory team in liaising with local villagers to check about the local use of forest plants. The ideal was for a particularly knowledgable villager to accompany the inventory team and identify all those NTFPs of particular local importance. This inevitably worked better in some places than in others, but a number of locally important plants were identified in the process. The list of plants enumerated was eventually finalised at 27 climbers, 17 herbaceous plants, and the 5 cane species that occur in Ghana. All the NTFPs are recorded using local names, and their botanical identity is checked by skilled botanists.

Sampling parameters

For many NTFPs, the parameters on which measurement should be based were not initially clear. The eventual choice of parameters was based largely on practical considerations, and was as follows.

- **Climbers**: The number of stems of each species in the plot was counted (whether rooted in the plot or not).

- **Herbaceous plants**: Given patterns of resource utilisation, a distinction between scattered, sparsely leaved plants and thickly leaved clumps was necessary. This was attempted by counting the number of distinct plant groups, but did not prove to be a very satisfactory measurement. It would probably have been more accurate to record the total ground cover, as an estimated fraction of the total plot area.

(continued/...)

Box 9.4 *(continued)*

- **Canes**: The number of cane stems and the number of clumps in the plot were used. Stems were categorised as immature (green stems extending more than 3 m into the canopy) or mature (brown stems with sheaves sloughing), and the number already cut was also recorded. Since the accurate identification in the field of seedling canes proved impossible, they were not recorded.

- **Chewsticks** (used for dental hygiene): Trees of *Garcinia* spp. and *Celtis* spp. are often harvested for this purpose when small (under 30 cm dbh), although large logs split into sticks are also acceptable to the market. Therefore all saplings over 5 cm dbh of the relevant species were enumerated (already under the national inventory all tree saplings of over 5 cm dbh were recorded in TSP sub-plots, but not throughout the plot).

Fieldwork

Enumeration was conducted by specially skilled teams of one Technical Officer and 3–4 labourers, working with the regular TSP inventory team. Three such teams participated in the entire TSP programme. The amount of time taken to enumerate a plot usually varied from half to two days. In comparison with tree measurements, the NTFP enumeration is not particularly time consuming or difficult. Recording NTFPs is most difficult in disturbed areas such as fire-damaged or logged plots with dense undergrowth. Many NTFP species grow prolifically in disturbed areas, but in clearing the undergrowth to see what is present, it is easy to destroy some of the plants to be enumerated (especially climbers).

Record-keeping, checking and data analysis

Separate field record forms are completed for climbing plants, herbaceous plants, and canes. As in the case of the regular TSP records, 10% of the plots enumerated are re-surveyed as check plots. The NTFP inventory has now been integrated into permanent sample plot (PSP) measurements, in order to gain an understanding of growth characteristics and change in the forest over time. Data from the NTFP inventory in TSPs have been entered into a computerised data-base, and are now being analysed. More information can be obtained from the Forest Department Planning Branch, Kumasi, Ghana.

Source: Julia Falconer (1995, pers. comm.)

Season of assessment. This is likely to be particularly important in forests which exhibit marked seasonal changes in vegetation. In such forests, many non-tree NTFP-yielding plants can only be observed at certain times of the year, and their assessment must be timed accordingly. The practical consequences of this can be immense. A series of assessments of different species through the year may be needed. Furthermore, the time at which most plants can usually be observed, the wet season, may be the most inconvenient for fieldwork.

Timing intervals for long-term monitoring. The optimum interval for re-assessing species occurrence for long-term monitoring will depend on the length of its life cycle – which may not even be known for all the NTFP-yielding plants to be assessed (particularly woody climbers and other plants which inhabit the forest canopy). An interval of five years is generally accepted as being appropriate for monitoring trees (even short-lived tree species have a life cycle longer than this), but many NTFP-yielding plants, particularly herbs, have a far shorter life cycle. Ideally, therefore, they should be monitored more frequently. However, this has obvious implications for cost, an issue discussed in the following section.

9.4 Economic Viability

Two particularly important economic issues highlighted in a number of the case studies are the costs of forest resource assessment, and, in the case of forest management initiatives with a commercial orientation, the availability of markets.

The Costs of Forest Assessment

The costs of forest resource assessment may vary widely, but the process is rarely cheap. The way in which these costs are distributed varies in the different case studies described in this book, but in all there has been some input from an outside funding organisation.

Labour
In many of the case studies, local people have provided their labour voluntarily or at a below-market rate. Time taken by local people in forest assessment work may represent lost opportunities for economic, subsistence or leisure activities, but it is certainly valuable to the individuals concerned. If new methods are being tested, an exceptional amount of labour may be required over the trial and error period. In such circumstances, it is commonly accepted that local people should be made fully aware of the trial nature of activities, and provided with greater support than might otherwise be available. How this support is given may vary greatly. An obvious option is providing participants with some form of compensation for their time (as in Ghana, where participants were given tools and reimbursed for travel and subsistence for a limited time period). The risk of this, of course, is that the whole 'participatory' approach could be undermined, with expectations of long-term salaries and other benefits being generated. Where forest assessment is primarily for commercial forest management, individuals may expect to be paid for their labour from the profits accrued. The Quintana Roo case study provides one example of how this can be organised. Much depends on the particular circumstances of the project, including precedents set by other development initiatives. It is also crucial that the matter is discussed openly at the outset of activities, to avoid any

misunderstandings arising.

Despite the high input of time needed in much forest resource assessment work, in no case has this been a major limitation to activities. Indeed, local people are often willing to provide many days of their time if they are confident that forest management will benefit them as a community.

Capital equipment and maintenance costs

Some of the equipment employed in the mapping, survey and inventory techniques described in this book is extremely expensive. Computers and GPS devices are not only expensive; they may need to be imported, and paid for in foreign exchange. Furthermore, regular maintenance costs may be incurred in their use. They have to be serviced, and spare parts purchased as necessary. Computers may need to be housed in an air-conditioned environment, requiring access to a suitable building with an electricity supply. All these matters may be difficult for local people to arrange without external assistance, particularly when large sums of foreign exchange are involved.

Professional expertise

Professional expertise is most likely to be needed, of course, when initiating and developing a suitable system of forest resource assessment. Depending on the particular circumstances, a wide range of personnel may be required, including a social development specialist, botanist, forest inventory specialist, statistician, and computer database manager. Such personnel are expensive. Although there is commonly an intention that they will train local counterparts who can take over their roles in the future, experience indicates that the time needed for this is often calculated optimistically. If complex procedures are being introduced, there may be a long-term need for external professional support, especially if any form of longer-term monitoring is envisaged, such as the establishment of PSPs and repeat sample surveys.

Given the high costs of capital equipment and maintenance, and of professional expertise, the question arises as to who should pay them. In the immediate term, all the case study initiatives have received some form of external funding to supply and maintain equipment, and for professional expertise. The question of longer-term funding, however, is often left unaddressed.

The feasibility of local people fully funding the cost of forest assessment in the future obviously depends on both the nature of that assessment and the potential income that can be derived from the forest. It is too simplistic to state that the best assessment methods for participatory initiatives are ones that demand only simple equipment and, once instigated, minimal professional support. Nevertheless, there are obvious advantages to such an approach, as demonstrated by the case studies from Ghana and Nepal. If a forestry operation is primarily commercial, and particularly if it is aimed at a specialist, premium market, costly assessment procedures may be justified and economically viable. This may be argued in the case studies described from Ecuador and Mexico. However, in any commercial forest management system (whether run by local people or by a private individual or company) a balance often has to be struck between the 'ideal' and the cost of operations. For example, Whitmore (1990) has noted that recommended post-harvesting silvicultural treatments for wood production in the tropics have largely been abandoned because of their cost.

The long-term implications of introducing high-cost forest assessment methods should be carefully considered and addressed. This is particularly important for funding monitoring activities which are of interest or benefit to a wider audience than local people alone. Expecting local people to cover the cost of maintaining PSPs for forest growth modelling or biodiversity monitoring is almost certainly unrealistic – an issue of concern raised in the case study from Uganda. One potential means of covering such costs is to establish a trust fund for the purpose, a suggestion that has been made under a number of projects funded by the GEF (Global Environment Fund), set up after the United Nations Conference on Environment and Development in 1992. However, the feasibility of introducing such innovative funding methods for long-term forest assessment has yet to be tried and tested.

> One potential danger of expensive forest resource assessment methods is that, in order to cover assessment costs, harvesting levels may be pushed to unsustainable rates. The likelihood of this occurring cannot be evaluated from the case studies.

The Availability of Markets

In community forestry initiatives of a primarily commercial orientation, a thorough investigation of available markets is an essential management activity. The forest resource assessment procedure adopted should be intimately linked with the marketing strategy – the latter influencing, and possibly determining, decisions over the detail of information collected. This may include the species recorded, and the parameters used (such as the minimum dbh for timber trees, etc.). Such decisions will not always be easy, as ideally they should reflect not only current marketing opportunities but potential future ones which may not be easy to predict. For example, the Quintana Roo Forestry Project in Mexico is now able to market over 15 different timber species, due to expanding markets for lesser-known species, whereas initially only two species (*Swietenia macrophylla* and *Cedrela odorata*) dominated the market. Had the project continued to include only these original two species in its inventory (as it was forced to do at the start because of lack of funds), it would have found itself in an extremely difficult position. As noted above, costs are an important factor. If a forestry operation has the potential to make considerable profits, a detailed forest inventory may be both desirable to inform marketing decisions fully, and justifiable in terms of the cost incurred.

There may be a need for a pro-active approach to developing new markets, involving the employment of personnel with appropriate marketing skills. Thus, for example, in the Ekuri case study from Nigeria, future work is focusing on the establishment of a co-operative which will consider the development of markets for forest products (amongst other activities). In some circumstances, limited or tightly controlled local market opportunities may result in local people deciding to establish their own processing units. These may range from portable sawmills that can be established on site to much more capital-intensive developments for more highly processed products. However, the discussion of such options is beyond the scope of this book.

A portable sawmill business in the forest colonisation zone near Santa Cruz, Bolivia. As a result of restricted local market opportunities, local people may decide to establish their own processing units. This sawmill was established by a family living in the settlement of San Julián. Photograph: Anna Lawrence

Certification

As noted in the introductory chapter, the certification of a forest as being 'sustainably' managed may enhance the prospects of marketing its products at premium price. Certification is currently carried out by a number of certification bodies, whose activities are evaluated and monitored by the Forest Stewardship Council (FSC). This independent, non-profit, non-governmental organisation was formally established in 1993 with an internationally recognised mandate to promote good forest management throughout the world. It does not itself certify forests or products, but oversees certification organisations which inspect forest operations and grant labels. The criteria used by each certification body differ slightly, although to be accredited by the FSC, they must conform to its principles and criteria.

For local people managing an area of forest for timber production on what they believe to be a sustainable basis, there are a number of disadvantages as well as advantages in seeking certification. The obvious advantage is in raising the profile of their products, thus attracting demand and a higher than average price. A number of trading companies such as the Ecological Trading Company, (see Chapter 3) actively seek sources of certified timber for import to Northern countries. By entering into an agreement with such a company, local people may be able to obtain a guaranteed buyer for all the timber produced from their forest. The disadvantages of certification largely rest on the size and cost of operations, and market opportunities.

- Certification is not free. Certification organisations have to charge for their services, although some are able to do this at a highly subsidised rate for small logging companies or community forestry projects that lack funds to pay.

- The requirements for certification may necessitate more rigorous and expensive inventories than might otherwise have been conducted. This will further increase costs.

- For timber export to be viable, the forestry project in question must be capable of supplying, on a regular basis, a certain minimum volume of timber of species in demand overseas. It must also be reasonably accessible to a reliable export point. Only if these circumstances obtain can certification improve export prospects.

For small forestry projects producing limited volumes of timber, certification may be of little benefit. Certification may not even be necessary to market timber as a product of sustainably managed forests, if a buyer is satisfied that this is the case. This is the current situation for the Awá Sustainable Forest Management Project, although it may not continue to be in future.

Decisions over whether or not certification should be sought for a particular community forestry initiative may rest in part on the national forest policy in the country concerned. Some countries argue that they aim to ensure that all their timber is produced on a sustainable basis, and that there is therefore little point in individual forests or projects being certified; a certification scheme on a country by country basis would be more appropriate. For example, Ghana seeks to ensure that all its timber is obtained from sustainably managed forests by the year 2000 (an international target originally set by the International Timber Trade Organisation and supported by a variety of organisations, but increasingly seen as optimistic at a world-wide level). In other countries, the certification of individual forests is strongly supported. In Bolivia, this is linked to the support of indigenous peoples in their forest management activities, as described in Box 9.5.

Box 9.5 The Introduction of the Green Seal (Sello Verde) in Bolivia's Indigenous Territories

The indigenous forest people of Bolivia are one of the country's most marginalised groups, lacking both economic resources and political support. They are, however, the inhabitants of large areas of tropical forests, and have been fighting for legal rights to their territories and the natural resources within them for many years. A number of organisations have been involved in investigating ways to support indigenous people in sustainable forest management. They include the BOLFOR project (a Sustainable Forest Management Project financed by USAID and the Government of Bolivia), the SNV (the Dutch Development Co-operation Service), and CIDOB (**Confederación Indígena del Oriente, Chaco y Amasonía Boliviana** – an indigenous peoples' NGO). The mechanism favoured is the introduction of a Green Seal (**Sello Verde**) for sustainably harvested timber, which will fetch a premium market price. The operational mechanisms for the Green Seal are yet to be finalised but substantial progress has been made under the BOLFOR project to define national certification standards according to the FSC's Guidelines and established Principles and Criteria of good forest management. The government is also interested in establishing a system of national certification. The Rainforest Alliance, through its Smart Wood Program, has been involved in an advisory capacity and will carry out the first certification evaluation in Bolivia with the Chiquitano Indians in the Lomerío Region in co-ordination with SNV, CICOL and BOLFOR in October 1995.

Source: John Nittler (1995, pers. comm.)

9.5 Local Participation Re-examined

Whatever the purpose of forest resource assessment, the need for it may be first identified by local people themselves, or by outsiders. Amongst the case study initiatives, the latter was far more common. Only the case study described from Indonesia documents instances of local people beginning the resource assessment process themselves and later seeking external support. In most cases local people sought assistance in forest management from outside agencies, and were advised that forest assessment was necessary. The need was thus externally perceived, but was agreed and implemented through a process of consultation or collaboration, and occasionally co-learning. In a few cases, it may be argued that the need for forest resource assessment has been entirely externally imposed, with local people merely co-operating in the activity.

Tailoring Assessment to Local Requirements

For local people's participation in forest resource assessment to be meaningful – at the level of collaboration or co-learning – it should entail the collection and use of information in a manner that can be locally understood. A quote from a member of one of Canada's indigenous peoples, the Inuit, serves to make this point.

> 'There are many ways to be poor, but in today's world not having the right kind of information represents a certain kind of poverty....Without information we are nothing at all and have no power to understand things or to change our life. If Inuit society is to develop we must be able to collect and use information according to our own terms.' (A Nunavik Inuk [1987], quoted by Kemp and Brooke, 1995).

As already noted, people of different cultural backgrounds and experience are likely to vary in the ease or difficulty that they find in understanding and implementing forest resource assessment. Experience from the case studies indicates some aspects of assessment that may be particularly difficult for local people to conceptualise, but categorical generalisations cannot and should not be made. Is the key to participation in forest assessment therefore specificity? Must foresters facilitating the process begin from scratch in each individual circumstance, jointly developing with local people a method that is appropriate for them, their objectives, and the forest in question? To a certain extent the answers must be 'yes', but this does not rule out the use of models that have been successful in similar circumstances and which may only require minor modification. As the case study from Nepal demonstrates, it is possible to institutionalise a system of participatory forest resource assessment, although it is probably a strength of the system that a certain degree of flexibility is retained in its implementation at district level.

Participation in Complex Technologies?

If data of statistical validity are needed, any flexibility in the design and implementation of forest resource assessment will be limited by statistical considerations. This said, the case study from Quintana Roo in Mexico provides an example of an inventory that has been developed to facilitate data collection by local people without compromising accuracy or precision. In terms of local people's participation, a more important feature of statistically rigorous assessment methods is the associated complexity of data processing and analysis. Many forest inventory specialists today would not consider conducting data analysis – except perhaps of simple stock surveys – without a computer. Similarly, the use of GPS (Global Positioning Systems) in increasing the accuracy of participatory maps introduces a tool that is conceptually difficult to understand and generally leads on to data processing by

Case study experience indicates that there may be a tendency for the mode of local people's participation to change from data collection to analysis. Data collection often entails collaboration or even co-learning, but data analysis is often outsider-controlled. This is particularly likely when inventories are involved.

computer, using complicated GIS (Geographical Information System) software. Given that expert advice is needed on statistical matters and in the use of complex technologies, their suitability for participatory approaches to forest resource assessment may be questioned. However, denying local people the opportunity to benefit from such methods on the basis of their limited ability (perceived or actual) to participate in them would be equally, if not more, questionable.

A reduction in level of local people's participation at the stage of data analysis may be inevitable, but experts themselves can play very different roles. They may simply provide recommendations and expect local people to follow them – thus controlling the decision-making process. Alternatively, they may serve as advisers, providing suggestions and explaining their reasons, but leaving final decision-making to local people themselves. The case study from Quintana Roo in Mexico provides an example of the latter approach.

The Inuit quoted above made a clear connection between information collection, understanding, and control over decision-making, the latter being the crucial feature. Perhaps the truest test of local people's participation in forest resource assessment lies in what the information collected equips them to do. Does it provide them with the knowledge they need to take decisions and become managers, or does it fall short of this, with decision-making being controlled by outsiders? Only the former implies a form of participation greater than mere consultation.

References

Alder, D. and **Synnott, T. S.** (1992) *Permanent Sample Plot Techniques for Mixed Tropical Forest*. Tropical Forestry Paper No. 25, Oxford Forestry Institute, Oxford University.

Amatya, S. M. (1989) *Ficus semicordata Buch. Ham. ex Sm. and its Taxonomy*. Forest Research Division Publication No. 1/89, Ministry of Forests and Soil Conservation, Kathmandu.

Applegate, G. B., Gilmour, D. A. and **Mohns, B.** (1988) 'The Use of Biomass Estimations in the Management of Forests for Fuelwood and Fodder Production', *Commonwealth Forestry Review* 67 (2):141–7.

Britt-Kapoor, C. (1994) 'A Tale of Two Committees: Villager Perspectives on Local Institutions, Forest Management and Resource Use in Two Central Himalayan Indian Villages'. *Rural Development Forestry Network Paper 17a*, ODI, London. Summer.

Brokaw, N. V. L. and **Scheiner, S. M.** (1989) 'Species Composition in Gaps and Structure of a Tropical Forest', *Ecology* Special Feature – Treefall Gaps and Forest Dynamics 70(3): 538–41.

Carter, E. J. (1991) 'Tree Cultivation on Private Land in the Middle Hills of Nepal: A Village Perspective'. DPhil Thesis, Department of Plant Sciences, University of Oxford.

Carter, J., Connelly, S. and **Wilson, N.** (1994) 'Participatory Forestry in Sri Lanka: Why So Limited? Change on the Horizon'. *Rural Development Forestry Network Paper 17b*. ODI, London. Summer.

Cernea, M. M. (ed.) (1991) *Putting People First, Sociological Variables in Rual Development* (2nd edn). Oxford University Press for the World Bank, Oxford.

Dawkins, H. C. (1961) 'New Methods of Improving Stand Composition in Tropical Forests', *Caribbean Forester* 22: 12–20.

Fisher, R. J. (1989) *Indigenous Systems of Common Property Forest Management in Nepal.* Working Paper 18, Environment and Policy Institute, East-West Center, Honolulu.

Fox, J. and **Fisher, R. J.** (eds) (1992) *Community Organizations and Government Bureaucracies in Social Forestry.* Working Paper 18, Environment and Policy Institute, East-West Center, Honolulu.

Freese, F. (1984) *Statistics for Land Managers: an Introduction to Sampling Methods for Foresters, Farmers and Environmental Biologists.* Paeony, Jedburgh, UK.

FSC (1994) *Forest Stewardship Principles and Criteria for Natural Forest Management.* Forest Stewardship Council, Oaxaca, Mexico, June.

Gomez-Pompa, A. and **Kaus, A.** (1990) 'Traditional Management of Tropical Forests in Mexico' in Anderson, A. (ed.) *Alternatives to Deforestation: Steps Toward Sustainable Use of the Amazon Rain Forest.* Columbia University Press, New York.

Gronow, J. and **Shrestha, N. K.** (1991) 'From Mistrust to Participation: The Creation of a Participatory Environment for Community Forestry in Nepal'. *Social Forestry Network Paper 12b*, ODI, London. Summer/Winter.

Hartshorn, G. (1989) 'Application of Gap Theory to Tropical Forest Management: Natural Regeneration on Strip Clear-Cuts in the Peruvian Amazon', *Ecology* Special Feature – Treefall Gaps and Forest Dynamics 70(3): 567–9.

Hobley, M. (1996) *Participatory Forest Management in South Asia.* Rural Development Forestry Study Guide No. 3, ODI, London.

Kemp, W. B. and **Brooke, L. F.** (1995) 'Towards Information Self-Sufficiency: Nunavik Inuit Gather Information on Ecology and Land Use', *Cultural Survival Quarterly* 18(4): 25–8.

Kleinn, C. (1994) Forest Resources Inventories in Nepal: Status Quo, Needs and Recommendations. Forest Resource Information System Project (FRISP), His Majesty's Government of Nepal/Finnida Finnish Forest and Park Service. FRISP, Kathmandu.

Martínez-Ramos, M., Alvarez-Buylla, E. and **Sarukhán, J.** (1989) 'Tree Demography and Gap Dynamics in a Tropical Rainforest', *Ecology* Special Feature – Treefall Gaps and Forest Dynamics 70(3): 555–8.

McGregor, J. (1991) 'Woodland Resources: Ecology, Policy and Ideology. An Historical Case Study of Woodland Use in Shurugwi Communal Area, Zimbabwe'. PhD thesis, Department of Geography, Loughborough University, UK.

Peters, C. M. (1993) 'Ecology and Exploitation of Non-timber Tropical Forest Resources: A Primer on Sustainability'. Draft Report II Biodiversity Support Program, Institute of Economic Botany, The New York Botanical Garden, New York.

Philip, M. S., (1994) *Measuring Trees and Forests* (2nd edn). CAB International, Wallingford, UK.

Poulson, T. L. and **Platt, W. J.** (1989) 'Gap Light Regimes Influence Canopy Tree Diversity', *Ecology* Special Feature – Treefall Gaps and Forest Dynamics 70(3): 553–5.

Redford, K. H. and **Padoch, C.** (eds) (1992) *Conservation of Neotropical forests Working from Traditional Resource Use*. Columbia University Press, New York.

Rusten, E. P. and **Gold, M. A.** (1991) 'Understanding an Indigenous Knowledge System for Tree Fodder via a Multi-method On-farm Research Approach', *Agroforestry Systems* 15(2 and 3): 139–66.

Salick, J. (1992) 'Amuesha Forest Use and Management: An Integration of Indigenous Use and Natural Forest Management' in Redford, K. H. and Padoch, C. (eds) *Conservation of Neotropical forests Working from Traditional Resource Use*. Columbia University Press, New York.

Schreuder, H. T., Gregoire, T. G. and **Wood, G. B.** (1993) *Sampling Methods for Multiresource Forest Inventory*. John Wiley and Sons, Inc. New York, Chichester, Brisbane, Toronto and Singapore.

Stewart, J. L., Dunsdon, A. J., Hellin, J. J. and **Hughes, C. E.** (1992) *Wood Biomass Estimation of Central American Dry Zone Species*. Tropical Forestry Papers 26, Oxford Forestry Institute, Department of Plant Sciences, University of Oxford.

Stockdale, M. C. and Wright, H. L., (1995) 'Rattan Inventory: Determining Plot Shape and Size' in Edwards, D. S. and Booth, W. E. (eds), Proceedings of the Conference on Tropical Rainforest Research: Current Issues, *Monographiae Biologicae*, Kluwer Academic Publishers, Dordrecht, Netherlands.

Tamang, D. (1990) *Indigenous Forest Management in Nepal: A Review.* Research Report Series 12, His Majesty's Government of Nepal Ministry of Agriculture/Winrock International, Kathmandu, Nepal.

Thomson, J. (1992) *A Framework for Analyzing Institutional Incentives in Community Forestry.* Community Forestry Notes No. 10, FAO, Rome.

Troup, R. S. (1922) *The Silviculture of Indian Trees* Vol. I–III. Clarendon Press, Oxford.

Veblen, T. T. (1989) 'Tree Regeneration Responses to Gaps along a Transandean Gradient', *Ecology* Special Feature – Treefall Gaps and Forest Dynamics 70(3): 541–3.

Whitmore, T. C. (1989) 'Canopy Gaps and the Two Major Groups of Forest Trees', *Ecology* Special Feature – Treefall Gaps and Forest Dynamics 70(3): 536-8.

Whitmore, T. C. (1990) *An Introduction to Tropical Rainforests.* Clarendon Press, Oxford.

Wyatt-Smith, J., Paton, W. P. and **Mitchell, B. A.** (1964) *Manual of Malayan Silviculture for Inland Forest.* Malayan Forest Record No. 23, Kuala Lumpur.

Acronyms specific to this chapter

CICOL   Central Intercomunal Campesina del Oriente de Lomerio

10 In Conclusion: Neglected Aspects and Future Developments

A number of forest resource assessment issues are either not covered in the case studies, or mentioned only briefly. Some of these are as follows:

- Tree inventories on private land.

- Sustainable non-timber forest product (NTFP) extraction: determining yields and monitoring harvesting impact.

- Monitoring forest condition and biodiversity.

- Using forest assessment for educational programmes.

This final chapter elaborates on these issues, although no claim is made to comprehensive coverage.

10.1 Tree Inventories on Private Land

The Study Guide has focused on local people's collective activities in assessing forest resources that they own or use communally. Interesting participatory initiatives in quantifying forest or tree resources on private land are also taking place in various parts of the world. This section considers three examples – in Brazil, Bangladesh and Nicaragua.

Valuing Farmers' Tree or Forest Resources

Tree or forest resources on private land can represent a considerable potential source of cash income to farmers in many situations (Chambers and Leach, 1987). However, it is not uncommon for farmers to be cheated of the true value of such resources by merchants or middlemen. One reason for this is that farmers tend to sell trees (particularly for timber) only rarely. They thus tend to be uncertain about current market prices, or how to assess the value of the standing crop. In addition, farmers typically resort to tree sale when they are in immediate need of cash – a time when they are not in a strong bargaining position. This common problem has been recognised in the very different settings of the Amazonian basin of Brazil and the agricultural plains of Bangladesh. In both, professional foresters are developing simple methods by which farmers can assess the value of their tree/forest resources and thus enter into dialogue with merchants or middlemen from a position of knowledge. It is hoped that through gaining a better price for their trees, farmers' interest in the planned, rationale management of the tree/forest resources on their land will grow.

Assessing the value of trees on forested land

The initiative in Brazil, outlined in Box 10.1, was essentially a small workshop that has since been backed by the distribution of an educational booklet (Mattos, Nepstad, and Vieira, 1992). One of the main exercises that farmers were taught was how to estimate tree volume using simplified calculations. The formula the farmers were taught may be compared against the standard formula:

$$v = ghf \text{ m}^3$$

where g = cross-sectional area, m^3
h = height (or length), m
f = the form factor (a coefficient employed to reduce the volume of a cylinder [$v = gh$] to that of the tree or log).

The relationship of g to circumference (girth), the measurement used in the workshop, is

$$g = \frac{c^2}{4\pi}$$

where c = circumference, m.

Clearly the volume formula taught to the farmers represents a considerable simplification. However, it is arguably a good example of 'appropriate imprecision', in PRA terms (Chambers and Guijt, 1995) – not going into detail where a rough estimate is adequate.

Box 10.1 Valuing Timber: A Short Course in Forest Inventories for Farmers and Extensionists in the State of Pará, Brazil

Timber extraction is a major industry in the state of Pará, and the town of Paragominas, where the initiative described took place provides a good example of activities. Some 112 sawmills exist in the town, processing over 80 timber species. Timber is being extracted further and further from the town itself, in a radius of 80–100 km. Investigations in the area revealed that when timber merchants negotiate with small farmers for timber on their land, the latter may be disadvantaged in various ways:

- Timber is commonly harvested from an area greater than that agreed. The farmer has no means of checking this.

- Trees of smaller diameter than that agreed are often harvested. Once felled, there is nothing that the farmer can do.

- Negotiations are usually conducted verbally, and payment for the timber is carried out in one or two instalments. Values are fixed, with no adjustments if harvesting takes place at a much later date, when market prices have increased.

Recognising the need to organise and direct the sale of timber by farmers, the Rural Workers Union of Paragominas (STR-P) invited four professional foresters (see source) to hold an intensive three-day training course for farmers on land surveying and mapping, forest inventory and calculating timber volume. This course was held in November 1991 and was given to a selected group of 13 participants, representing six farm communities.

The course began with a discussion of the basic concepts of length, area and volume. Comparisons were made between measurements commonly used by farmers (such as the distance from the end of the nose to the out-stretched hand, and paces) and conventional measurements (using measuring tapes and sticks).

A practical session was then held. This entailed conducting a survey of part of a forest owned by a participating farmer to obtain an estimate of its area, and then carrying out a simple forest inventory by opening up transects for sampling. This farmer had sold the timber rights of his forest and the loggers had already begun to extract logs from the area. Demonstrations were given of how to measure girth at breast height (gbh) and to estimate the height of standing trees to calculate timber volume. These same measurements were conducted on felled trees, for comparative purposes.

Since many of the farmers could not do long division, a simplified formula for calculating timber volume was used. This employed the local term **rôdo** (girth at breast height), and substituted the values for the form factor and pi for less complex numbers. The resulting formula was:

$$\text{volume(m}^3) = \textbf{rôdo}(m) \times \textbf{rôdo}(m) \times \text{height(m)} \times 0.06.$$

(continued/...)

The front cover of the booklet produced from the short course on forest inventory. This course is described in Box 10.1.

Box 10.1 *(continued)*

A basic class in mathematics was needed for the farmers to gain confidence in making calculations. This was successfully achieved. The measurements and volume calculations obtained were then used to demonstrate how to calculate the average number of stems per unit area of a given species, the monetary value of each tree, and, finally, the true market value of the timber. The concept of sampling, and the merits of sampling versus a complete stock survey depending on the area of forest entailed, were also discussed.

To calculate the true market value of timber a series of factors should be taken into account, notably:

- timber quality (the local system recognises standard, first, second or third class)
- the distance from the sawmill (affecting transport costs)
- the type of equipment required for extraction and transport
- local market prices for timber.

These costs were discussed with the farmers, noting that those of extraction and transport are significant. It is estimated that a logger in the state of Pará makes on average 19–25% profit on an operation, and that only 4–7% of his total expenses go on timber purchase. Thus farmers were advised that to obtain a reasonable estimate of the value of their standing timber in the forest, they should calculate 4–7% of the price per m^3 of timber arriving at the sawmill. This point was reinforced by the example of the forest inventory that the participants had conducted. They estimated that the farmer whose forest they had surveyed was paid one-tenth of the market value of his timber.

Following from the course, a booklet was produced setting out all the information that had been covered in clear language, with numerous illustrations. This has been distributed throughout Brazil to farmers and extension agents, and is now in its second printing. In addition, a course was taught to 17 extension agents from across Amazonia on how to help smallholders determine the fair market prices for their timber.

Source: Mattos, Nepstad, Vieira and Assis (1994); Daniel Nepstad (1995, pers. comm.)

Measuring individual trees in fields

Box 10.2 describes an initiative aimed at assisting farmers in Bangladesh to value individual trees growing on their land. As can be seen, it entails a comprehensive determination of biomass – quantifying all tree products and not just timber. The process of determining a simple system of valuation is outsider-controlled, and currently involves no more than the co-operation of the farmers concerned. However, it is intended that farmers will become more actively involved in testing and of course implementing the method developed.

The principle of measuring biomass is not difficult, and entails the following (Philip, 1994):

• Fell (or dig up) a representative sample of trees.

• Take small representative samples of the different parts of the tree (bole, branches, leaves and roots).

• Weigh the samples green, and then oven-dried.

• Calculate from the samples the sum biomass for the tree.

• Establish relationships with parameters easily measured on the standing tree and develop predictive mathematical models to avoid destructive sampling in future.

The problems are in:

• Selecting representative trees and parts of trees.

• Developing unbiased predictive models.

• Ensuring that the sum of the predictive parts equals the prediction of the whole.

Box 10.2 Measuring Individual Trees in Private Farmers' Fields in Bangladesh

In many parts of Bangladesh little or no natural forest remains, and tree cultivation on private farm land is common – both around homesteads, and in cropped fields. An important incentive for farmers to grow trees is the high value of tree products, especially wood. Where there is an acute shortage of wood products, systems for the marketing of private trees are highly developed. Major wood-using industries and concerns operate through echelons of large and small contractors, who actively seek out and buy individual trees from farmers. Since most farmers have up to now sold only occasional trees at times of distress, they have little experience of price negotiations and little knowledge of factors affecting tree value. The Swiss-sponsored Village and Farm Forestry Project (VFFP), a village-based programme of tree planting oriented towards private small farms, is therefore assisting farmers to improve their terms of trade with wood buyers. This is being done in a number of ways, one being the provision of training in scaling tree volumes so that farmers can negotiate price from a firm knowledge base.

The volumes of many commercial timber species may be estimated from standard volume tables, with reference to diameter at breast height (dbh) and sometimes height. However, most of the trees grown by farmers are species that have previously been considered 'non-commercial' by the Forest Department (FD), so standardised volume tables are not available. FD Volume Tables exist for some species grown by farmers, but they refer to trees grown in dense plantations in which the growth and form are very different from trees grown at wide spacings in crop fields. The VFFP has therefore undertaken measurements of a sample of different sized trees of species commonly grown on farms, in order to develop a 'form factor' for each species under farm conditions. The 'form factor' will then be used to estimate timber volumes, fuelwood and other biomass components, based on simple tree measurements such as dbh and height.

The information collected has already proved of additional value to the VFFP, by providing a means of estimating the contribution of trees from farmers' fields to regional and national wood production. This has been used in drafting a national Forestry Master Plan, and has also been helpful in countering a powerful agricultural lobby that opposes tree planting in crop fields.

Data collection

The measurements needed for developing a form factor that can be used for partitioning tree biomass into a range of products are more extensive than those for timber alone. The VFFP trained field staff of its partner NGOs in the appropriate methodology; they in turn trained participating farmers. The sampling of different tree species was conducted opportunistically, as far as possible using only those trees that farmers already planned to harvest for their own purposes. For a few species, it was necessary to seek out and request the purchase of individual trees because the available sample proved to be too small. It was also sometimes necessary to compromise on the size range of certain species sampled. In the first data collection exercise, each NGO sampled ten trees of one species common in crop fields in their operational areas.

(continued/...)

Box 10.2 *(continued)*

The samples collected included 28 different tree species, many of which were represented by only one or two specimens. This is clearly insufficient for analysis to develop form factors or to predict growth. Larger numbers are needed, probably a minimum of eight per species. The samples will be gradually increased over a year or two until they are sufficient for the calculation of 'form factors'.

The data being collected on each tree are as follows:

- Length (height) from ground level of up to three selected main axes (stem plus principal branches).

- Girth over bark at 1 m intervals along each selected axis.

- Length of main timber log, from ground level to a minimum 90 cm girth.

- Girth under bark in the middle of the main timber log.

- Fresh weights of timber, poles, small branches, fodder (small tender twigs and leaves), wood chips, and stump plus roots.

- Fresh and dry weights of a wood sample, dried to constant weight.

- Fresh and dry weight of a fodder sample; weight of material rejected by livestock fed.

Analysis and interpretation
The total quantity of data to be collected is relatively small and can be easily managed within the VFFP Co-ordination Office, with technical advice from a visiting forestry consultant. Once the data collection has been completed, the raw data will be screened manually and entered into a formal data structure on a computer spread sheet. It will then be subject to further checking.

Analysis will take into account the main parameters identified as important for the marketing of the major tree products. These include size (girth and length) of the main bole (log), weight of woody material, and weight of leafy material (whether as fodder or fuel). The output required from the analysis will be a set of simple predictors that can be measured easily by the farmers themselves and then used by them to place a monetary value on their tree products. Ideally, the main predictor will be *gbh*, which in most cases will provide an adequate estimate of the marketable products. In some species, or under some kinds of management systems such as pollarding, additional predictors such as *height* and perhaps some indicator of *branchiness*, may be needed.

Source: Drake Hocking (1995, pers. comm.); VFFP (1994)

Inventory Methods Developed by Farmers Themselves

In some circumstances, farmers may develop their own methods for inventorying their tree/forest resources. This has been reported by CIPRES (1993). A study by CIPRES in three farming communities in Nicaragua revealed that small farmers have a detailed knowledge of forest management, and have developed their own system of quantifying the forest resources on their land, without any outside intervention. CIPRES documented the procedure used by the farmers, identifying the twelve following steps:

- Determine the reasons for conducting the inventory.

- Form a group to conduct the work.

- Go to the forest, taking a machete, pencil and paper.

- Note all the trees – the species, their estimated size (height and circumference) and quality.

- Count the trees near water sources – these must not be felled.

- Record the position of the trees, using known reference points (i.e. obvious features in the landscape).

- Note which are seed trees.

- Note the uses of all the trees.

- Draw a sketch map, marking boundaries, the position of the trees, and the watercourses.

- Tell other small farmers about the procedure.

- Explain the need for inventory to other farmers.

- Take forest management decisions based on knowledge.

Details of these procedures are reported in CIPRES (1993). The researchers noted that farmers' estimates of tree size were not only accurate in themselves, but that they could also make a good estimate of the volume of timber and fuelwood obtainable from each tree. Farmers also demonstrated a clear respect for environmental conservation by choosing not to fell trees growing close to water courses or important seed producers.

As a result of these findings, CIPRES produced a cartoon depicting the farmers' inventory procedure, which it has distributed to other interested communities. The study clearly demonstrates the importance of determining existing forestry knowledge and practice amongst local people, and developing participatory forest assessment and management techniques from this, if and as appropriate.

10.2   Sustainable NTFP Extraction: Setting Yield Limits and Monitoring Harvesting

The experience of NTFP assessment documented in this book has largely involved the collection of baseline data – in other words, quantifying the existing resource. The one exception to this is the Bwindi Impenetrable National Park case study from Uganda, where a method for determining the sustainable harvesting potential of different species has been put into operation, yield limits for certain species have been set, and some preliminary measurements of harvests have been conducted. However, even in this case, the whole procedure for managing the sustainable harvest of NTFPs is at a very early stage. This section briefly considers what management steps are required to move from the collection of baseline data on NTFP occurrence to the establishment of a system of sustainable harvesting, as set out by Peters (1993). A further text that the reader may find useful is Cunningham (1997). The section is included as a point of reference and comparison with the case studies from Uganda, but also as an indication of the type of issues that some of the other case study initiatives (particularly those from Ghana and East Kalimantan) may need to address in future. It also provides a conceptual background to the example of participatory biodiversity monitoring given in Box 10.3.

Peters (1993) sets out six basic 'steps to sustainability', as follows:

- species selection
- forest inventory
- yield studies
- regeneration surveys
- harvest assessments
- harvest adjustments

Species selection

The selection of species to include in forest resource assessment has been discussed in the previous chapter with regard to the importance of involving local people in the decision and of considering market potential. For sustainable NTFP harvesting, it is also necessary to consider the potential of the species to be managed on a sustained yield basis according to its ecological characteristics. One system for such assessment is that developed by Cunningham (1992), and used in the Bwindi Impenetrable National Park, for the Species Vulnerability Assessment. Peters (1993) adopts slightly different guidelines, based on the following criteria:

- **Life-cycle characteristics** – unpredictably yielding species (e.g. plants which fruit irregularly) are less easy to manage than species that produce the desired product on a fairly predictable basis.

- **Type of resource produced** – the harvesting of some products (e.g. fruits, leaves, latex) is less destructive and more easy to manage than others (e.g. bark, stem tissue, roots).

- **Density and abundance in different forest types** – abundant species are easier to manage than ones occurring in low-density scattered populations. A species confined to one forest type occupying only a small area has less potential for sustainable exploitation than one found widely.

- **Size-class distribution of populations** – the relative health of a population may be assessed by sampling its size-class distribution. A healthy population typically has abundant natural regeneration, and fewer individuals in larger size classes. If a population has an abundance of stems in one size class or exhibits poor regeneration, it is probably unsuitable for sustainable exploitation (see Section 10.3).

The first two sets of information can often be obtained through discussions with local collectors, forest observations, and reference to available texts. The latter two require a formal inventory.

Forest inventory and yield studies

Forest inventory procedures for NTFPs have been discussed in the preceding chapter. Yield studies should add to these data by providing an estimate of the productive capacity of the species to be exploited. Such data should be collected from individuals of all age-classes, forming a representative sample of the population (ideally, the individuals sampled should be permanently marked so that they can be re-traced). The data are then plotted in a yield curve to show the relationship between plant size (on the x axis) and yield (on the y axis). Combining inventory data on the number of productive plants of each size class in a given area of forest with data on yields should give a satisfactory estimate of total potential production; the size class of plants responsible for the greatest percentage of this production; and the forest types providing the highest yield. With these data, systematic forest management for NTFP production can begin.

Regeneration surveys, harvest assessments and harvest adjustments

These three procedures should provide a basis for determining and monitoring sustainable NTFP production. As Peters (1993) points out, regeneration surveys form a demographic 'yardstick' by which to measure the long-term impact of harvesting. Whether harvesting kills a large number of the adult population, lowers adult vigour to the point that reproduction is affected, or removes an excessive number of seeds, the effect can be seen in natural regeneration levels. The standard method by which regeneration can be monitored is by the regular inventory of permanent sample plots (at a suggested interval of five years). Whether five-year intervals are appropriate for some or indeed any non-tree NTFP-yielding plants is debatable.

Harvest assessments entail observations of the condition of adult plants, conducted concurrently with harvesting activities. Visual inspections should take into account the apparent health and vigour of the plant, and the existence and condition of nearby seedlings (for example, if they are being trampled by collectors, this should be noted). In addition to such observations, yield measurements should be repeated at regular intervals (e.g. every five years) and yield curves plotted to detect any change in productivity by size classes.

The sustainability of existing harvesting levels can be assessed from the results of the two monitoring operations, using the seedling and small sapling densities recorded in the first regeneration survey as a threshold value. If levels fall below this, harvesting should be reduced. Similarly, if observations of plant condition reveal evidence of damage or stress, harvesting levels should be reduced.

The 'steps to sustainability' outlined are inevitably simpler in theory than in practice. To date, there is very little practical experience anywhere in the world of the latter steps – whether participatory or outsider-controlled. However, the steps are no more complicated than forest resource assessment activities already being conducted by local people in some of the case studies and examples in this book. Indeed, as collectors and regular forest observers, local people are better placed than outsiders to undertake many of them.

10.3   Monitoring Forest Condition and Biodiversity

The above section concerns forest management for sustainable production; in this section, the emphasis is more on management for conservation, although it is clear that the two are not mutually exclusive. Where a participatory approach is adopted, the harvesting of selected species is in fact likely to be a part of management for conservation. The steps outlined above may thus be highly pertinent, although the monitoring of biodiversity poses additional and particular challenges.

The monitoring of both forest condition and biodiversity may entail the keeping of detailed records of the forest population by species and size class over regular intervals. Alternatively, and more practically, it may entail the monitoring of carefully selected indicator species. One project that has adopted the latter approach is working to conserve the Kilum/Ijim Forest of North Western Cameroon, described in Box 10.3. From the outset, this project has sought the participation of local people in its activities. The system of forest condition and biodiversity monitoring that it has now set in place focuses on selected tree species (based on their use and importance to local people), and on bird species as biodiversity indicators. Project staff are confident that local people will be able to conduct monitoring by themselves in the future, although at present data analysis is handled by outsiders.

The use of size-class distributions to assess forest condition draws directly from Peters (1993). He describes three common types of population structure, Types I, II, and III. As already indicated above, the population structure of a given species can indicate its overall health. However, the information must be treated with caution. Different population structures may also reflect different regeneration strategies under gap theory (see Section 9.3 in Chapter 9).

- Type I structure is particularly common to shade-tolerant, climax (or primary) tree species. It is also considered to represent a 'normal', healthy population – an ideal that managers should seek to maintain or create in natural populations of NTFP-yielding trees.

- Type II structure has abundant natural regeneration, but is characterised by 'peaks' and 'valleys' in larger size classes. This is common to late pioneer (secondary) species that require small gaps in the canopy to regenerate. However, it may also represent a population that has undergone temporary periods of stress, possibly inflicted by excessive harvesting.

- Type III structure is commonly exhibited by light-demanding, early pioneer species that require large gaps in the canopy to regenerate. However, it may also be found in longer-lived pioneer and climax species if their regeneration has been interrupted, in which case it is a sign of serious ill-health in the population.

In the Kilum/Ijim forest, *Syzygium staudtii* exhibits Type I structure, and is considered to be a population in good health. Amongst the other species mentioned, Type II structure is not represented, but *Polyscia fulva* provides an example of Type III structure – in this case indicating serious ill-health in the population. The management of the Kilum/Ijim forest provides a good illustration of ecological theory being put into practice with local people. If the current momentum of its activities continues into the future, it should provide an extremely instructive example to other initiatives of a similar nature.

Box 10.3 The Biodiversity/Forest Condition Monitoring Programme in the Kilum/Ijim Forest of the Bamenda Highlands, North West Province, Cameroon

The contiguous Kilum/Ijim Forest is the largest remaining remnant of West African montane forest, covering about 20,000 ha most of which lies above 2,200 m elevation. It is an area of great national and international importance for conservation, as well as a source of many subsistence products and a certain cash income for the local population. Some 200,000 people, from four ethnic groups, live around the forest. In the past, excessive forest exploitation was prevented through well enforced indigenous management systems, but in the last twenty years enforcement has broken down and the forest has declined rapidly in area and condition.

Eight years ago, BirdLife International (formerly the International Council for Bird Preservation) began working with local people to conserve the remaining Kilum/Ijim forest and its biodiversity. This was addressed by promoting conservation and sustainable forest use through the appropriate development of the surrounding farming and grazing lands. It was found that, due to ethnic tensions, it was most effective to establish two projects – one working on the Kilum Mountain with the majority **Oku** people, and one on the Ijim Mountain with the majority **Kom** people. Recent changes to Cameroon's forest legislation provide further incentive for local people to regulate the use of the nearby forests.

Since 1994, there has been legal provision for formal local community control over forest management. Some of the forest users of Kilum have already organised themselves into Forest Users Groups (FUGs), and it is envisaged that eventually the entire Kilum/Ijim forest area will be managed by a number of such FUGs. Each FUG will, with the assistance of the projects, draw up a forest management plan for an agreed portion of the forest. Co-ordination of forest management as a whole will take place through an elected Community Forest Management Council (CFMC) which will have responsibility for implementation. Part of each management plan will be an undertaking by the users to regulate forest product use and ensure that the level of exploitation is sustainable both for their own benefit, and to ensure that biodiversity conservation objectives are met. A programme of participatory biodiversity/forest condition monitoring has been developed to this effect. It is split between faunal and forest monitoring, using the endemic birds as the main indicators of biodiversity, and forest inventory as a measure of forest condition.

Forest users trained in monitoring techniques
Plant and bird lists which include both local and scientific/English names have been compiled and are used to translate local names to scientific names. Two forest users who already have extensive knowledge of the flora and fauna of the forest have now also learned the scientific names of all trees in the forest and the English names of all birds. The two forest users and two scribes (secondary school-leavers) have been trained in the bird transect count methodology and in appropriate forest inventory and forest structure measurement techniques.

(continued/...)

Box 10.3 *(continued)*

The monitoring team collects all data in the field, unsupervised, and later enters the data on to a computer database ready for analysis. The analysis itself is currently conducted by BirdLife International staff, but in the long term it is hoped that this responsibility, together with that of paying the salaries of the monitoring team, will be transferred to a partner organisation in Cameroon.

Birds as biodiversity indicators

BirdLife International uses birds as indicators of biodiversity since the distribution and status of birds is better known on a world-wide basis than for any other biological taxon. Fifteen montane bird species endemic to Cameroon are found in the Kilum/Ijim forest, of which two (Bannerman's Turaco and Banded Wattle-eye) are found only in this area. The bird monitoring programme is based on transect counts, with specific adaptations to the counting methods for the latter two endemics. The baseline data are currently being analysed. From these data, it will be possible to determine the habitat preferences of the endemics and the areas of forest with the highest bird biodiversity.

Forest condition monitoring

This is conducted on the same transect routes as used for the bird counts, and will be used to determine sustainability of NTFP harvesting and bird-habitat associations.

Eleven transects, totalling 20.9 km in length, have been established in the Kilum/Ijim forest. Transect routes were selected to reflect the natural range of variation in forest type, forest condition, and altitude (2,000–2,900 m); eight were based on existing forest paths.

Permanent marker pegs at 100 m intervals divide each transect into 100 m long plots.

Measurements were conducted in a 10 m wide band either side of the transect route (total width 20 m), giving each plot an area of 0.2 ha. Diameters (dbh) of all trees over 10 cm were measured throughout each plot, whilst a sub-sample of smaller trees and saplings (dbh 1–10 cm) and regeneration (dbh below 1 cm) was taken in 20 circular sub-plots of 2.5 m radius within each 100 m plot (total sampling area 0.039 ha per 100 m plot).

The sub-plots were positioned at 10 m intervals along either side of the transect at a perpendicular distance of 10 m from the transect.

Totals of the smaller trees in the sub-plots were multiplied by a factor of 5.09 to give a total area of 0.2 ha for comparison with data from the 0.2 ha plots (see diagram of plot layout).

Trees with more than one stem at breast height were common in the forest. Each stem was measured separately, converted to basal area, and summed before converting back to the theoretical dbh had the tree had only one stem.

(continued/...)

Box 10.3 *(continued)*

Diagram of plot layout for dbh and natural regeneration measurement

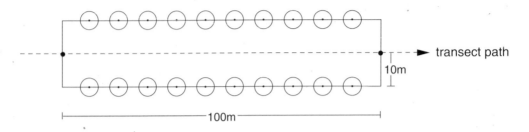

- • 100m marker post
- ⊙ 2.5m radius regeneration plots

Results of baseline forest condition monitoring

Results have been calculated for the Ijim forest transects, representing five transects of total length 8.7 km. The total sampling area was 17.4 ha, a 0.44% sample of the total Ijim forest area of approximately 4,000 ha.

The size-class distributions of four forest tree species, selected to represent differing levels of resource use, are shown in Figures 1 to 4.

Figure 1 Size-class distribution of *Syzygium staudtii* – no specific resource use

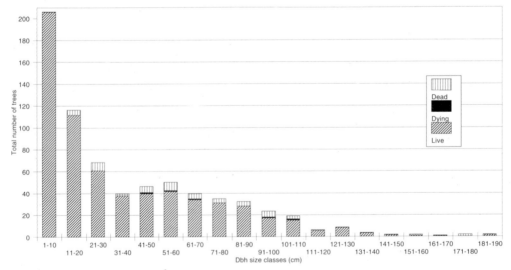

The size-class distribution of this dominant species in the high canopy forest shows the classic 'normal' distribution, representing a 'healthy' population structure. There are many small trees, and fewer in each successive size class due to natural mortality.

(continued/...)

Box 10.3 *(continued)*

Figure 2 Size-class distribution of *Nuxia congesta* **– a favoured fuelwood tree**

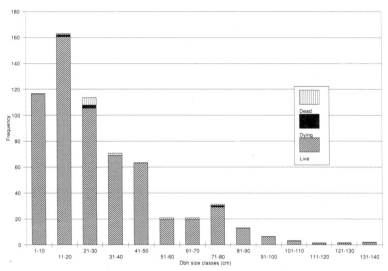

Another dominant species in the high canopy forest, this species has an almost normal size-class distribution. However, there are fewer individuals in the smallest size class than expected, suggesting poor regeneration. There is no obvious reason for this, but careful monitoring is required.

Figure 3 Size-class distribution of *Prunus africana* **– a species of high commercial value, its bark being used for commercial drug production; also a favoured fuelwood tree**

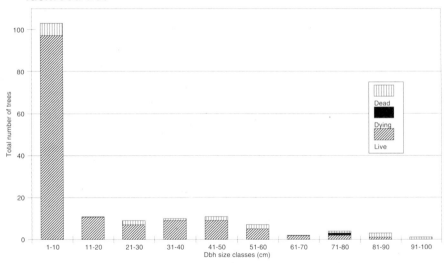

This has a distinctly unhealthy size-class distribution, with a large proportion of the trees measured being dead or dying from ring barking. The smaller size classes are also poorly represented. The species is clearly being over-harvested. However, the smallest size class is well represented, indicating that with appropriate management the species should be able to recover.

(continued/...)

293

Box 10.3 *(continued)*

Figure 4 Size-class distribution of *Polyscia fulva* – the most favoured carving tree

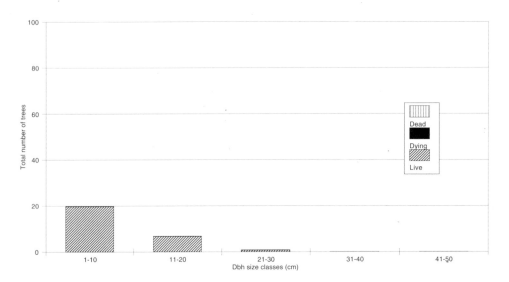

This species is now extremely scarce in the forest, and its size-class distribution shows that it is close to extinction. No trees were found of dbh over 40 cm (the size suitable for carving into stools, etc.), and very few young trees were found either. It is likely that the species can only be reinstated in the forest through enrichment planting. In the meanwhile, the project is working with carvers to establish *Polyscia fulva* plantations at lower altitudes, where it has a faster growth rate.

Combining sustainable use management and biodiversity/forest condition monitoring
The system for controlling and checking use levels is still to be devised and developed by the forest users, but the results of the above monitoring exercise will be discussed with them as an aid in their decision-making. It is proposed that the monitoring programme should continue with vegetation monitoring every two years, and bird monitoring every five years. The results should be compared with the NTFP extraction data recorded by the FUGs (however they decide to do this), to determine whether or not harvesting levels are sustainable, and whether they affect biodiversity. It is hoped that the CFMCs will then use this information to plan, agree and implement forest resource management in the future.

Source: McKay and Young (1995)

10.4   The Use of Forest Assessment for Educational Programmes

The focus of this Study Guide has been on local people's participation in the quantification of tree and forest resources in order to gain control over and/or manage these resources. This section briefly draws attention to the potential use of forest resource assessment in campaigns for increasing local awareness of the value of forests. In some communities, of course, there may be no need for such education. Any educational programme should be preceded by a careful appraisal of existing local knowledge and information needs. Nevertheless, where appropriate, quantifying forest resources can be a useful educational exercise, acting as a catalyst to local action in forest management.

Placing a monetary or equivalent value on resources that are considered to be 'free', or the true market value of which is unknown, can be a particularly effective exercise with local people. This was the rationale behind the attempts to assist farmers to place an accurate value on their trees, outlined in Section 10.1. Drawing again from Brazil, colleagues of those involved in the timber valuation workshop have been working with local communities investigating their use of NTFPs. The programme has combined research and education. Research objectives included conducting an inventory of the fruit, game, fish and medicinal plants consumed by 45 families over a year and determining the population of four important NTFP-yielding species (selected by the community). Educational objectives included demonstrating the economic contribution of NTFPs to household economies, offering an assessment of the sustainable commercial extraction of selected NTFPs, and developing participatory methods for collecting and returning NTFP data to communities (Shanley, Luz and Galvão, 1995). The latter included the following, all of which could have application elsewhere:

- Household notebooks, whereby each participating household undertook to weigh or count (as appropriate) all the NTFPs that they consumed over the year. The data compiled were subsequently presented to the community at workshops in which people were asked to guess the cost of the products consumed (as calculated in prices fetched at the nearest town and translated into bags of the food staple farina, since these were more meaningful to participants than monetary values). Values proved to be far higher than people expected.

- Role plays, in which community members took the part of key players such as poor farmers, loggers, fruit collectors, and traditional healers. These focused on the relative values of different forest products and showed, for example, the far greater value of a tree giving a regular fruit harvest than one sold for a small, one-off payment for timber.

- Posters illustrating the value of NTFPs in terms of bags of farina.

- Travelling shows, along themes such as 'How I was fooled by a logger'.

- Illustrated booklets depicting relevant ethno-botanical, ecological and market information.

As this example shows, forest resource assessment can be used as a basis for much interactive educational work with communities.

This potential could be worth considering when developing forest management plans with local people.

10.5 Conclusion

Inevitably, this final chapter has presented a number of quite diverse topics and field examples. Even this coverage leaves a number of important issues untouched. It is notable, for example, how little participatory work is reported in quantifying animal populations as part of forest resource assessment. Yet wildlife are often an extremely valuable forest resource, with hunting being seen by local people as an important right. The quantification of the non-tangible benefits of forests, such as cultural, environmental and aesthetic values, is also an issue that might be addressed more rigorously in participatory forest assessment.

It is clear that much remains to be learned about appropriate methods for working with local people in quantifying forest resources that they use. Furthermore, the appropriateness of any given method depends so much on individual circumstances – on the people and forest concerned, the purpose of assessment, the detail of information required, and a potential host of other factors. It is hoped that the case studies and shorter examples provided in this book have, at least, provided a stimulus for thought – and further innovation in the forest.

References

Chambers, R. and **Guijt, I.** (1995) 'PRA – Five Years Later. Where are we now?' *Forests, Trees and People Newsletter* No. 26/27 April: 4–14.

Chambers, R. and **Leach, M.** (1987) 'Trees to Meet Contingencies: Savings and Security for The Rural Poor'. *Social Forestry Network Paper 5a*, ODI, London. October.

CIPRES (1993) *Investigacion: Methodologia campesina de inventario forestal Nicaragua*. Centro de Investigacion y Promocion para el Desarrollo Rural y Social (CIPRES), Convenio FAO/CIPRES, Nicaragua.

Cunningham, A. B. (1992) 'People, Park and Plant Use – Research and Recommendations for Multiple Use Zones and Development Alternatives around Bwindi Impenetrable National Park, Uganda'. Report prepared for CARE-International, Kampala, Uganda.

Cunningham, A. B. (1997) *People and Wild Plant Use*. Chapman and Hall, London.

Mattos, M. M., **Nepstad, D. C.** and **Vieira I. C. G.** (1992) *Cartilha sobre mapeamento de área, cubagem de madeira e inventário forestal*

Belém, Brazil. Obtainable through Woods Hole Research Center/EMBRAPA, Belém, Brazil.

Mattos, M. M., Nepstad, D. C., Vieira I. C. G., and **Assis, Santos de, W.** (1994) 'Valorizando a Madeira: um mini-curso para Agricultores e Extensionistas em Inventários Florestais'. Unpublished mimeo, obtainable through Woods Hole Research Center/EMBRAPA, Belém, Brazil.

McKay, C. and **Young, J.** (1995) 'Developing a Monitoring Programme for Combined Community and Forest Management in the Kilum/Ijim Montane Forest, Cameroon'. Unpublished paper obtainable through BirdLife International, Cambridge, UK.

Peters, C. M. (1993) 'Ecology and Exploitation of Non-timber Tropical Forest Resources: A Primer on Sustainability'. Draft Report II Biodiversity Support Program, Institute of Economic Botany, The New York Botanical Garden, New York.

Philip, M. S. (1994) *Measuring Trees and Forests* (2nd edn). CAB International, Wallingford, UK.

Shanley, P., Luz, L. and **Galvão, J.** (1995) 'Translating Dry Data for Forest Folk: Science Offers Incentives for Conservation'. Unpublished mimeo, Woods Hole Research Centre/EMBRAPA, Belém, Brazil.

VFFP (1994) *Measuring Trees and Crops.* Technical Information Series 2. Village and Farm Forestry Project, Swiss Development Co-operation, Dhaka, Bangladesh.

Acronyms specific to this chapter

CFMC	Community Forest Management Council (in Cameroon)
CIPRES	**Centro de Investigacion y Promocion para el Desarrollo Rural y Social** (Centre for the Investigation and Promotion of Rural and Social Development) (in Nicaragua)
FUG	Forest User Group (in Cameroon)
VFFP	Village and Farm Forestry Project (in Bangladesh)

A Appendix: Geomatics: A Guide to the Technology

Compiled by Peter Poole

Scope and Local Potential of Geomatics

Geomatics, a useful new term, refers to the elaboration of traditional mapping methodologies by advanced information technologies for the recording, storage, manipulation and analysis of geographical imagery. They comprise three technologies: remote sensing, global positioning systems (GPS), and computer-based image manipulation and analysis. All three are steadily becoming cheaper and more user-friendly, and thus more accessible to remote communities.

These technologies are being used locally for applications generally assumed to be the preserve of sophisticated research institutions and centralised agencies. For example, simple video and digital cameras can mimic a "spectral window" as viewed by a multispectral scanner used by imaging satellites. (A multispectral scanner is an instrument used to capture reflectants only in specific parts of a spectrum, enabling researchers to identify features that would otherwise be invisible. For example, crop disease can be seen in the infrared band of a spectrum. In this case the infrared band would be the spectral window.) GPS positioning enables such local, highly detailed images to be directly compared with satellite images, which cover larger areas but in far less detail. This suggests a dual utility for local mapping and geomatic applications: not only can they serve local needs in biodiversity conservation but they can also be used to extend, amplify and verify the information gathered by global monitoring systems. There is scope for the mutually beneficial exchange of global and local environmental data.

At the local level, geomatic technology has the potential to amplify the capability of groups with limited resources to map and monitor large areas of land. For example, it has been estimated that one-third of the Amazon Basin, 210 million hectares, will revert to indigenous control. Altogether, as much as 13% of the Americas will fall under some measure of indigenous control, almost double that committed to protected areas. However, indigenous communities have virtually no resources at all to protect their lands. From that perspective, these emerging local applications for geomatic technologies show how to do much with little.

GPS: The Global Positioning System

The GPS is a web of 24 navigational satellites originally installed by the Pentagon so that submarines could locate themselves. A GPS receiver works like a transistor radio; once it is exposed to the sky and receives signals from three satellites, it will compute its triangulated position and display it as coordinates. Reception of four satellites will produce a 3-dimensional fix. GPS units can also be used to navigate between a set of "waypoints" entered by co-ordinates.

Geocoding with GPS

Geocoding, or georeferencing, is simply the identification of any bit of information by its geographic coordinates. GPS receivers are ostensibly accurate to 30m. However, the Pentagon may degrade signals accessible to civilian units to accuracy within 100m. This "selective availability" can be circumvented, but at a cost.

Differential GPS: Improving accuracy

Differential GPS uses two units: a base unit left at a site with verified coordinates and a mobile unit taken into the field. While the mobile unit is in use, the base unit records noise and signal variations in the GPS web. Post-mission software subtracts noise from the mobile unit's positional record. The resulting accuracy will match that of the base unit. Accuracy within 2 to 3 meters can be achieved at some extra cost, while positions within a few centimetres are obtainable at far more expense. Reliable GPS units are obtainable from $400. Systems for the more accurate differential GPS can cost from $10,000 to $20,000. However, alternatives for achieving differential GPS accuracy are being devised, and this cost is sure to decrease soon.

[*Howard Wright, Forestry Research Programme, University of Oxford adds:* Single receiver systems will only record the commonly degraded (Selective Availability) signal. This provides a geodetic position accuracy of 100m which improves to 25m if the signal is not degraded. Differential GPS uses an additional receiver located at a control point and positions relative to that control point can be accurate to 10m if the two systems are less than 100km apart. Sophisticated systems may have far greater accuracy. In the majority of cases, differential GPS can only provide greater geodetic accuracy with respect to the second (reference) receiver, which is still subject to the same degraded SA signal influence. The only way a differential system may provide greater accuracy is if the reference receiver is placed at a known geodetic position.

It is important to realise that there is a clear distinction between local accuracy (precision) with respect to a differential GPS reference, and geodetic accuracy. Users also need to be aware that the datum to which their GPS unit is set must match that used for their map. Many GP sets allow a wide range of datum points to be used.]

Coupling GPS with other Technology
GPS can be coupled, or integrated, with photo and video cameras so as to automatically geocode the imagery. This is an unnecessary expense for most ground work but is useful in the air. One new instrument combines a GPS with a laptop computer. With a digitised aerial image on the screen, the user is shown as a point of light moving over the landscape.

Field Operational Problems and Limitations
GPS has its limitations. For example, forest canopies interfere with reception. A method is needed for raising the GPS antenna above the canopy. Also, battery life is low at 4–6 hours: each AA cell lasts about one hour.

Satellite Remote Sensing
For practical purposes, satellite images are defined in terms of their ground cover and ground resolution. They are derived from digital scanners or conventional cameras on the space-craft. The major satellite sensing systems include:

- *LANDSAT (US)* produces images in four spectral bands which cover 160km x 160km at a ground resolution of 30m. *SPOT (France)* images cover 36km x 36km, with ground resolutions of 20m for multispectral (colour) and 10m for panchromatic images.

- *A Russian system* uses conventional cameras in the satellite. This means that the images cannot be retrieved in real time, but they are of higher resolution (apparently to within 2–5 meters). This technology is now becoming available sporadically.

- *RADARSAT (Canada)* is due to be launched this year and promises panchromatic imagery with resolutions in the 20–30m range. Although radar imagery is low in resolution and spectral information, it has the advantage that it can "see" through cloud cover. In the Colombian Pacific forest, for example it is virtually impossible to obtain satellite images free of cloud cover with current satellite systems.

Satellite imagery has proven useful in areas where maps are non-existent or inaccurate, and in Brazil its use has been accepted for providing legal evidence of illegal activity in indigenous lands. Images cost from $2,000 to $6,000 each, although year-old imagery can be cheaper. For the Yuqui demarcation, SPOT images were obtained at an educational discount for $1,000 each.

Aerial Imaging

This usually means images from airplanes, although kites, balloons and dirigibles have been used for the same purpose. For local mapping, four imagers have potential: photo, video, digital and radar (similar to satellite radar).

Air Survey Photography

Conventional aerial photography, which uses 230mm x 230mm (9" x 9") stereoscopic mapping cameras, is very accurate but expensive. It is generally thought to be justifiable only in covering large areas for topographic mapping.

Black and white aerial survey photography, 230mm x 230mm , has proved useful in the course of local PRA (Participatory Rural Appraisal) exercises. But the scale (between 1: 20,000 and 1: 60,000) is considered too small for useful local discussions. Several studies have independently concluded that a scale of 1: 5,000 is optimum as a stimulus for local discussions, as villagers are able to easily recognise significant features.

Small Format Photography

Over the last ten years or so, researchers have experimented with small format cameras (70mm and 35mm), in some cases using up to four cameras filtered to enable each unit to gather data in a specific spectral band. Small format photography has a potential for such applications as crop and forest disease detection, land use sampling, urban and settlement studies, and wildlife census. Its advantages include its low cost, simple operations and processing, and the wide range of film and lens types. The one disadvantage is the limited image ground cover by comparison with standard mapping cameras. Small format is suitable for obtaining selective data to upgrade existing maps, but not for topographic mapping itself.

Aerial Videography

Aerial video is attracting interest for a similar range of local and specific applications. The advantage over photo survey is that tape is cheaper than film and carries no processing cost. The disadvantage is lower resolution. Aerial video data can either be interpreted directly as a moving image or can be converted to a series of still images by the use of a "frame grabber". These images, like still photo images, can then be either interpreted directly or digitised for computer-based analysis. Digitisation causes a loss in image resolution but a gain in image manipulation. Although some reports refer to a new generation of "digital video recorders", these do not obtain imagery in digital form, they simply place a digitiser within the camera. Moving video has been used for locating point sources of pollution and for coastal studies, in fact for many small format photo applications which tolerate low resolution.

Digital Frame Cameras

Direct digital aerial imagery can be obtained using one of the new digital frame cameras. These are still cameras which resemble photo cameras but which use an array of digital receptors instead of film. At present, data storage capacities limit the utility of digital cameras in light aircraft. One currently available system requires 1.3 megabytes per image. However, once this problem is resolved, these cameras will be competitive with the video/frame-grabber combination.

Coupling Aerial Imagers with GPS

When coupled, or integrated, with GPS, photo/video combinations in light aircraft have great promise for a wide range of mapping and monitoring missions. For monitoring environmental change with differential GPS navigation, flight lines or selected photo sample plots can be replicated to an accuracy of less than 5m. Where traditional lands are recognised on paper but not demarcated on the ground, their borders can easily be monitored with GPS/video to produce image transects.

GIS: Geographic Information Systems

These range from relatively cheap and simple methods for image manipulation and map production to powerful analytical technologies capable of correlating and manipulation and map production to powerful analytical technologies capable of correlating and manipulating large numbers of "layers" of geographical information. There is wide interest in geographic information systems, but only a few groups so far have used this technology to its full extent. There are accounts of technological overkill; vendors at a recent GIS conference in Vancouver estimated that 80% of the GIS obtained by First Nations groups are not being fully utilised. Various reasons were cited for this: lack of initial training, lack of follow-up service, and hidden and incremental costs. Many groups using more sophisticated GIS have become obliged to hire full-time operators.

At the simpler end of the GIS scale, emerging low-cost systems have proved valuable in simply integrating geocoded data, gathered locally with GPS, and producing maps as evidence of traditional land use and occupancy. These are compatible with basic computer systems and software and cost $500–$1,000.

Experience to date suggests that advanced GIS makes sense when working on a regional basis with associations of communities or with long-term environmental management institutions emerging from land claim settlements. For making local maps at the community level in preparation for negotiations, simple map-making systems compatible with standard computer systems may be quite adequate.

Matching Applications with Geomatic Technology		
Application	*Data Needed*	*Geomatic Technology*
Land use and occupancy	Maps based upon local knowledge and practice	Sketch mapping basic mapping GPS for more accuracy
Demarcation	Positional base/ images if available	GPS
Gathering & protecting traditional knowledge	Traditional environmental knowledge	Sketch mapping basic mapping GPS for more accuracy GIS for map-making
Boundary monitoring	Sequential visual data	GPS and aerial video satellite imagery radarsat imagery
Resource mapping	Local data upon base maps	Aerial video/photo & GPS GIS for map-making
Ecological recuperation	High resolution imagery	Aerial photography
Impact monitoring	Aerial imagery	Aerial video/photo & GPS
Resource management	Comprehensive cultural and ecological	Aerial video/photo & GPS satellite GIS for analysis
Local communication	Local views and land- scape data	Ephemeral maps sketch maps aerial photos

IN BRIEF:

Basic Mapping... has proven effective on its own account. The process by which traditional knowledge is gathered remains essential, however sophisticated the geomatic technology.

Global Positioning System... technology offers the best return on training and financial investment. It can be grafted on to local knowledge gathering, it transforms informal maps into the cartographic forms familiar to external agencies, and it radically reduces the potential costs of land demarcation.

Satellite Imagery... has been used but its local utility is limited by low ground resolution, aggravated by problems of accessibility, cost, and performance in cloud-covered areas.

Aerial Imagery... when available, has been found useful at scales of 1:5,000. There is potential for emerging, low-cost systems combining GPS with video or photo in light aircraft.

Geographic Information Systems... are useful at two levels:
- As computer-based mapping programmes capable of producing maps from locally acquired geocoded data.

- As advanced, analytical, GIS: more appropriate for community umbrella or support association.

This appendix is reprinted with permission from *Cultural Survival Quarterly*, Winter 1995, pp. 16–8.

B Appendix: Study Questions

1. Draw up a table of the different purposes for which forest assessment may be used, and the outputs that are needed for each. You should structure your table in the following manner, completing it as far as possible.

Securing land tenure	Establishing usufruct rights	Claiming compensation	
• boundaries established	• boundaries established • quantities of resources assessed	• boundaries established • quantities of resources assessed • value of resources estimated.....	
• map(s)	• management plan	• valuation.....	

2. Following from the above table, choose **one** purpose of forest resource assessment pertinent to a situation known to you. Describe which participatory methods would be most appropriate to achieve the necessary outputs, explaining your reasons.

3.   Construct a diagram whereby the x axis represents increasing levels of local people's participation in decision-making, and the y axis represents the complexity of tasks undertaken by them, as follows.

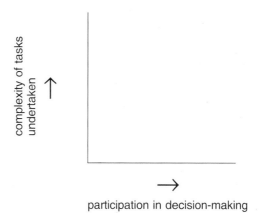

participation in decision-making

Locate the different case study initiatives on this diagram (treating the two Nepal projects and the three Ugandan projects separately). What can you deduce from your completed table?

4.   What aspects of forest resource assessment do you personally find most difficult to conceptualise? Compare your background and experience against that of the users of a particular forest who are known to you. What aspects of forest resource assessment might you anticipate them finding particularly difficult, and why?

5.   What similarities may be drawn between the forest inventory procedure adopted in the case study from Nigeria (Chapter 2) and in the case study from Ecuador (Chapter 3, focusing on the current baseline inventory and the planned stock surveys)? What are the differences?

6.   Compare the participatory mapping exercises used in community forestry in Nepal (Chapter 6) with those used in East Kalimantan, as described in Chapter 7. Describe the similarities and differences, paying particular attention to the purpose of mapping in each case. Supplement your discussion as far as possible by further comparisons with other participatory forest mapping exercises known to you.

7.   Briefly describe a participatory forestry initiative known to you, and outline the method(s) of forest resource assessment employed. Consider the training needs of all parties concerned, and draw up a tentative training programme.

8.   Which of the case studies do you feel demonstrates the highest degree of local people's participation in forest resource assessment, and which demonstrates the lowest? Why?

9.   Is it both unnecessary and limiting to define the degree of local people's participation in forest resource assessment by their understanding of the methods used? Discuss this, with reference to your own experience as well as the pertinent case studies in this book.

10.   'Markets are a crucial factor governing the type of inventory conducted in a forest under any form of commercial management.' Discuss this statement with reference to participatory forest management initiatives known to you, drawing on the case studies in this book where relevant.

C Appendix: Glossary

accuracy	In statistical terms, freedom from error or the closeness of a measurement or estimate to the true value. More broadly, it is the degree to which a statement or quantitative result approaches the truth (Schreuder, Gregoire, and Wood, 1993).
basal area (tree)	The cross-sectional area of a tree stem at breast height.
basal area	The sum of the cross-sectional areas at breast height of all trees (forest stand) on a defined area.
bias	A systematic error introduced into sampling, measurement, or estimation by selecting or encouraging, possibly intentionally, one outcome or answer over others (Schreuder *et al.*, 1993).
biomass	The amount of living matter, quantified by weight or volume, in an individual organism (e.g. tree, animal) or unit area (e.g. of forest).
breast height	The point on a tree stem at which diameter is commonly measured, 1.3 m above ground level.
error	The difference between an observed or calculated value and the true value. There are four main types of error: human (mistake), accidental, bias, and sampling error (Schreuder *et al*, 1993).
geocoded data	Data which may be identified by their geographical coordinates (latitude and longitude); also known as geo-referenced data.
geographical information system (GIS)	A computer-based system for producing geographical imagery (see Appendix A).
geomatics	The elaboration of conventional mapping methods using advanced information technologies for the recording, storage, manipulation and analysis of geographical imagery.

global positioning system (GPS) A system for accurately locating any point on the earth's surface using a web of navigational satellites (see Appendix A).

hypsometer An instrument used for the purpose of estimating height through the geometric principle of triangulation.

mensuration The measurement of lengths, areas, and volumes. Forest mensuration provides information about the current state of a tree or crop, but also concerns change over time - the measuring and predicting of tree and crop growth.

morphological characteristics In biological terms, these concern the form or shape of an organism (both whole, e.g. a tree, or part, e.g. a leaf)

non-timber forest product (NTFP) Non-timber plant or animal product derived from the forest or forest habitat. NTFPs include foods (fruits, nuts, mushrooms, vegetables, spices and bushmeat), fodder, oils, gums, resins, medicines and fibres.

parameter A characteristic of a population that usually can be expressed in a numerical form.

participatory rural appraisal (PRA) A semi-structured process of learning by, with and from communities communities about their own situation and way of life (see Chapter One, Section 1.2).

permanent sample plot (PSP) A permanently demarcated area of forest, typically of 1 ha, which is periodically remeasured. PSPs are maintained over a minimum of five years, and usually very much longer. They provide estimates of changes in forest stocking and volume, information which is essential for rational forest management (Alder and Synnott, 1992).

phenological characteristics These concern phenomena which re-occur at timed intervals (often dictated by seasonal climatic changes) e.g. in plants, flowering, fruiting, leaf fall, etc.

population In statistical terms, an assembly of individual units usually formed in order to measure the units quantitatively (Philip, 1994).

precision In statistical terms, relative freedom from random variation, expressed in sampling as the standard error. Precision is the degree to which measurements or estimates cluster about their own average. Precision is a function of the calibration of instruments, the variation that exists in a population, and the fact that an estimation is based on an assumption. The precision of an estimate based on sampling can be increased by increasing the number of sampling units (Philip, 1994).

rapid rural appraisal (RRA) A systematic semi-structured activity conducted in the field by a multi-disciplinary team, in order to acquire new information on, and construct new hypotheses about, rural life and production systems (see Chapter One, Section 1.2).

relascope An instrument used for determining stand basal area rapidly and accurately. It discriminates between trees on the basis of whether or not the tree subtends an angle equal to or greater than that of the relascope when viewed from the sampling point. When using a relascope the observer stands with the gauge at a point in the forest and records the number of trees subtending an angle equal to or greater than a fixed and known angle. This record is multiplied by the 'relascope factor' to give a direct reading of basal area per hectare.

sample
A part of a population used to obtain estimates of characteristics of that population.

standard error
The measure of the random errors that affect precision. The smaller the standard error of an estimate, the more precise is that estimate (Philip, 1994).

swidden agriculture
A form of agriculture or forest farming also known as shifting cultivation in which primary or secondary forest is cleared, cultivated for a period of time, and then temporarily or permanently abandoned.

Taungya system
A system of re-afforestation once employed by forest departments in many parts of the world. Under it, local people plant and tend tree seedlings on land belonging to the department and are permitted to cultivate crops between the trees in the early years of establishment. Typically, cultivation is allowed for no longer than three years, but this depends partly on the growth rate of the trees. The system is less commonly used today, as in most cases it is neither very advantageous to local people nor particularly efficient in terms of re-afforestation.

temporary sample plot (TSP)
An area of forest temporarily demarcated for sampling in an inventory.

tenure
The nature of property rights under which a resource (land, forest, tree, etc.) is held and used.

usufruct
The right to use and enjoy the yield of resources (land, trees, livestock, etc.) that belong to someone else.

References for Glossary

Alder, D. and **Synnott, T. S.** (1992) Permanent sample plot techniques for mixed tropical forest. Tropical Forestry Paper No. 25, Oxford Forestry Institute.

Philip, M. S. (1994) *Measuring trees and forests.* (2nd edn) CAB International, Wallingford, UK.

Schreuder, H. T., Gregoire, T. G. and **Wood, G. B.** (1993) *Sampling methods for Multiresource Forest Inventory.* John Wiley and Sons, Inc. New York, Chichester, Brisbane, Toronto and Singapore.

D Appendix: Species Index

E Appendix: General Index